DIRECT-CURRENT MACHINERY

DIRECT-CURRENT MACHINERY

BY

HEMPSTEAD S. BULL

Assistant Professor of Electrical Engineering
University of Michigan

NEW YORK

JOHN WILEY & SONS, Inc.

London: CHAPMAN & HALL, Limited

1939

Printed in U. S. A.

Printing	Composition	Binding
F. H. GILSON CO.	TECHNICAL COMPOSITION CO.	STANHOPE BINDERY
BOSTON	BOSTON	BOSTON

PREFACE

The author has endeavored to include in each chapter only such material as will be most useful to electrical engineering students who are beginning their work with electrical machinery. Frequent references to collateral reading are provided in the hope that the reader will find time and incentive to depart occasionally from the main highway in order to experience the exhilaration that follows a strenuous climb over a faintly blazed trail to a commanding peak.

The book contains numerous problems of varying degrees of difficulty. Scant use is made of photographs of machine parts, in deference to the modern tendency to utilize lantern slides and manufacturers' bulletins as valuable supplements to a formal textbook.

The somewhat unconventional topical sequence makes possible a more intimate correlation with the laboratory instruction without sacrifice of logical development. The general picture of the shunt motor and its governing equations is developed early in the text so that laboratory studies of motor torque, speed and current relations may be started in the second or third week.

Particular attention is directed to the methods of presenting certain aspects of armature windings, armature reaction and commutation which are, it is believed, original.

The author is grateful to his colleagues at the University of Michigan for their unfailing encouragement and support, and in particular to Professor A. D. Moore, whose criticism of sections of the manuscript has been invaluable.

H. S. BULL

January 15, 1939

CONTENTS

v

TABLES AND CURVES

DIRECT-CURRENT MACHINERY

CHAPTER 1

ELECTROMAGNETIC RELATIONS

1. General Features of Magnetic Fields. There are several familiar methods for determining the existence of a magnetic field, its strength, and its directional characteristics. The force which it exerts upon a delicately suspended magnet can be observed and measured. Iron filings may be scattered on a sheet of glass, which is then placed in the region to be studied, and tapped gently. The filings gradually arrange them-

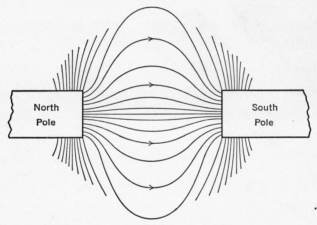

Fig. 1. The field between unlike poles of very long magnets.

selves in a definite pattern which conforms closely to the forces of the field. Some of the observations that these tests bring out may be summarized as follows:

A. Force reactions between magnets.
  (*a*) The force effects are concentrated in the end portions or poles of the magnets.
  (*b*) Poles of like sign or polarity repel each other.
  (*c*) Unlike poles attract each other.
B. The pattern of the field between two magnet poles of unlike polarity.

1

(*a*) The region between the poles appears to contain a large number of lines of force, terminating at the poles.

(*b*) These lines appear to be in a state of tension, trying to draw the poles nearer each other.

(*c*) They likewise seem to have a mutual repulsion for one another so that lines which are close together at the poles are spread far apart in the space between the poles.

C. The pattern of the field between two poles of like polarity.

(*a*) The region appears to be filled with force lines arranged in two independent groups, each group terminating on one pole and curving back to avoid mingling with the members of the other group.

(*b*) The individual lines of each group likewise seem to be subject to a mutual repulsion.

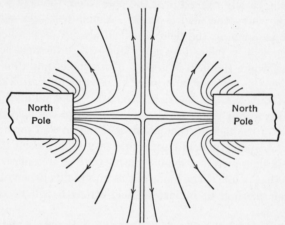

Fɪɢ. 2.   The field between like poles of very long magnets.

2. Definitions and Concepts. It is well known that a freely suspended magnet will assume a north-south position if influenced by the earth's magnetic field alone. By common agreement the end of the magnet pointing toward the geographical north is called a north pole and the other end is termed a south pole.

Any attempt to isolate the north pole of a magnet from its companion pole by breaking or subdividing the magnet results in the immediate formation of new poles on each side of the break. However, the ends of a magnetized steel rod, whose length is great compared to the dimensions and strength of its poles, behave practically as isolated poles. For many purposes it is convenient to invent the concept of a completely isolated point pole whose companion pole is infinitely far away and whose dimensions are extremely small. This concept will be discussed in Chapter 7.

It is often desirable to speak of a magnetic field as having direction, the term being defined as follows: the direction of a magnetic field at any point is the direction in which an isolated north pole will tend to move if placed at that point. Thus magnetic lines are considered to point *out* or *away from* a north pole, and *enter* or *point toward* a south pole.

Another important characteristic of a magnetic field is its strength. There are two useful methods of indicating magnetic field strength. One involves the use of a concept called flux density, and the other defines field strength in terms of its force effect on a unit point pole.

To get a clear understanding of the first term it may be helpful to think of the magnetic field which surrounds the north pole of a long, thin magnet. The pattern of this field is approximately radial, the lines of force being closely packed near the pole where the field is strong and more sparse where the field is weak. A unit test area moved about from point to point in the field and held always perpendicular to the lines of force will be pierced by many lines where the field is strong and by few lines where the field is weak. The number and direction of the lines piercing the unit test area may be used as indicators of the magnitude and direction of the field strength. The number of lines of force piercing a unit test area at a given point in the field is called the flux density of the field at that point, and the lines of force are termed flux lines. A magnetic field has unit density at any point if one line of force, or flux line, pierces a square centimeter test area placed normal to the field at that point. The name of this unit of flux density is the *gauss*.

The other method of indicating field strength will be discussed in Chapter 7.

3. Electrons and the Electric Current. Although a detailed treatment of the electron theory with its various modern ramifications is beyond the scope of this book, the concept of the electric current generally employed in electrical engineering cannot be appreciated fully without reference to some of this background material.

The atom, once considered the ultimate unit of matter, has more recently been pictured as composed of a positively charged nucleus with a large number of negatively charged particles called electrons moving about it. The atoms of an insulating material restrict the motion of most of their component electrons to orbital paths around the nucleus. A similar restriction is exhibited by the atoms of a conducting material, but it affects a much smaller number of the component electrons and a relatively large number of electrons are free to wander from atom to atom. If a steady difference of potential is maintained between the ends of a conductor, as by connecting it to the terminals of a battery, a slow drift of free electrons occurs through the material of the conductor from the negative to the positive battery terminal. This drift of negative charges toward the positive battery terminal is called the electronic current.

For a long time before the discovery of the electron it was assumed that when the positive and negative terminals of a battery were connected by a metallic conductor a transfer of positive electric charge occurred through the external conductor from the positive to the negative terminal, flowing from a high to a low potential. Any reference in this book to the electric current, or, more briefly, current, is based on this conventional concept.

4. Electromagnetic Relations. The discovery by Oersted in 1819 that a magnetic needle is deflected when brought near to a conductor carrying current was an epoch-making event. Extensive laboratory investigations of this new phenomenon were soon under way, culminating in Faraday's famous experiments in electromagnetic induction, 1831; and a considerable fund of information concerning electromagnetic fields is now available. Some of these important facts will now be listed.

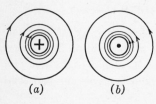

(a)   *(b)*

Fig. 3 (a) Flux around a conductor carrying current away from the observer. (b) Flux around a conductor carrying current toward the observer.

(a) All electric currents are encircled by magnetic lines of force. When the conductor is far removed from magnetic materials the pattern of the field around the wire is a symmetrical one, resembling groups of concentric circles. The flux density is high near the wire and low at a more distant point.

(b) The direction of the lines may be determined by means of an exploring magnetic needle. A definite relationship to the direction of current in the wire will be found. This relation is shown in Fig. 3, in which the usual symbols for current direction are employed. The cross and dot within the conductor sections stand for the tail and point respectively of an arrow moving with the current.

(c) The strength of the field is directly proportional to the current producing it, if the region in the vicinity of the conductor does not contain any magnetic material.

(d) The shape of the current path has considerable influence on the magnetic field strength. A strong electromagnetic field can be produced at a certain point more easily by forming the conductor into a one-turn circular loop with its center at the point of interest than by means of a long, straight wire. If the loop radius is decreased and more turns of wire used, further increases in field strength can be obtained without increasing the current. For example, suppose that 1 unit of flux density will be produced at a distance of 5 cm. from a long, straight wire carrying 25 amperes. If the wire is bent into a loop of 5-cm. radius a density of π units will be produced at the loop center with the same current. A 10-turn coil of 2.5-cm. radius carrying 25 amperes will produce a density of about 62 units at the center.

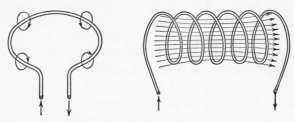

Fig. 4.   Flux lines generated by a loop and by a long coil.

(e) The nature of the material in the close vicinity of the conductor has a great influence on the strength of the field produced by a given current. If a magnetic material such as iron or steel is placed near the conductor there will be a marked increase in the field strength.

5. Force Effects of a Magnetic Field. In a similar manner some important force effects may be listed.

(a) If a conductor carrying current is located in a magnetic field other than the one due to its own current, experiment shows that it tends to move out of the field in a direction which is mutually perpendicular to the axis of the conductor and to the direction of the magnetic field. This fact may well be considered to be the basis for most of the theory of dynamoelectric machinery, and therefore deserves careful attention. Figure 5 shows the proper space relationships of the conductor and the field to produce the maximum force. Notice that the conductor is perpendicular to the field in this case. By experimenting with the conductor placed at various angles with the field it may be shown that

$$F \propto \sin \theta,$$

θ being the angle between the conductor and the field. The directions of the force, the field and the current are evidently oriented like the familiar X, Y, Z coordinates.

A convenient method for predicting the force direction for any com-

bination of current and field directions is illustrated in Fig. 6.   Draw
two parallel lines, *A–A*, and arrowhead them to indicate the direction of the magnetic field.   Draw a circle between the lines to represent the conductor section, and mark the direction of the field due

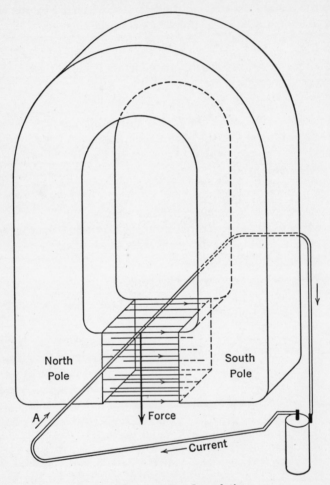

North
Pole

South
Pole

A

Force

Current

Fig. 5.   Force-current-flux relations.

to the current by means of smaller arrows, *B–B*, above and below
the conductor.   One of these smaller arrows will evidently point in
the same direction as the main field and the other one will point
against the main field.   The conductor will tend to move toward the
region of opposing fields, or downward in the example shown in the
figure.

(b) Familiarity with the space relationships of the force, the field and the current is not sufficient. The quantitative results of experiments with these factors are important also.

If the current carried by the conductor is varied and all other influential factors are held constant the force exerted by the field on the conductor will be found proportional to the current:

$$F \propto i.$$

Variations in field strength, other factors being constant, produce proportional changes in the force:

$$F \propto B.$$

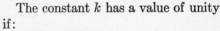

Similarly, variations in the active length of conductor (that part of the conductor lying in the field and perpendicular to it) affect the force proportionally:

$$F \propto l.$$

FIG. 6. Prediction of force direction.

The dependence of F upon $\sin \theta$ has already been mentioned. Therefore a complete expression for the deflecting force can be obtained by combining these separate results into the following complete equation.

$$F = kBil \sin \theta. \tag{1}$$

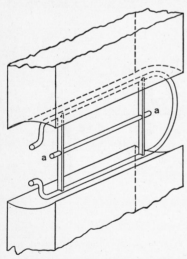

The constant k has a value of unity if:

F, the deflecting force, is in dynes.

B, the flux density, is in gausses.

i, the current, is in abamperes.

l, the conductor length, is in centimeters.

θ is the angle between the conductor and the field.

This equation may be used in the determination of the turning moment or torque produced by a magnetic field on conductors that are free to turn about a central axis.

FIG. 7. Production of torque.

EXAMPLE. A frame pivoted at a–a supports a conductor between the north and south poles of a magnet, as shown in Fig. 7. Each portion of the conductor parallel to the axis is 20 cm. long, and the distance separating the two portions is 10 cm. The magnetic field surrounding the conductor is assumed to have a density of 10,000 gausses.   If the ends of the conductor are connected by flexible leads to a battery and a current of 2 abamperes is produced in the conductor, what will be the value of the torque tending to produce rotation?

The force in dynes acting on one portion of the conductor is equal to 10,000 × 2 × 20 or 400,000.   The lever arm at which this force is acting is 5 cm.   Therefore its torque is 400,000 × 5 or 2,000,000 dyne-cm.   An equal effect is produced by the other portion so that the total torque is 4,000,000 dyne-cm.   An instant later the conductor will have turned to a different location in the field where the density is perhaps 7000 gausses.   The torque at that instant will be proportionally reduced, if the flux is assumed to be radial to the coil axis so that the motion of the conductor will continue to be perpendicular to the flux.

6. Generation of Voltage.   The following facts are of interest relative to the generation of voltage in a conductor moving through a magnetic field.

(*a*) If a conductor is placed normal to a magnetic field, as in Fig. 5, and then is moved in a direction normal to both the field and the conductor, a voltage will be generated in the conductor while it is moving.   The direction of the voltage is definitely related to the direction of the field and the direction of the motion, and it can be predicted for any combination of directions by proceeding as shown in Fig. 8.   Draw the straight line *A–B* indicating the direction of the magnetic field.

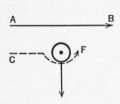

FIG. 8.   Prediction of voltage direction.

Draw a circle below it to represent the conductor cross-section, and attach an arrow to indicate the direction of its motion relative to the magnetic field.   Draw the line *C–F*, thinking of it as a field flux line like *A–B* which has been struck by the conductor and curved by the impact.   Notice whether the new direction of *C–F* is clockwise or counter-clockwise.   If it is clockwise the induced voltage is acting away from the observer; if counter-clockwise it is toward the observer.   Thus in Fig. 8 the induced voltage is toward the observer, or out of the paper.

Fleming's right-hand rule, may also be used for this purpose.   It is usually stated as follows: If the thumb, first finger and middle finger of the right hand are held mutually perpendicular to each other, and if they are so directed that the thumb indicates the direction of motion of the conductor and the first finger the direction of the flux, the middle finger will point in the direction of the induced voltage.

(*b*) A quantitative study of the relationship of the above factors, by means of experiments similar to those described in connection with the determination of the force effects, leads to the conclusion that the induced voltage is proportional to the flux density of the field, the velocity with which the conductor is moving across the field, the length of the conductor which is cutting the flux, and the sine of the angle between the conductor and the field; or, expressed in the usual symbols,

$$e = kBlv \sin \theta. \tag{2}$$

The constant k has a value of unity if:

e, the induced voltage, is in abvolts.

B, the flux density, is in gausses.

l, the conductor length, is in centimeters.

v, the velocity of the conductor, is in centimeters per second.

θ is the angle between the conductor and the field.

(c) Equation 2 can easily be put in a more useful form. If velocity is expressed as distance divided by time, and the conductor is assumed to be normal to the flux, the equation becomes

$$e = \frac{Bl\,ds}{dt} \text{ abvolts.}$$

Since the product $Bl\,ds$ can be replaced by $d\Phi$, the flux " cut " by a conductor of length l moving through a distance ds, the expression becomes

$$e = -\frac{d\Phi}{dt} \text{ abvolts.} \tag{3}$$

The reason for the insertion of the minus sign will be discussed in Art. 8.

A study of equation 3 suggests other ways by which voltage may be induced in a conductor. Any process which brings about a time rate of change of the flux lines associated or linking with the conductor will result in the production of voltage in the conductor. Accordingly experiment shows that voltage may be produced in a stationary conductor by passing magnets across the conductor.

A less obvious variation which also fulfills the stated requirements can be secured by keeping both the magnet and the conductor stationary and altering the field strength by changing the current in the coils of wire which are producing the field. Voltage is evident only while the flux is actually changing.

In order to secure the greatest benefit from any of these schemes the condition of mutual perpendicularity of flux, conductor and motion must be satisfied.

EXAMPLE. Let Fig. 9 represent an end view of the machine shown in Fig. 7. Let the initial position of the coil be at A, and assume that it is given angular acceleration until it attains an angular velocity of 10 radians per second at B, which is maintained until it reaches C. Assume that the flux is radial and has a constant density in the region between B and C of 10,000 gausses. If the coil length is 20 cm., and its span or distance between coil sides is 10 cm., find the voltage generated in the coil during its travel from B to C.

The tangential velocity of the coil sides is easily determined.

$$v = 10 \times 5 = 50 \text{ cm. per sec.}$$

By the application of equation 2 the abvolts generated in one coil side is equal to $10,000 \times 20 \times 50 = 10^7$. The total abvolts generated $= 2 \times 10^7$.

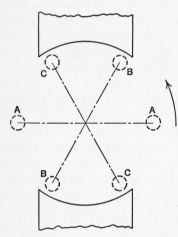

EXAMPLE. In Fig. 9 let us assume that the flux is so distributed that the density affecting the coil sides varies sinusoidally with the coil position. That is, the density for position A is zero, and for any other position such as B the density is proportional to $\sin \beta$, where β is the angle turned through in going from A to B. Assume that the coil starts from position A and turns through an angle of 180° at a constant angular velocity of 10 radians per sec. Let the maximum value of flux density be taken as 10,000 gausses; let the coil length be 20 cm. and its span 10 cm. Write the expression for the voltage generated in the coil at the instant it is in position B. Compute the value of the maximum voltage. Compute the value of the average voltage generated during the 180° shift in the position of the coil.

FIG. 9. Generation of voltage.

The tangential velocity will be $10 \times 5 = 50$ cm. per sec. The total conductor length is 40 cm. The flux density will be $10,000 \sin \beta$ gausses. Therefore the expression for the voltage at this instant is $Blv \sin \beta = 2 \times 10^7 \sin \beta$ abvolts.

Evidently the maximum value of the generated voltage will be 2×10^7 abvolts.

The average voltage may be found most easily by the aid of the calculus. Let e_m be the maximum value of the generated voltage. Then the voltage at any instant may be written as $e = e_m \sin \beta$, and the average value,

$$e_{\text{av.}} = \frac{1}{\pi} \int_{\beta=0}^{\beta=\pi} e_m \sin \beta = \frac{e_m}{\pi} \left[-\cos \beta \right]_0^{\pi} = \frac{e_m}{\pi} 2 = 0.636 e_m.$$

This amounts to 1.272×10^7 abvolts.

7. Current and Voltage Interactions.

Although the production of a deflecting force on a conductor carrying current in a magnetic field, and the generation of voltage in a conductor moving across a magnetic field, have been discussed as separate phenomena, the armature conductors

of motors and generators usually exhibit them simultaneously. The
arrangement shown in Fig. 5 may be used to investigate this possibility.

Let it be assumed that the wire is movable and that the current and
magnetic flux directions are as shown. A downward motion will be
given to the conductor. As soon as the conductor acquires velocity all
the requirements for the generation of voltage are fulfilled and an
induced voltage will appear whose direction (by application of Fleming's
rule) will be opposite to the direction of the current already present in
the conductor. A reduction in the amount of current in the conductor
may therefore be expected. This can easily be verified by noting the
behavior of a suitable current-measuring instrument in the conductor-
battery circuit.

If in the arrangement shown in Fig. 5 the battery is disconnected
and the wire is then moved vertically upward, a voltage will be generated during the motion whose direction will be as indicated by the
arrow marked A. If the open ends of the wire are joined so that a
closed circuit is provided, the voltage induced during the motion will
set up a current in the direction indicated by arrow A. As a result
of this current a deflecting force is brought to bear on the moving
conductor which is downward and therefore opposite to the force orig-
inating the motion. The tendency of this deflecting force to reduce
the velocity with which the conductor is moving can easily be verified
experimentally.

8. Flux Linkages. A conductor of N turns linking with Φ maxwells
of flux in the manner of two links of a chain is said to constitute NΦ
flux linkages. Even a single conductor lying in a magnetic field may
be thought of as linking with that field if it is part of a closed electrical
circuit. The conductor-battery circuit in Fig. 5 encircles and links with
the flux through the permanent magnet.

In gaining an understanding of the behavior of coils of one or more
turns which are encountering a changing flux, the concept of flux linkages is quite helpful. The position of the coil in Fig. 7 is such that no
linkages with the main field exist; the plane of the coil is parallel to the
field. If current is supplied to the coil from an external source it tends
to turn to a new position 90° from the position shown, where it will be
" filled " completely with flux. Furthermore, if the magnetic field and
current directions are carefully observed after the coil has turned to
its new position, it will be apparent that the flux lines produced by the
current in the conductor pass through the coil in the same direction
as the main field lines.

In Fig. 10 the coil is free to move in its own plane. Current supplied
to the coil in the indicated direction will cause it to move as shown by

the arrow. In the upper figure the motion is clearly such as to fill the coil with flux. The apparent contradiction indicated by the motion in the lower figure really does not exist. The outward motion brings it into the path of the returning flux lines which will fill the coil without "clashing" with the flux produced by the coil current. In other words, if a coil carrying a constant current is placed in a magnetic field it tends to move so as to increase the total number of linkages.

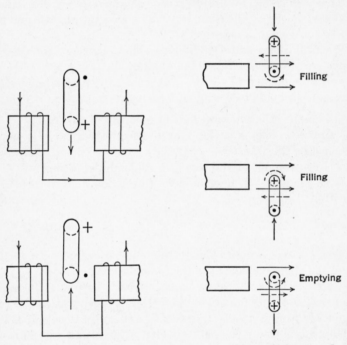

FIG. 10. Filling a coil with flux.   FIG. 11. Effect of changing flux linkages.

If a closed coil is made to move across a magnetic field a voltage is induced in it during its motion. The resulting current produces a flux whose direction is such as to oppose the main field if the coil is filling with flux or increasing its linkages, and to assist the main field if the coil is emptying or reducing its linkages. In Fig. 11 the horizontal solid arrows indicate the direction of the main field, the vertical arrow the direction of motion imparted to the coil and the dashed arrow the direction of the field due to the coil current.

When these statements are correlated with the observations noted in Art. 7 regarding current and voltage interactions a general law may be formulated which is usually stated as follows: Whenever a closed coil undergoes a change in flux linkage a voltage is induced in it which tends to produce a stabilizing current in the coil — a current which opposes the *change* in flux linkage. This statement is known as Lenz's law.

The significance of the minus sign in equation 3 should now be apparent. When the rate of change of flux is positive (which would properly be associated with an increase in the number of flux linkages) the voltage induced by the changing flux opposes the increase and hence should be considered as negative.

9. Practical Units and Definitions. The following definitions and concepts are stated briefly on the assumption that the reader needs merely to be reminded of them. Any modern textbook on electricity and magnetism should be consulted for a more extensive treatment.

The coulomb: The practical unit of quantity of electricity.

The ampere: The practical unit of electric current. It may be defined as the transfer of electricity from one point to another in an electric circuit at the rate of 1 coulomb per second.

One ampere = 1/10 abampere. Equation 1 may therefore be written

$$F = \frac{kBIl \sin \theta}{10} , \tag{4}$$

where I is the current carried by the conductor expressed in amperes, and the other symbols have the same meaning as before.

The volt: The practical unit of electric potential. It may be defined as the difference in potential between two points when 1 joule of work is done in transferring a charge of 1 coulomb between the points. One volt = 10^8 abvolts. Equation 2 may be written

$$E = \frac{kBlv \sin \theta}{10^8} \text{ volts}, \tag{5}$$

and equation 3 may be written

$$E = - \frac{d\Phi}{10^8 \, dt} \text{ volts.} \tag{6}$$

The watt: The practical unit of power. When work is done at the unit rate of 1 joule per second, that rate is called 1 watt.

Since the volt = 1 joule per coulomb, and the ampere = 1 coulomb per second, their product = 1 joule/coulomb $\times$ 1 coulomb/second = 1 joule per second = 1 watt.

The watt-second: The practical unit of energy or work. It is equal to 1 joule.

The watt-hour: A derived unit of energy equal to 3600 watt-seconds. The ohm: The practical unit of resistance. It may be defined by means of Ohm's law, which states that a conductor has a resistance of 1 ohm when a steady difference of potential of 1 volt is produced between its terminals by a current of 1 ampere.

Some useful conversion factors are listed below.

$$1 \text{ pound of force} = 444,800 \text{ dynes} = 453.6 \text{ grams.}$$
$$1 \text{ inch} = 2.54 \text{ centimeters.}$$
$$1 \text{ square inch} = 6.45 \text{ square centimeters.}$$
$$1 \text{ inch-pound} = 1.13 \times 10^6 \text{ dyne-centimeters.}$$
$$1 \text{ foot-pound} = 13.56 \times 10^6 \text{ dyne-centimeters.}$$
$$1 \text{ horsepower} = 550 \text{ foot-pounds per second,}$$
$$= 746 \text{ watts.}$$

10. Ohm's Law. The voltage which must be applied to a conductor whose resistance is R ohms, in order to produce a current of I amperes in it, is equal to RI volts. This statement of Ohm's law is so well known as to require no amplification.

It is necessary, however, to keep in mind that there are certain limitations to Ohm's law. The conductor must be metallic, it must have a constant resistance, and the current must be steady and uniform. If the passage of current through a conductor is accompanied by temperature or chemical changes, or if the current flow occurs between moving or stationary contacts, or through gases, the governing laws are more complex.

11. Factors Affecting Resistance. If the resistances of various homogeneous metallic specimens, which are identical as to material and sectional area and differ only in length, are measured, the resistance of each will be found directly proportional to its length. Similar tests conducted with other specimens of identical material and length but with different sectional areas indicate that the resistance of each is inversely proportional to its sectional area. These relationships may be combined in the following equation:

$$R = \rho \frac{L}{A} \tag{7}$$

where R is the resistance of the specimen in ohms.

L and A are its dimensions.

ρ is the resistivity or specific resistance of the material.

The value of ρ depends upon the material and temperature of the specimen, and upon the units in which L and A are expressed.

12. Resistivity Units. So many problems in electrical engineering practice require the calculation of resistance by means of equation 7 that several different ways of expressing resistivity are in common use.

(a) Microhms per centimeter cube. This is the resistance at some specified temperature, usually 20°C., of a centimeter cube of the material, measured between opposite faces. As the material is usually a metal, the resistance of a cube of the specified size will be so small that it is expressed conveniently in microhms.

In order to calculate the resistance of a particular specimen when ρ is expressed in microhms per centimeter cube the length of the specimen (measured along the current path, in centimeters) must be substituted for L in equation 7, and the sectional area (measured at right angles to the current path, in square centimeters) must be substituted for A.

(b) Circular mil-ohms per foot. This is the resistance at some specified temperature, usually 20°C., of a specimen 1 ft. in length and having a sectional area of 1 circular mil. This method of expressing resistivity is particularly useful for wire of circular cross-section because of the ease with which the area of a circular section can be determined and expressed in circular mils.

The circular mil (abbreviated C.M.) is a special unit of area, being defined as the area enclosed by a circle 1 mil (0.001 in.) in diameter. Certain convenient relations proceed from this selection.

A circle 2 mils in diameter will have an area of 4 C.M.

A circle n mils in diameter will have an area of n^2 C.M.

To obtain the area of any circular section in circular mils express its diameter in mils and square it.

The circular mil is a smaller unit of area than the square mil, since a circle 1 mil in diameter can be inscribed within a square mil. The conversion factor relating the two units is evidently $\pi/4$. For example, an area measured in square mils may be changed to circular mils by multiplying the number of square mils by $4/\pi$.

An area given in square inches may be changed to circular mils by multiplying the number of square inches by $4/\pi \times 10^6$.

(c) Circular mil-ohms per inch. This is the resistance at some specified temperature, usually 60°C., of a specimen 1 in. in length and having a sectional area of 1 C.M. This unit of resistivity finds special application in calculating the resistance of motor and generator field coils. Copper wire at typical field coil temperatures of around 60°C. has a resistivity of 1.0 C.M.-ohms per inch, so that the resistance of a field coil can be computed very easily by dividing the wire length, in inches, by its sectional area in circular mils.

See the table following Art. 13 for the resistivities of some common materials.

13. Temperature Coefficients. The resistivities of most metals increase with increases in temperature. Copper, aluminum, silver and other metals of the usual commercial standards of purity show very appreciable increases, but many special alloys have been developed which are practically unaffected by temperature changes of ordinary magnitude.

Fortunately the curve relating resistivity and temperature is nearly a straight line so that the effects of temperature changes may be computed easily. If ρ_t is the resistivity of a certain metal at t°C. the resistivity ρ_T at a higher temperature T°C. may be approximated closely by the following relation:

$$\rho_t = \rho_T \left[1 + a(T - t)\right]. \tag{8}$$

The coefficient a is called the temperature coefficient of resistance of the material.

The resistivities and temperature coefficients of three metals and two common alloys are listed in the following table.

TABLE I

Material	Resistivity		Temperature Coefficient at 20°C.
	Microhms cm. cube at 20°C.	C.M.-ohms per foot at 20°C.	
Aluminum........	2.828	17.01	0.00403
Copper..........	1.724	10.37	0.00393
Tungsten........	5.5	33.1	0.0047
Constantan......	49.	295.	0.000005
Nichrome	112.	675.	0.00016

14. Resistances in Series and Parallel. The current drawn by a single resistance unit from a constant supply voltage may be calculated easily by the application of Ohm's law. A 5-ohm resistor, for example, will draw a current of 20 amperes from 100-volt mains. The flow of a current of I amperes through a resistance of R ohms may be pictured as creating a counter-voltage, RI volts, which is necessarily equal to the applied voltage, E.

In a series circuit composed of several resistance units the current will be the same in all parts of the circuit, and its value may be computed by dividing the applied voltage by the sum of the individual resistances.

$$I = \frac{E}{R_1 + R_2 + R_3 + \cdots}. \tag{9}$$

The summation of the RI drops created in the various resistance units by the flow of current will be equal to the applied voltage. For example, three resistances of 4, 6 and 10 ohms respectively are connected in series to a 120-volt supply. The current will be

$$I = \frac{120}{4 + 6 + 10} = \frac{120}{20} = 6 \text{ amperes,}$$

and voltage drops of 24, 36 and 60 volts respectively will occur in the three resistances, adding up to 120, the applied voltage.

When several resistance units are connected in parallel across constant-voltage mains the current in each resistor will be determined entirely by its own resistance and by the value of the applied voltage. The total current drawn by all the resistance units will be the sum of the currents of the individual units. Thus a 5-ohm and a 4-ohm resistor connected in parallel across 100-volt mains will draw currents of 20 amperes and 25 amperes respectively, making a total current of 45 amperes. The addition of another resistor, say 10 ohms, in parallel with the two units already connected to the supply mains will not change their individual currents if the supply voltage remains constant. The total current, however, will be increased by the 10 amperes now entering the 10-ohm resistor.

Occasionally it may be desirable to compute the equivalent resistance which, when substituted for a combination of parallel resistances, will draw the same total current. This may be done by means of the following equation:

$$R = \frac{1}{\dfrac{1}{r_1} + \dfrac{1}{r_2} + \dfrac{1}{r_3} + \cdots}, \tag{10}$$

where $r_1, r_2, r_3, \ldots$ are the resistance values of the separate units which are in parallel and R is the equivalent resistance of the combination. Obviously the value of R will always be less than the value of the smallest resistance unit in the parallel combination. It should also be evident that the above equation cannot be used if one or more of the individual paths contain sources of voltage, such as batteries or rotating machines.

PROBLEMS

1. A conductor 20 in. long, carrying a current of 10 amperes, is acted upon by a force of 2.2 lb. when placed in a magnetic field. What must be the flux density of this field, in gausses? (The conductor lies perpendicular to the field.)

2. How much current would a conductor 40 cm. long have to carry in order to receive a deflecting force of 1000 dynes in a magnetic field of 10,000 gausses density, which is acting along a line making an angle of 40° with the normal to the conductor?

3. A conductor 10 in. long, bent to a right angle at its middle, carries 400 amperes and lies in a magnetic field of 50,000 gausses density. The direction of this field is normal to the plane of the conductor. Find the resultant force in pounds acting upon the conductor.

4. A conductor is bent into the arc of a circle of 10-in. radius, and carries a current of 100 amperes. The central angle subtended is 60°. A magnetic field of 60,000 lines per square inch density is acting on the conductor in a direction normal to the plane of the conductor. Find the resultant force in pounds acting on the conductor.

5. A horizontal wire, stretched parallel to the direction in which a magnetic compass points, carries a current of 1000 amperes flowing toward the north. The wire is 250 meters long, the density of the earth's field is 0.58 gauss and the magnetic dip is 63°. Calculate the force in pounds with which the earth's field acts on the wire, and specify its direction.

6. Let the coil of Fig. 7 be turned to a position 90° from the one shown. Let the average flux density acting on the coil sides be 30,000 lines per square inch and its direction perpendicular to the plane of the coil. The length of the coil sides is 10 in., and it carries 10 amperes. Calculate the force in pounds acting on each coil side, and indicate its line of action.

7. The axle of an ordinary railway coach has a length of 8 ft. Assume the density of the earth's field to be 0.6 gauss and its angle of dip 70°. When the car is traveling 70 miles per hour due east, what voltage is generated between the ends of the axle? Does the direction of travel affect the value of this voltage?

8. A wire 22 cm. long is moving with a velocity of 40 cm. per sec. perpendicular to a magnetic field whose average density is 5000 gausses. Compute the average voltage generated in the wire.

9. How fast would a conductor 12 in. in length need to move across a magnetic field of 20,000 lines per square inch average density in order to generate 0.02 volt?

10. If a straight conductor 2 ft. long is revolved at 1000 rpm. about an axis through one end and perpendicular to the conductor, what voltage will be generated in the conductor when it moves in a magnetic field which has a direction parallel to the axis and a strength of 50,000 maxwells per square inch?

What torque in pound-feet will have to be overcome in order to sustain this motion, if the induced voltage is permitted to produce a current of 100 amperes by completing an electric circuit between the ends of this revolving conductor? Assume the system to be frictionless.

What mechanical horsepower will be used to maintain rotation? Calculate from the foregoing how many volt-amperes or watts of electrical power generated correspond to each horsepower of mechanical power consumed.

11. An armature is rotating at a constant speed of 1200 rpm. in a 2-pole frame. Its radius is 5 in., and its active conductors are 15 in. long. The flux lines under the poles are assumed to be radial and to have a constant density of 60,000 lines per square inch everywhere under the pole. The pole span is such that any given conductor is cutting flux 70% of the time. Draw the voltage-time curve for one conductor, and compute its average value for 1/2 revolution.

12. The flux of each pole of a certain 6-pole generator is 4.8×10^6 maxwells. The generator armature rotates at 450 rpm. The portion of the armature circumference covered by the pole faces amounts to 70%.

(a) Calculate the voltage generated in a single conductor while it passes under one pole.

(b) Calculate the average voltage generated in a single conductor in 1/6 revolution of the armature.

13. A rectangular one-turn coil is centrally located in the air gap between two magnet poles which are so large compared to their separation that the flux density may be assumed to be uniform and constant throughout the entire gap. The axis of rotation of the coil is perpendicular to the flux lines, the length of the coil side is 10 cm. and the distance from the coil side to the axis is 2 cm. The angular velocity of the coil is constant at 20 rps., and the air-gap flux density is 10,000 lines per square centimeter.

What is the maximum value of the generated voltage?

Write the expression for the instantaneous voltage in terms of its maximum value and the angular position of the coil.

What is the average value of the voltage generated in one complete revolution? In 1/2 revolution?

14. A conductor is " cutting flux " at the average rate of 100,000 lines per second. Compute the average induced voltage, in volts and in abvolts.

15. A coil of 200 turns is linked with a magnetic circuit which requires 0.1 second for the flux to build up from zero to 1,400,000 lines. What will be the average value of the voltage induced in the coil by the changing flux?

16. An average voltage of 2.5 volts is desired in a coil linking a certain magnetic circuit. How many turns must the coil have if the flux changes from +250,000 to −250,000 lines in a time interval of 1/2 second?

17. If the flux linking with a coil of N turns varies sinusoidally with time, write the expression for the voltage induced in the coil at any instant. Do you see any important fact growing out of this relationship?

18. Assume that the accompanying figure represents the voltage wave in a certain armature coil. Calculate the average value of that portion of the wave lying between O and A.

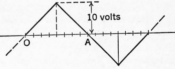

Prob. 18, Ch. 1.

19. Let the diagram of Problem 18 represent the flux linking with a one-turn coil, each horizontal scale division being 1/10 second and the peak value of the flux being 500,000 maxwells. Draw the corresponding wave of induced voltage, and state its maximum value.

20. A copper disk is rotated with a constant angular velocity underneath the north pole of a bar magnet, as shown in the figure. If a galvanometer is connected to brushes B and A, what will be the direction of the current through it? If the galvanometer is connected to brushes B and C? To C and D?

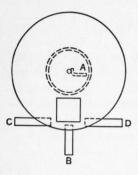

21. The bar magnet and the brushes are removed from the apparatus shown in the preceding problem and a magnetic needle is held in a central position just above the disk so that it is free to turn in a plane parallel to the disk. What will happen to the needle when the disk is rotated at a constant speed? Explain.

22. A copper rod 2 cm. in diameter has a resistance of 0.001 ohm. What will be its approximate resistance when drawn into wire 0.1 in. in diameter?

23. What will be the resistance at 20°C. of a copper bus bar 15 ft. long, 1/4 in. thick and 4 in. wide?

24. A set of motor field coils has a measured resistance of 100 ohms at 70°F. What resistance will it have at a temperature of 85°C.?

25. How many degrees temperature rise would be required to cause a 15% increase in the resistance of an aluminum conductor? Assume that the original resistance is measured at 20°C.

26. An annular block of copper is to be heated inductively, by placing it over a cylindrical iron core carrying an alternating flux. Its inner radius is 10 cm., its outer radius is 20 cm. and its thickness is 5 cm. The section of the annulus is rectangular. With the help of the calculus find the resistance of the annulus at its initial temperature of 20°C.

27. An electric heater has three elements. When all are placed in parallel across 220 volts they take 1, 4 and 9 amperes respectively. What will be the total current if all are placed in series across the same line?

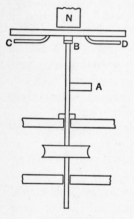

Prob. 20, Ch. 1.

28. Three resistances of 3, 5 and 6 ohms respectively are connected in parallel. What is their equivalent resistance?

29. Four resistances of 6, 4, 10 and 15 ohms respectively are connected in parallel, and this combination is then connected in series with an ammeter and an unknown resistance to 100-volt mains. If the ammeter indicates a current of 20 amperes, what is the value of the unknown resistance?

CHAPTER 2

MEASURING INSTRUMENTS

15. Measurable Current Effects. The presence of current in a conductor is made evident by the various effects it produces, as the chemical effect when a suitable solution is made a part of the circuit, or the heating effect, or the force effect. One or more of these effects can often be utilized to indicate the magnitude of the current. For example, two electrodes might be immersed in a silver nitrate solution and the rate of deposition of silver on one electrode determined. This rate of deposition might be taken as a measure of the current.

If the force effect is used as a measure of current, certain advantages are secured which are not attained by other methods. Inspection of equation 4 suggests two possibilities in the utilization of the force effect for current measurement. A conductor might be placed in a field of constant density and measurements taken of the deflecting force produced when the conductor carries current. Or the conductor might be placed in a field whose density bears a known relationship to the current to be measured. The amount of current in the conductor corresponding to a measured deflecting force might then be determined. The first possibility is the more practical.

16. Permanent Magnet Ammeter. Suppose that a permanent magnet (*A*, Fig. 12) is shaped so that its poles, *BC*, are quite close together, and a few turns of fine wire are wound on a non-magnetic rectangular form, *D*, pivoted as shown. For the indicated flux and current directions the conductors nearest *B* will be given an upward force impulse and those nearest *C* will experience an equal downward force, thus producing a clockwise torque about the axis of support. A study of the pattern of the magnetic field in the region between the poles reveals an uneven distribution of the flux lines, so that as the pivoted coil turns owing to the above-described torque the density of the flux lines linking with it is continually changing. If a stationary iron cylinder is placed within the coil and the magnet poles *BC* are provided with curved faces which flare out and partially surround the cylinder so that the entire space between the magnet poles is filled with iron (except the narrow gaps needed to allow freedom of motion to the form holding the movable coil), three distinct benefits are observed. The air-gap field pattern becomes radial and practically uniform in intensity, and the magnitude of the density in the gap is greatly increased.

21

17. Necessity for Counter-torque.   Consider what happens in such an instrument when current is sent through the coil.   If the coil sides are lying in a high-density field a considerable amount of torque will be

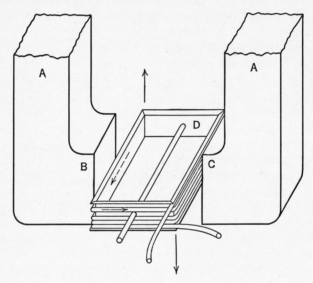

Fig. 12.   Coil in the field of a permanent magnet.

built up immediately — much greater than the frictional torque at the pivots — and an angular acceleration, α, will be imparted to the coil. The factors determining the magnitude of α are expressed in equation 11,

$$\alpha = \frac{T}{J}, \tag{11}$$

where α = angular acceleration in radians per second per second.

   T = net or unbalanced torque in gram-centimeters.

   J = moment of inertia of the coil in gram-centimeters^2.

The resulting angular velocity will be sufficient to cause serious damage to the coil when it reaches its limit of travel unless some kind of counter-torque is brought to bear on the moving coil as soon as it begins its motion.   Spiral hair springs serve this purpose admirably, since they not only bring the coil to rest easily, but also serve as electrical connectors for the moving coil and are very light in weight.

18. Production of Uniform Scale.   Consider an assembled instrument of this type as shown in Fig. 13.   Assume that the scale divisions are to be marked in their proper places by connecting the instrument in series with one which has already been calibrated and passing various amounts of current through both. If the position of the pointer is carefully marked when the calibrated instrument reads 1 unit of current, and again when the calibrated instrument reads 2 current units, the angle through which the pointer moves when its coil carries 2 units is found to be just twice the angle it deflects for 1 unit. Similar observations for other current values indicate that the entire scale is uniformly spaced, provided that the total angle of twist is not so great as to bring the coil sides very near the tips of the magnet poles. The reason for this uniformity can easily be discovered.

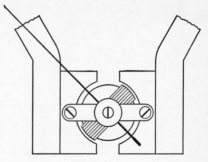

FIG. 13. Permanent magnet ammeter.

It is well known that the resisting force produced by a spring when it is elongated is proportional to the amount of elongation, provided that the elastic limit of the spring is not exceeded. This also applies to the spiral springs attached to the coil of the instrument shown in Fig. 13, if we substitute counter-torque for resisting force, and angular deflection for elongation. If the torque developed in the coil by electromagnetic reactions is doubled, angular motion begins and continues until the springs have been wound up enough to produce a doubled counter-torque, and the coil then becomes stationary in this new position. The only remaining step in this analysis is to answer the question how much increase in current through the coil would be required to produce a doubled torque. Since this is a permanent-magnet instrument with a constant, uniform field density, equation 4 shows that the current would have to be doubled. This can now be summarized:

1. Torque developed electromagnetically is proportional to the current.

2. Counter-torque is proportional to deflection angle.

3. At equilibrium, developed torque equals counter-torque.

4. Therefore, deflection angle is proportional to current, which results in a uniform scale.

19. Damping Devices. The permanent-magnet ammeter as so far described lacks one feature that is very important to the user of the instrument. The moving system is so light and so delicately pivoted that bearing friction is almost negligible in comparison to the strong forces acting on the coil. As a result a sudden current change, even of small magnitude, will cause the coil to swing beyond its ultimate position of balance, and accurate readings of the pointer position are impossible until the oscillations have died out. Some device is needed which will "damp out" these oscillations quickly without affecting the ultimate position of the coil. An air vane attached to the moving system and partially enclosed by a stationary chamber will accomplish the desired result very nicely and is used on many instruments.

Another method which might be called electromagnetic damping is of more interest as it is particularly suited to permanent-magnet instruments. A light, low-resistance material such as aluminum is required in the construction of the rectangular "bobbin" which supports the turns of wire. The sequence of events by which damping is produced by a metallic bobbin may be summarized as follows:

1. The wires on the bobbin receive current from some external source.
2. The bobbin is caused to turn on its pivots.
3. The sides of the bobbin cut the magnetic field and have voltages induced in them.
4. These voltages combine to produce a circulating current in the bobbin.
5. The circulating current reacts with the magnetic field to produce a counter-torque.
6. The counter-torque retards the motion of the bobbin.

The more violent the initial motion due to the instrument current, the larger the circulating current in the bobbin and the more powerful is its counter-torque. As the velocity of motion reduces, the damping torque reduces with it, becoming zero when the coil becomes stationary, so that the accuracy of the instrument is not affected by the use of electromagnetic damping.

20. Ammeter Shunts. It is quite obvious that the moving coil of a permanent-magnet ammeter must be designed to carry very small currents if high accuracy and extreme sensitivity are to be expected. Large current capacity would mean large wire size and a heavy moving element. When it is desired to measure large amounts of current with this type of instrument a by-pass must be designed which will carry most of the current, and will allow only a small, known fraction of it to pass through the moving coil of the instrument. Such a by-pass is usually called an ammeter shunt.

It is quite common practice to design ammeter moving coils for a maximum current of about 20 milliamperes and to adjust the resistance of the moving-coil circuit so that an applied voltage of 50 millivolts will produce the exact current required for full-scale deflection. Figure 14 shows a typical ammeter circuit. The shunt has two heavy terminals by which the current to be measured enters and leaves. Two small terminals are connected to the instrument posts by special low-resistance leads. The narrow metallic strip bridg-

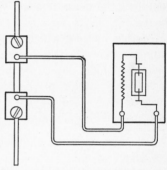

ing the heavy terminal blocks must have an accurately determined resistance. The following example will illustrate the computations necessary to determine the proper value of this resistance.

Assume that the instrument itself requires 25 milliamperes to produce full-scale deflection and has a resistance of 2 ohms, so that 50 millivolts must be applied to its terminals for full-scale deflection. It is required to determine the resistance of a shunt which when used with this meter will cause it to function as a 25-ampere ammeter. The current through the shunt must be 24.975 amperes. In other words, the ap-

Fig. 14.   Ammeter   and   shunt connections.

plication of 50 millivolts to the combination of shunt and instrument must produce a current of 0.025 ampere in the instrument and 24.975 amperes in the shunt. The resistance of the shunt must be 0.050/24.975 or 0.002002+ ohm. This shunt would be called a 50-millivolt, 25-ampere shunt.

If this combination of instrument and shunt is to be a permanent one the shunt will probably be mounted within the case of the instrument and the scale marked in amperes. An instrument intended to be used with a number of external shunts usually has no name attached to its scale divisions, and the instrument user must determine the actual meaning in amperes of a given pointer position by noting the shunt rating and the number of scale divisions. For instance, 47 scale divisions on an instrument with a total of 100 divisions used with a 50-ampere shunt would mean 23.5 amperes in the main circuit.

21. Voltmeters and Voltmeter Multipliers. Since the resistance of such an instrument as just described is constant, the pointer deflection is also proportional to the voltage applied to the instrument terminals. In this sense any ammeter of this type may likewise be considered as a low-range voltmeter.

Moving coils especially designed for voltmeters have resistances of the order of 100 ohms and deflect to full scale with about 0.01 ampere, so that a voltage as high as 1 volt can be applied directly to the coil terminals. If voltages in excess of this amount are to be measured, a resistance must be connected in series with the moving coil. The amount of series resistance needed to give the instrument any desired range can be calculated easily as shown in the following example.

A 150-volt voltmeter is to be provided with a moving coil of 100 ohms resistance, and 0.01 ampere is required for full-scale deflection. The total resistance of the instrument circuit must be 150/0.01, or 15,000 ohms. The series resistance needed is therefore 14,900 ohms. If a 15-volt instrument is needed, the total resistance must be 15/0.01 or 1500 ohms. The two ranges may be provided in one instrument by the arrangement shown in Fig. 15.

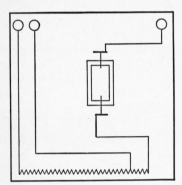

Fig. 15. Voltmeter circuit.

Assuming that a 150-volt voltmeter is available, the student will find it profitable to compute the additional resistance needed to give it, say, 20 times its usual range. A resistance unit designed to increase the range of a voltmeter is sometimes called a multiplier or a volt box.

22. The Oscillograph. The oscillograph is a very sensitive direct-current ammeter modified in design to suit it to the task of measuring a rapidly changing current. Figure 16 shows its essential parts. A single loop of wire with a tiny mirror fastened to it is suspended vertically in a strong, unidirectional magnetic field produced by direct-current electromagnets or by permanent magnets made of special alloy. An intense beam of light is directed on the mirror, and the reflected beam serves as the pointer of the instrument. The current to be studied is passed through the wire loop. Variations in the magnitude or direction of the current produce corresponding variations in the position of the mirror mounted on the loop, and the reflected beam can be made to trace a line on a rapidly moving photographic film. The displacement of the line from its position for zero current in the loop is a measure of the actual current value instant by instant, and the

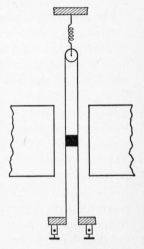

Fig. 16. Oscillograph element.

trace is recorded on the film for future study. For a more extended discussion of the constructional features of the oscillograph and its applications consult any modern textbook on alternating currents.

23. Iron-vane Instruments. If two pieces of iron are placed close together within a coil, parallel to each other and to the coil axis, a current through the coil will magnetize each piece in the same direction so that a force of repulsion will be set up between them, since like poles will be adjacent.   If one iron piece is fixed and the other movable this repulsion can be made to actuate a pointer and a restraining force can be created by spiral springs which will cause the pointer to take a definite position for each value of current in the coil. Figure 17 shows the most satisfactory arrangement, in which the stationary and movable pieces are little iron bands shaped about the coil axis as a center. The pivots of the moving system are also on the coil axis, and the only motion which the repulsive force can produce is an angular one which turns the inner band away from the outer one. This type of instrument has a non-uniform scale and an air-vane damping system.

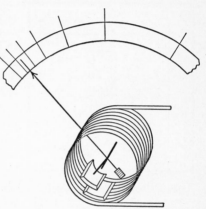

FIG. 17.   Iron vane instrument.

24. Electrodynamometer Voltmeter. If, in Fig. 13, the permanent magnet and central iron core are removed and two coils are placed one on each side of the moving coil so as to produce the same kind of magnetic effect as the magnet poles, and if the moving coil is electrically connected to the polar or field coils so that the same current passes through all, we have the essential features of the so-called electrodynamometer type of instrument.   For use as a voltmeter the field coils would be wound with many turns of fine wire, and the meter would have a high resistance and would require only a small current for full-scale deflection. The construction of a low-resistance ammeter on this principle is also possible.

The density of the magnetic field by which the moving coil is affected is not constant in this type of instrument, but varies in direct proportion to the value of the current in the field coils.   Furthermore, the flux is not distributed as uniformly about the path of the moving coil as in the permanent-magnet instrument.   Thus a doubled current in the moving coil will be acted upon by an approximately doubled field density, which causes the torque to be about four times its original value.   The scale will evidently be non-uniform.

This type of instrument must be protected from external magnetic fields. It should not be placed near other instruments or near con-ductors carrying large currents unless the manufacturer has surrounded the essential parts with a good magnetic shield.

25. Electrodynamometer Wattmeter. The wattmeter is an ingenious instrument in which some of the features of the ammeter and the volt-meter are combined. When properly connected to the wires supplying power to a load, say a bank of lamps, its deflections are proportional to the product of the current in the wires and the voltage across the circuit. Figure 18 shows its essential features. The main magnetic field is pro-duced by two coils, B–B, which consist of a relatively small number of turns of heavy wire and are connected to the external circuit in the same manner as an ammeter would be connected. The moving coil, pivoted in the central space between the two fixed coils, consists of many turns of fine wire, and together with its series resistance, R, is connected across the external circuit as a voltmeter would be connected. The current through the moving coil is evidently proportional to the voltage of the external circuit. The flux produced by the field coils (often called current coils) is directly proportional to the amount of current passing through them, since the instrument is built with-out iron in the magnetic circuit. The torque produced is therefore closely proportional to the product of the circuit voltage and line current, or to the power delivered to the receiving circuit. Exact proportionality cannot be expected as the moving coil changes its position relative to the fixed coils with every variation in the current of each and will be affected by the non-uniformity of the field produced by the fixed coils. It has, therefore, a non-uniform scale. Spiral springs produce the necessary counter-torque, and air-vane damping is usually employed.

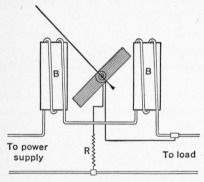

To power supply   R   To load

FIG. 18. Wattmeter circuit.

It is customary for manufacturers of portable wattmeters to place ± marks upon one terminal of the current or field circuit and one terminal of the potential or moving-coil circuit even though the instrument may be provided with a reversing switch. The user is advised to con-nect the ± potential terminal to the same polarity of the power supply as the ± current terminal. Unless this procedure is followed there is danger of instrument error as well as a possibility of insulation break down. This will be understood if it is remembered that the moving and fixed coils are actually very close together, and, if their circuits are so connected that one is at the potential of the + line when the other is at − potential, damage may result.

A careful inspection of Fig. 18 will show that the instrument will be caused to deflect slightly as soon as connected to line voltage, even though there is no receiving circuit drawing current through the meter. This deflection is due to the reaction between the current in the potential coil and the magnetic field produced by that same current as it passes through the current coils on its way to the potential coil. To avoid this error most good wattmeters have a compensating coil which is an additional field coil coaxial with the regular field coils and connected in series with the potential coil. It is wound in such a way that the field set up by its current just neutralizes the field set up by the same current in the main field coils so that the resultant field is zero and there will be no deflection of the needle until the actual load current passes through the meter.

26. Watt-hour Meter. A meter designed to record the total amount of electrical energy drawn from the supply mains is called a watt-hour meter. There are two common types of direct-current watt-hour meters: the mercury flotation type and the commutator type. Each consists of three essential parts: a motor element, a braking element and a recording element, and the only radical difference between the two types is in the motor element.

The commutator type serves to illustrate better the important features of watt-hour measurement. Hence we shall confine our discussion to this type and refer the reader to several of the textbooks listed at the end of the chapter for ample treatment of the mercury flotation type.

Figure 19 shows a commutator type of watt-hour meter in diagrammatic form. The motor element consists of two low-resistance field coils, SC, connected in series with the load or receiving circuit, and a high-resistance armature, AA, mounted in the space between the field coils. The armature with its series resistance, R, is connected across the supply line in the same manner as the potential coil of a wattmeter. Since the magnetic circuit of the motor element contains no iron the magnetic field strength will be directly proportional to the current in the field coils, which is the load current. The high-resistance armature circuit draws a current that is proportional to the load voltage. Therefore (by equation 4) the motor torque will be proportional to the product of load voltage and load current, which is the power in watts drawn by the load.

To produce enough torque in the motor element to take care of friction and have the meter always on the verge of starting so that the slightest current drawn by the load will be sufficient to start registration, a friction compensator is provided in the form of an adjustable field coil, *FC*, coaxial with the main field coils but connected in series with the potential circuit.

The braking element utilizes the production of torque by electromagnetic action. An aluminum disk, *D*, fastened to the motor shaft passes between the poles of one or more permanent magnets, *DM*. When the disk is set in motion by the torque created in the motor ele-

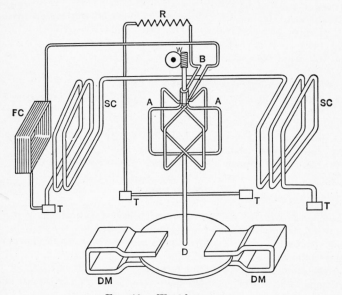

Fig. 19. Watt-hour meter.

ment, voltages are induced which cause circulating currents to flow in the disk, and these react with the magnets to produce a retarding torque which is closely proportional to the speed of the disk.

The recording element is simply a revolution counter attached to the meter shaft by suitable gearing, *W*, with the ratio adjusted to enable the counter dials to be graduated in watt-hours or some convenient multiple thereof.

Summary of watt-hour meter performance:

1. Strength of magnetic field of motor element is proportional to load current.
2. Armature current is proportional to load voltage.
3. Torque on armature is proportional to load watts.
4. Acceleration results from production of torque in motor element.

5. Retarding torque is built up in disk which is proportional to speed.

6. When torque equilibrium is reached, disk speed will be proportional to load watts.

7. Number of disk revolutions in a given time will be proportional to energy delivered to load in that time.

SUGGESTED BIBLIOGRAPHY

A. General information on electric meters.
  1. Standard Handbook for Electrical Engineers, 6th edition, 1933, Section 3.
  2. Electric Meters, JANSKY, McGraw-Hill, 2nd edition, 1917.
B. Theoretical study of electric meter design.
  1. Electrical Measuring Instruments, DRYSDALE and JOLLEY, Benn, Ltd., 1924.
C. Practical information on various makes of meters.
  1. Handbook for Electric Metermen, National Electric Light Association, 4th edition.
D. Calibration and use of meters.
  1. Experimental Electrical Engineering, Vol. I, 4th edition, KARAPETOFF and DENNISON, John Wiley & Sons.
  2. Electrical Measurements, F. A. LAWS, McGraw-Hill Book Co.

PROBLEMS

1. The moving element of a certain permanent-magnet voltmeter has a resistance of 75 ohms and requires 12 milliamperes for full-scale deflection. Specify the value and circuit connections of the series resistances necessary to make this instrument a triple-range voltmeter: 0–3, 0–150 and 0–300.

2. A 150-volt voltmeter has a total resistance between its terminals of 14,000 ohms. Compute the amount of additional resistance that will be needed in series with this instrument to give it a full-scale range of 750 volts.

3. Two voltmeters are connected in series across a line. Voltmeter 1 has a scale of 0–150, a resistance of 4000 ohms and indicates 130. The scale of voltmeter 2 is 0–300 and its resistance is 6000 ohms. Find (a) the current through the meters; (b) the reading of voltmeter 2; (c) the voltage of the line.

4. Three voltmeters are connected in series across an unknown voltage. Voltmeter 1 has a resistance of 15,000 ohms and a scale of 0–175 volts; voltmeter 2 has a resistance of 29,000 ohms and a scale of 0–300; voltmeter 3 reads 130 and is carrying 10 milliamperes. Determine the readings of the other meters.

5. A certain permanent-magnet type of ammeter has 100 scale divisions and a resistance including flexible leads of 2.0 ohms. Full-scale deflection is produced by 25 milliamperes. What must be the resistance of a shunt for use with this meter in order to make it function as a 100-ampere ammeter? What will be the per cent error in the reading if the true line current is 50 amperes and the meter circuit resistance is changed to 2.2 ohms by the use of a different pair of connecting leads?

6. In order to measure a current greater than the range of any of the ammeters that were available, three ammeters were connected in parallel by heavy copper connectors. These ammeters were of 100-, 50- and 25-ampere scales, and had resist-

ances of 0.0025, 0.0040 and 0.0125 ohm respectively. What is the maximum current that can be read on this combination?

7. Three ammeters are connected in parallel with each other by means of heavy copper connectors. Their full-scale ranges are 25, 10 and 50 amperes respectively. Each requires 0.05 volt at its terminals for full-scale deflection. How will a total line current of 65 amperes be divided among the three ammeters?

8. Two ammeters are connected in parallel by means of heavy copper connectors. Ammeter A has a range of 100 amperes and requires 0.05 volt for full-scale deflection. Ammeter B has a range of 200 amperes and requires 0.04 volt for full-scale deflection. How will a current of 150 amperes be divided between these meters?

9. The coil of a permanent-magnet type of voltmeter has a resistance of 100 ohms and requires a current of 10 milliamperes for full-scale deflection. Specify 'the value and show the connections of the series resistance required to make this instrument serve as a double-range voltmeter with the scales 0–15 and 0–300.

10. If the moving system of a voltmeter weighs 3 grams and the area of bearing surface on the thrust bearing is 0.001 sq. mm., calculate the pressure exerted on the bearing in pounds per square inch.

11. If the moving system of an undamped galvanometer is deflected and the deflecting torque is then removed, the resulting oscillation can be considered as an example of simple harmonic motion if friction is negligible. Let the torsion constant of the suspension be 50 dyne-cm. per radian and the moment of inertia of the moving system 5.2 gram-cm.^{2} Derive the equation by which the time required for one complete oscillation may be calculated, and determine the time in seconds.

12. Show that the ratio of the moment of inertia of a rectangular coil to its weight is given by the expression

$$\frac{I}{W} = \frac{b^2}{4} \times \frac{h + \frac{1}{3}b}{h + b}$$

where h = coil length, b = coil width and the axis of rotation passes through the coil center of gravity and is parallel to h.

CHAPTER 3

MOTOR ELEMENTS

27. An Elementary Motor. A study of the arrangement shown in Fig. 12 suggests the possibility of obtaining motor action with such a device. In order to produce unidirectional rotation it is evidently necessary to bring about a reversal of either field polarity or coil current every half revolution. The reversal of coil current is the more easily accomplished of the two. Figure 20 shows a one-turn coil provided with a simple reversing switch, or two-part commutator. If this coil is

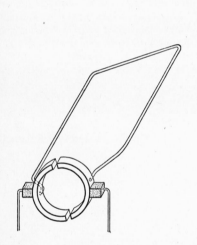

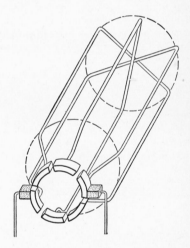

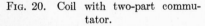

FIG. 20. Coil with two-part commutator.

FIG. 21. Six-part commutator.

pivoted between the poles of suitable magnets two unidirectional pulsations of torque are produced every revolution. By the use of three symmetrically spaced coils and a six-part commutator six torque impulses per revolution can be obtained, thus smoothing out the operation and preventing stalling on a "dead center." See Fig. 21 for this arrangement.

The average torque to be expected from this motor is very small at best. Even though powerful permanent magnets are used, the air gap between the poles is so large that the field strength in the air gap will be very small. Higher gap flux densities may be secured by substituting electromagnets with iron cores in place of the permanent magnets, and by filling most of the central space between the poles with an iron cylinder or armature provided with projecting shafts and bearings so that it can rotate easily. By laying the conductors in slots cut in the cylinder parallel to the axis of rotation they will be protected from injury, and the air gap can be made shorter.

Figure 22 shows an improved machine having its armature conductors connected to form what is called a continuous drum winding. The principles governing the winding connections will be discussed in detail

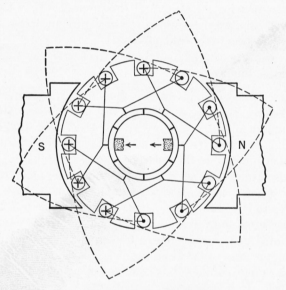

Fig. 22.   Drum-wound armature.

in Chapter 9. It is apparent, however, that all the conductors are carrying current; that the direction of the current in each conductor is such as to produce clockwise torque for the given magnetic field polarities; and that there are two paths in parallel between the brushes, each path containing six conductors.

28. Construction of a Modern Motor. Familiarity with the constructional features of a modern motor and an understanding of the function of each part are prerequisites to an effective study of its theory of operation. The principal parts may be listed as follows:

(a) The yoke which forms the frame of the motor.

(b) The field poles which project from the yoke and carry the flux to and from the armature.

(c) The field coils which surround the poles and produce the magnetic flux.

(d) The armature core which occupies the space between the poles and supports the armature conductors.

(e) The armature coils whose current reacts with the field flux to produce the motor torque.

(f) The commutator which is the automatic reversing switch for the current in the armature coils.

(g) The brushes and brush holders by which contact is made between the rotating armature and the external supply circuit.

(h) The bearings which support the armature and keep it properly aligned with respect to the field poles.

(i) The end frames which are bolted to each side of the yoke and serve to house the bearings.

These parts will now be discussed in the order listed above.

29. The Yoke. The yoke serves a number of purposes. It is usually the main support for all the motor parts and has some kind of footing integral with it by which the motor may be secured firmly to its foundation. Another function of the yoke is to furnish suitable paths for the magnetic flux; it must therefore have good magnetic properties.

Materials which meet the above requirements of strength and high permeability, and in addition are cheap and workable, are limited to cast iron, cast steel and rolled steel. The latter two have now practically supplanted cast iron for motor frames.

A small motor nearly always has its yoke cast in a single piece, or if rolled steel is employed the slab is bent to a circular form and the joint is butt-welded. In a large motor a split yoke is used to facilitate the removal of the armature for repairs, and the two halves are bolted together. The yoke of a 3500-hp., 600-volt motor is shown in Fig. 23. Notice the narrow commutating poles between the main poles, and the heavy pole-face windings designed to reduce armature reaction.

30. The Field Poles. The field poles such as are shown bolted to the inner surface of the yoke in Fig. 23 usually consist of stacks of sheet-steel punchings held together tightly by bolts or by long rivets. Each punching is curved at one end to accommodate itself to the inner surface of the yoke, and the other end is flared in width to form what is called the face of the pole. The reason for the use of laminated rather than solid steel poles will be discussed when the armature core is described (Art. 32).

Small motors usually have two or four poles. In large motors the number of poles used in the design depends largely upon the speed desired. A large high-speed machine is likely to be designed with four poles; a slow-speed motor of the same power rating might require eight

FIG. 23.   Yoke of large machine, showing poles and pole-face windings.
(*General Electric Co.*)

or more poles. It is obvious that an even number of poles is always required, and that the polarity of any two adjacent poles must be opposite.

31. The Field Coils. The magnetic flux required in each pole is produced by one or more coils of wire surrounding the pole and supported by it. These are termed field coils. The kind of field coil used, the number of coils on each pole and the method of connecting them to the power supply are different for the three main classes of direct-current motors and are largely responsible for this classification.

In the shunt motor there is one coil per pole consisting of many turns of fine wire, and all the field coils are usually connected in series and supplied with current from mains of the motor's rated voltage.

The series motor also has one field coil per pole, but it is made up of a few turns of heavy wire. All the field coils are connected in series, and the group is then connected in series with the motor armature.

The compound motor has two field coils per pole, a shunt coil of many turns and a series coil with few turns. The series coils are grouped together and are connected in series with the motor armature while the group of shunt coils is connected directly across the

Fig. 23a. Pole and field coils of compound machine. (*Westinghouse Elec. & Mfg. Co.*)

motor supply mains. Figure 23a shows the pole and field coils of a large compound motor. Here the series coil is formed of copper strap, wound edgewise with small air spaces separating the turns. This type of construction facilitates the cooling of the coils.

32. The Armature Core. The outer portion of the armature which supports the armature conductors and provides an iron path for the flux after it has crossed the air gap under the pole face is called the armature core. It consists of rolled-steel punchings or laminations stacked up in cylindrical fashion and bolted or clamped tightly together. In small machines these punchings are circular disks with their edges slotted and with a central hole for the shaft. In large machines the punchings are not complete circles but are sectors which are firmly dovetailed to a central supporting structure called a spider. Figure 24 shows an armature spider, and the method of assembling the core punchings on the spider is well illustrated in Fig. 25.

The reason why motor and generator armatures are built of laminations can now be stated. It was shown in Chapter 1 that voltages are induced in conductors which are moved across flux lines. If the armature were solid the voltages induced in the teeth on each side of any armature conductor would produce large currents in the teeth because the whole cylinder would offer itself as a path for such currents. Consequently the iron would be considerably heated and the counter-torque associated with this current would be unduly great. By laminating the core the eddy-current paths become restricted largely to the boundaries

Fig. 24.   Armature spider for large machine.   (*Westinghouse Elec. & Mfg. Co.*)

Fig. 25.   Armature core partially assembled on spider.   (*Westinghouse Elec. & Mfg. Co.*)

of the individual laminations, owing to the high contact resistance between adjacent surfaces of the punchings, and the path resistance is greatly increased. The voltages which are the primary cause of the eddy currents are induced as easily as before, but they are now unable to produce large current values.

The unevenness of the iron surface of the armature due to the presence of the slots causes rapid flux pulsations in the poles and quick changes in the distribution of the flux in the pole face as the armature rotates. These are of sufficient magnitude to cause appreciable eddy currents in the pole face unless it or the entire pole is laminated. The polar laminations may be somewhat thicker than the armature punchings so that it is comparatively easy to make the pole rigid, and little difficulty is encountered in fastening the poles to the yoke.

33. Armature Coils. Figure 26 shows a typical armature coil. The usual method of forming such a coil is as follows: a sufficiently long piece of copper stock is selected, the cross-section being either circular or rectangular, depending on the size of the machine and the purpose for which it is designed. An ingenious machine coils and then spreads it until the sides have the proper span, after which it is wrapped with insulating tape. This process is repeated until a suf-

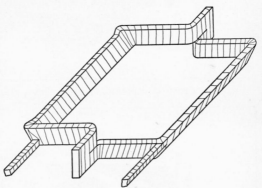

FIG. 26. Form-wound coil.

ficient number of coils is completed to fill the slots in the armature.

The process of installing the finished coils in the armature slots is called armature winding. This subject will be considered in some detail in Chapter 9. Some characteristic features of a simple winding were mentioned in Art. 27 in discussing Fig. 22. Three additional requirements may now be stated.

1. The winding must be symmetrical.
2. Every coil must have the same span.
3. The coil span must be such that, when one side is placed in a slot that is directly under the center of a pole, the other side will occupy a slot which is in approximately the same position under an adjacent pole.

In Fig. 27 a large armature with a partially completed winding is shown.

FIG. 27.   Armature with winding partially completed.   (*General Electric Co.*)

34. The Commutator.   The constructional details of the commutator of a modern motor have several interesting features.   In order to function properly each segment must be insulated from its neighbors

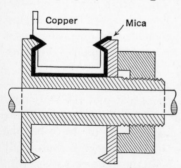

FIG. 28.   Commutator section.

and from the machine's shaft, and yet must present a smooth area of contact to the brush.   It must also resist the powerful centrifugal force created by the rapid rotation of the armature. Some such scheme as shown in Fig. 28 is usually adopted.   Each segment is slightly wedge shaped and has two V-shaped notches cut in it.   The necessary number of segments with their mica separators are assembled on a V-ring mounted on the shaft.   A second V-ring is then brought up against them and tightened.   The resulting pressure has a considerable radial component which draws the tapered segments inward toward the shaft and packs them together rigidly.

Each segment is provided with a projecting shoulder or riser which is slotted to receive the ends of the armature coils, and the ends are held in place by means of solder. The armature is then placed in a lathe and the commutator turned down and carefully smoothed, after which the mica separators are slightly undercut to reduce brush wear and excessive brush chattering.

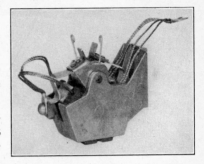

35. Brushes and Brush Holders. Brushes are needed to bring current from the external source of supply to the commutator surface. They must be so located as to send current through every active armature coil in such a direction as will produce the maximum useful torque. The number of positions around the commutator surface requiring contact with a brush is always even; but whether it is 2 or some multiple of 2 depends upon the number of poles and the type of armature winding.

FIG. 29.   Brush holder with brushes.
(*General Electric Co.*)

Figure 29 shows a brush holder designed for a large machine. The twin brushes have separate springs by which the proper contact pressure can be maintained. Notice the stranded copper connections called pigtails which provide low-resistance current paths between brush and terminal.

If the current to be handled at each brush position is very large the current density in the brush is kept within reasonable limits by means of two or more brushes side by side on the same brush arm. Figure 29a shows a close-up of the commutator and brush rigging of a large machine.

Carbon or graphite brushes are used in machines operating under normal conditions. Machines designed for very low voltages are sometimes supplied with copper brushes.

36. Bearings. In order to allow the armature to rotate freely and to maintain proper mechanical clearances between it and the stationary field poles it is necessary to support each end of the shaft in specially designed bearings. Figure 30 shows a modern type of sleeve bearing designed particularly for motors. As the shaft rotates, oil is continually carried up to the upper surface of the shaft by the brass ring which dips in the oil well in the bottom of the bearing housing. This insures uniform lubrication of the contact surfaces.

Fig. 29a.   Close-up of commutator and brush rigging.   (*General Electric Co.*)

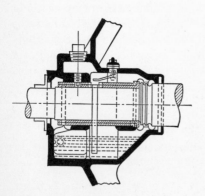

Fig. 30.   Sleeve bearing.

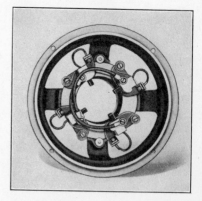

Fig. 31.   End frame of small motor.
(*Fairbanks, Morse & Co.*)

The lining of the bearing which comes into actual contact with the steel shaft is usually a soft alloy called babbitt metal. There are several reasons for the extensive use of this material for bearing surfaces. It has a low coefficient of friction, which assists in keeping the frictional drag small. It has a low melting point so that, if the oil supply becomes exhausted and the bearings begin to overheat, the linings will melt and stop the motor before the shaft temperature reaches a level that will damage it seriously. Furthermore, it is comparatively inexpensive to replace when the original linings have been worn down.

For many motor applications ball or roller bearings have been used with very satisfactory results, but in general sleeve bearings are less expensive and are therefore preferred.

Fig. 31a. Exploded view of small motor. (*Fairbanks, Morse & Co.*)

37. End Frames. Figure 31 shows an end frame for a small motor. It is a one-piece casting of the so-called open type which allows plenty of air to circulate around the motor coils. An exploded view of a small motor is shown in Fig. 31a.

When a motor must be operated in a dust-laden atmosphere or where there is danger of igniting explosive gases by sparks from the commutator it is necessary to use a different form of end frame which has no ventilating openings and is dust and vapor proof. A totally enclosed motor is frequently provided with forced ventilation by means of inlet and outlet ducts built into the end frames and connected by piping to a blower.

SUGGESTED BIBLIOGRAPHY

The best sources of information on the structural features of modern motors are the sales bulletins published by the various electric manufacturing companies.

CHAPTER 4

THE SHUNT MOTOR

38. The Shunt Motor. It has already been pointed out that direct-current motors are usually classified in accordance with the type of field coils they possess and the connection scheme used to supply them with current. The field coils of a shunt motor consist of many turns of fine wire, and they are connected across supply mains of practically constant voltage. The armature is also connected to these supply mains as a separate current path. Figure 32 shows a conventional way of representing the circuits of a shunt motor.

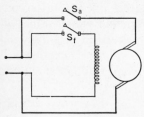

FIG. 32.   Shunt motor operating circuit.

Suppose that switch S_f is closed. A current of the value V/R_f will be produced in the field coils, where V is the voltage of the supply mains and R_f is the resistance of the field circuit. This field current will set up a flux in the motor magnetic circuit, and, so long as the supply voltage and field-circuit resistance remain constant, the magnetic flux and the average flux density in the air gap between the pole face and the armature for our present purposes may be considered constant.

39. The Starting Torque. If switch S_a is now closed a starting current will pass through the armature circuit whose initial value will be V/R_a, where V has already been defined and R_a is the resistance of the armature circuit. This starting current will divide among the several groups of armature conductors with the result that all the conductors lying under a north pole will have deflecting forces exerted on them tending to produce rotation, let us say in a clockwise direction, while at the same time a similar group of conductors under a south pole will have similar force effects tending to produce the same clockwise rotation. The total torque thus produced is called the motor starting torque.

40. Motor Acceleration. The starting torque is normally very large, much greater than the retarding torque produced by friction. In order to simplify the discussion it will be assumed that no mechan-

44

ical load is attached to the motor shaft. A large angular acceleration can therefore be expected, which will continue until either the retarding torque is increased in some manner, or the starting torque is reduced. In this behavior a motor armature is no different from any other rotating mass, and the relationship between its moment of inertia, its angular acceleration and the unbalanced torque causing the acceleration is the familiar one expressed in equation 11.

As a necessary result of acceleration the peripheral velocity of the armature conductors with respect to the stationary field poles rises from zero to greater and greater values. This brings into action a very important phenomenon which will be discussed next.

41. Counter-emf. It has been shown that, if conductors are made to move across or " cut " magnetic flux lines, voltages will be induced in them, and for the most effective production of voltage the velocity of the conductors must be normal to the flux lines. The armature conductors of the motor under discussion fulfill this requirement exactly.

Furthermore, it is evident that all the voltages generated in the conductors passing across one pole will be in the same direction. Since all the conductors under one pole are part of one electrical path between the brushes, the voltages generated in the individual conductors will add up to a considerable amount when the contributions of all the conductors in one path are totaled.

This induced voltage must exert an influence on the current already present in the armature conductors. Application of the method for predicting the direction of an induced voltage (see Art. 6 and Fig. 8) will indicate that the voltage induced in a motor armature opposes the armature current and tends to reduce it. The reasonableness of this conclusion may be confirmed by a process of " reasoning to the ridiculous." Assume that the induced voltage tends to increase the armature current. The acceleration produced by the starting current would cause a rapid increase in induced voltage which would then cause the current to increase to a still larger value. This would increase the acceleration and the induced voltage, and cause another increase in current. The process thus begun would continue until the motor protective devices would be forced to open the supply circuit. Hence this assumption must be considered as contrary to fact, and the conclusion that the induced voltage opposes the armature current is confirmed.

The induced voltage in a motor armature is usually called counter-electromotive force (abbreviated counter-emf., or cemf.).

42. The Counter-emf. Equation. In order to develop an equation for the counter-emf. generated in a motor armature, equation 6 may be restated as a starting point.

$$E = -\frac{d\Phi}{10^8 dt} \text{ volts.} \tag{6}$$

Since the minus sign merely indicates that the voltage induced by a changing flux is opposed to the action which produces it, the average voltage induced in a conductor which cuts Φ lines of flux in t seconds is

$$E_{av.} = \frac{\Phi}{10^8 t} \text{ volts.} \tag{12}$$

Let Φ = the number of flux lines crossing the air gap from one pole to the armature.

p = the number of poles.

N = armature speed in revolutions per minute.

m = number of groups of armature conductors connected in parallel between the brushes.

Z = number of conductors on the armature.

E_g = counter-emf., in volts.

As the armature rotates, any one conductor cuts Φ lines as it passes each pole, and therefore cuts $p\Phi$ lines in every complete revolution of the armature.

The armature is making $N/60$ revolutions per second. Therefore one conductor will cut $p\Phi N/60$ flux lines per second, and the average voltage generated will be $p\Phi N/60 \times 10^8$ volts.

Since Z/m represents the number of armature conductors in series in any one of the paths between the brushes, the total average voltage which will appear at the brushes will be

$$E_g = \frac{Z}{m} \frac{p\Phi N}{60 \times 10^8} \text{ volts.}$$

Rearranging these terms,

$$E_g = \frac{10^{-8}}{60} \frac{pZ}{m} \Phi N \text{ volts.} \tag{13}$$

For a given machine, p, Z and m will have constant values. Therefore the above equation can be written

$$E_g = K\Phi N \tag{14}$$

which is a very useful form for many purposes.

43. Regulating Action of Counter-emf. The analysis of shunt motor behavior during the starting period can now be continued.

1. Closing the armature circuit causes a large rush of current of the value V/R_a to pass through the armature.

2. The reaction of this large current with the magnetic field produced by the shunt field produces a large torque which accelerates the armature rapidly.

3. The velocity imparted to the armature conductors causes them to generate a counter-emf. as they cut the field flux. The higher the velocity, the greater this counter-emf. becomes.

4. The growth of counter-emf. in the armature circuit reduces the net voltage available to force current through the armature, and the armature current begins to drop in value.

5. The torque developed by the armature conductors becomes less, which reduces the acceleration.

6. The velocity continues to increase, but at a slower and slower rate.

7. The counter-emf. continues to increase, but at a slower and slower rate.

8. The armature current and the developed torque continue to decrease, but at a slower and slower rate.

9. A steady operating speed finally results, at which sufficient counter-emf. is produced to hold the armature current to the exact value needed to maintain rotation. There now is perfect balance between the developed torque and the opposing torque produced by friction.* No change in operating speed can occur so long as this torque balance is maintained.

When the armature is rotating, the expression for the value of the armature current cannot be V/R_a, on account of the presence of counter-emf. in the circuit. The equation which does express the voltage-current relationship can be written as follows:

$$I_a = \frac{V - E_g}{R_a},\qquad(15)$$

where I_a is the armature current in amperes, and V, E_g and R_a have already been defined. This can be expanded to

$$I_a = \frac{V - K\Phi N}{R_a}\qquad(16)$$

or
$$V = K\Phi N + R_a I_a\qquad(17)$$

* The term friction torque is used here and elsewhere in Chapters 4 and 5 to mean the complete no-load counter-torque composed of friction, windage, eddy-current torque, etc.

44. The Torque Equation. The various factors affecting the torque developed in a motor armature have been discussed qualitatively. An expression can easily be derived which will state these relationships in a quantitative way.

If it is recalled that equation 4 was built up from certain experimental facts, it becomes a convenient starting point for the following derivation. In Fig. 33 the armature conductors acted upon by the flux from one pole are numbered for convenient reference. Assume that each conductor is carrying a current of I amperes and has a length of L centimeters along the axis of rotation. Then the force in dynes which will tend to move conductor 1 across the field may be written

$$F_1 = B_1 L \frac{I}{10}$$

where B_1 is the average flux density in lines per square centimeter in the region where conductor 1 is located. This is a direct application of equation 4. The above equation can easily be transformed into a more convenient form.

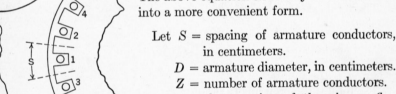

Let S = spacing of armature conductors, in centimeters.

D = armature diameter, in centimeters.

Z = number of armature conductors.

ϕ_1 = that portion of the air-gap flux per pole which is acting on conductor 1.

FIG. 33.　Armature torque.

S may be inserted in both numerator and denominator of the above equation:

$$F_1 = B_1 L S \frac{I}{10S},$$

and since LS is an area with conductor 1 at its center and possessing an average flux density B_1

$$F_1 = \phi_1 \frac{I}{10S}.$$

Substituting the expression $\pi D/Z$ for S,

$$F_1 = \phi_1 \frac{IZ}{10\pi D}$$

NOTE: Art. 44 is built upon material taken by permission from "The Principles of Electrical Engineering," Vol. II, 1919, by Gisbert Kapp.　Edward Arnold & Co.

Similarly,

$$F_2 = \phi_2 \frac{IZ}{10\pi D}$$

is the expression for the force exerted by one pole on conductor 2.

The total force exerted on all the armature conductors that lie under the influence of one pole is

$$F = F_1 + F_2 + F_3 + \cdots,$$

which can be expressed as

$$F = (\phi_1 + \phi_2 + \phi_3 + \cdots)\frac{IZ}{10\pi D},$$

or more simply

$$F = \Phi \frac{IZ}{10\pi D},$$

where Φ is the total air-gap flux per pole.

The total force exerted upon all the conductors by all the poles will be

$$pF = p\Phi \frac{IZ}{10\pi D},$$

where p = the number of poles.

The total torque tending to produce rotation will be

$$T = p\Phi \frac{IZ}{10\pi D} \times \frac{D}{2} = p\Phi \frac{IZ}{20\pi} \text{ dyne-cm.}$$

To express the torque in kilogram-meters it is necessary to divide the above expression by $980,700 \times 100$, which produces

$$T = p\Phi \frac{IZ}{6.1619 \times 10^9} \text{ kg-meters.}$$

To express it in pound-feet it is necessary to multiply the kilogram-meter torque value by 2.205×3.281, which results in

$$T = 0.1174 \times 10^{-8} \, p\Phi IZ \text{ lb-ft.}$$

Since $I = I_a/m$, where I_a is the total armature current and m is the number of conductor groups connected in parallel between brushes, we can write

$$T = 0.1174 \times 10^{-8} \frac{pZ}{m}\Phi I_a \text{ lb-ft.} \tag{18}$$

For a given machine, p, Z and m will have constant values. Therefore the above equation can be written

$$T = c\Phi I_a. \tag{19}$$

Notice the similarity between c in equation 19 and K in equation 14. They contain the same factors and differ only by a number. Their relationship can easily be determined.

$$c \approx 7.05K. \tag{20}$$

45. Effect of Increasing Load Torque. In Art. 43 the regulating effect of the motor counter-emf. during the starting period was considered. The counter-emf. exhibits a similar regulating action if the retarding torque is changed after the starting process is completed. If a mechanical load such as a friction brake is placed on the pulley and held constant, an analysis of the ensuing transition period may be made as follows:

1. The balanced condition which existed between the torque developed in the motor armature and the friction torque is disturbed by the addition of the load torque.

2. Negative acceleration occurs as a result of the unbalanced torque now acting on the armature, and the motor slows down.

3. The motor counter-emf. is decreased by the decrease in speed.

4. The net voltage available to force current through the armature is increased, causing an increase in armature current.

5. The increased current strengthens the developed torque.

6. The difference between the total retarding torque and the developed torque is decreased.

7. The value of the negative acceleration is reduced. In other words, the rate of decrease of speed is reduced.

8. These changes continue until the motor-developed torque is built up to equal the sum of the load and friction torques. The motor speed then becomes constant at a value somewhat less than the no-load value, and there is a permanent increase in the value of I_a.

In Fig. 34 these changes are indicated graphically. Convenient ordinate scales are chosen to represent speed, applied voltage, counter-emf., armature current, developed torque and counter-torque. Time is plotted horizontally. At time t_1 the load torque is added and the transition period begins. It ends at t_2, when the torques become balanced again.

The reader is urged to construct a similar chart to show what happens when the load torque is changed from a large to a small value.

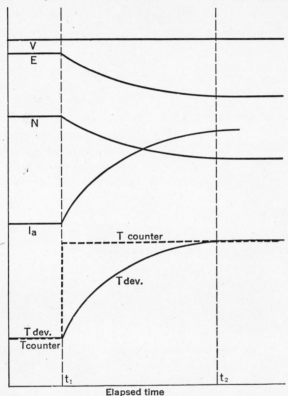

Fig. 34.   Chart of transition period.

46. Effect of Increasing Armature Circuit Resistance. A shunt motor operating at steady speed with a constant-load torque added to its friction torque undergoes a similar transition period if a change is made in the value of its armature circuit resistance. An analysis of such a case follows.

Assumed operating conditions: V, Φ and T_{load} are constant. R_{a1}, N_1 and I_{a1} are the initial values of armature circuit resistance, speed and armature current respectively. R_{a1} is changed to a value R_{a2}, such that $R_{a2} > R_{a1}$.

1. I_{a1} decreases to a value I_{a2}; such that

$$R_{a2} \times I_{a2} = R_{a1} \times I_{a1}.$$

2. This decrease in armature current produces a decrease in the

torque developed in the motor armature and disturbs the balance which existed between the developed torque and the countertorque.

3. Negative acceleration occurs as a result of this unbalanced torque, and the speed decreases.

4. The counter-emf. decreases as the result of the speed decrease.

5. The decrease in counter-emf. permits the armature current to increase again, and the torque developed by the armature is correspondingly increased.

6. The difference between the developed torque and the countertorque becomes smaller, and the negative acceleration begins to fade out. The rate of speed decrease becomes smaller and smaller.

7. These changes continue until the developed torque again equals the counter-torque. This will require a current I_{a1}, the same as the original current, as will be evident from a review of the operating conditions assumed. However, a permanent change in speed has occurred, the new speed N_2 being somewhat less than N_1.

The reader is advised to chart this transition period and the reverse case picturing the effects of a decrease in R_a.

47. Effect of Increasing Armature Applied Voltage. Assumed operating conditions: A loaded shunt motor operating at steady speed; Φ, R_a and T_{load} remaining constant. The voltage applied to the motor armature is increased.

1. I_a increases, owing to the increase in net voltage available to produce it.

2. An increase in the developed torque occurs which brings about an unbalance in the relationship between the developed torque and the counter-torque.

3. Acceleration occurs as a result of this unbalanced torque, and the speed increases.

4. An increase in counter-emf. is produced by the increase in speed.

5. The increase in counter-emf. produces a decrease in the net voltage acting in the armature circuit, which reduces the armature current.

6. A reduction in the developed torque begins so that the net torque available to produce acceleration is lessened.

7. The speed continues to increase, but at a slower and slower rate.

8. These changes continue until the developed torque again equals the sum of the load and friction torques. This will require

I_a to be the same value that was passing through the armature previous to the change in V. However, a permanent change in speed has occurred, the new speed being greater than the old.

The reader is advised to construct charts for the transition period brought about by an increase or a decrease in V.

48. Developed and Delivered Torque. In many problems dealing with motor performance it is necessary to distinguish clearly between the torque produced within the armature by the interaction of the armature current and the field flux, and the torque appearing at the shaft as a part of the mechanical power available to do work. The term developed torque will be used for the former and delivered torque for the latter.

The developed torque is always the greater since it must include the torque needed to overcome friction and other forms of counter-torque which are unavoidably present in the motor even when it is running idle. However, the numerical difference between them is always small.

Delivered torque is always equal and opposite to the counter-torque produced by the mechanical load which the motor is driving.

49. Power Output. If a motor is turning at a constant speed of N revolutions per minute and is driving a mechanical load which is producing a constant counter-torque it is possible to express the mechanical power delivered by the motor in terms of the values of speed and torque. For this purpose let the delivered torque be expressed as a force of F pounds acting at a lever arm equal to the armature radius, R, in feet. When the armature has completed one revolution in response to this force the work done is

$$W = F \times 2\pi R \text{ ft-lb.}$$

If this force causes the armature to rotate at a speed of N rpm. the work done per minute is

$$P = F \times 2\pi R \times N \text{ ft-lb. per min.}$$

Since 33,000 ft-lb. per min. are equivalent to 1 hp., the power of the armature can be expressed in horsepower as follows:

$$\text{hp.} = \frac{F \times 2\pi RN}{33,000} = \frac{TN}{5250}, \tag{21}$$

where T is the torque delivered to the load, in pound-feet, and hp. is the quantity of power delivered in horsepower.

Further details concerning the power relationships in a motor and the matter of losses and efficiency will be considered in Chapter 10.

50. Shunt Motor Performance Curves. Assuming for the present that the motor field flux is unaffected by changes in load torque, inspection of equation 19 shows that variations in developed torque require proportional changes in armature current, and the curve of developed torque plotted against armature current will be a straight line beginning at the origin of the coordinate system. The unavoidable presence of friction causes the curve of load torque vs. armature current to be shifted slightly to the right as shown in Fig. 35.

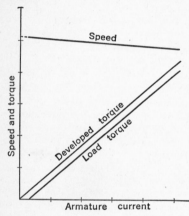

FIG. 35.   Shunt motor speed and torque relations.

If equation 17 is expressed in slightly different form we can tell by inspection the effect of changes in load torque on the speed of a shunt motor. From equation 17

$$N = \frac{V - R_a I_a}{K\Phi}. \qquad (22)$$

If the load torque is zero, I_a will be almost zero since very little is needed to take care of friction, and the speed will be approximately equal to $V/K\Phi$, since $R_a I_a$ will have a very small value if I_a is small. For increasing values of torque, $R_a I_a$ will change almost proportionally and the speed-current plot will be a straight line.

51. Effect of Armature Current on Field Flux. It happens frequently if a shunt motor is forced to operate at a fairly high-speed level under varying load conditions that the relationship between speed and load torque becomes noticeably non-linear. As the load torque is increased, the speed drops slowly and uniformly at first, then levels off and finally shows a tendency to increase. The motor behaves as though its shunt field current were being reduced gradually as the load increases. For the present the following facts may serve to explain this phenomenon. A more detailed discussion will be found in Chapter 11.

1. If the armature of a shunt motor is supplied with current while the shunt field circuit is open, a magnetic field will be produced in and near the armature.

2. The direction of this field is approximately perpendicular to the line of action of the main field flux, and its magnitude is approximately proportional to the armature current.

3. The combined effect of current in the armature and current in the shunt field coils is to create a resultant magnetic field.

4. One component of this resultant field tends to reduce the average flux density in the air gap.

5. Under the operating conditions stated at the beginning of this article the reduction in average density may be sufficient to have a noticeable effect on the speed-armature current relation.

PROBLEMS

1. A shunt motor has sufficient load to cause it to draw a line current of 20 amperes from 200-volt supply mains, and to operate at 1000 rpm. The measured resistances of field and armature circuits are 100 ohms and 1 ohm respectively. Find the value of the armature current.

2. A shunt motor is operating at 900 rpm. Its armature current is 16 amperes, its armature resistance is 0.4 ohm and the supply voltage is 115. Compute the value of the counter-emf. which it is generating, and determine the value of $K\Phi$.

3. A shunt motor is producing 205 volts of counter-emf. when running at a speed of 1000 rpm. What value of counter-emf. will be produced if sufficient resistance is inserted in the armature circuit to reduce the speed to 800 rpm.? The field flux remains constant.

4. A shunt motor has an effective flux per pole of 2.4×10^6 lines, and is running at 1000 rpm. It has 4 poles, 4 parallel paths in the armature and 280 conductors. What is the value of its counter-emf.? If its armature current is 40 amperes, what torque is it developing?

5. A motor has the following constants: $V = 220$; $R_a = 0.3$; $R_f = 80$; $I_a = 22$; $N = 800$.

(a) Compute the pound-feet of torque being developed in its armature.

(b) Assuming friction to be negligible, compute the operating speed if the load torque is doubled. The field remains constant.

6. A shunt motor has an armature resistance of 0.3 ohm and a no-load speed of 700 rpm. Its no-load armature current is 2.5 amperes, and the applied voltage is 110 volts. Find the no-load speed if the armature applied voltage is raised to 150 volts, the field current remaining constant. Find the speed if $I_a = 50$ amperes, $V_a = 150$ volts, as before, and there is no change in field current.

7. A shunt motor has the following constants: $V = 110$; $R_a = 0.3$; no-load $I_a = 2.5$; no-load $N = 700$ rpm. Find N and T developed when the load is adjusted to cause the armature to draw 25 amperes from the supply mains. The field remains constant.

8. A shunt motor has the following constants: $V = 220$; $R_a = 0.35$; no-load $I_a = 2.2$; no-load $N = 1650$. Find N and T developed when the load is adjusted to require an armature current of 35 amperes. The field remains constant.

9. A shunt motor has an armature resistance of 0.6 ohm and a no-load speed of 1100 rpm. Its no-load armature current is 1.2 amperes, and the supply voltage is 220 volts. Find the motor speed when sufficient load is added to bring the armature current up to 20 amperes. Find the speed if a 2-ohm resistor is placed in series with the armature and no change is made in the load torque.

10. A shunt motor has the following constants: $V = 220$; $R_a = 0.4$; no-load $N = 1000$; $I_a = 2.0$. Outline the steps by which the motor regains equilibrium when 1 ohm is suddenly added to the armature circuit. What will be the final value of speed if the motor remains unloaded?

11. A 220-volt motor is operating at 600 rpm. with an armature current of 25 amperes. An external resistance of 3.04 ohms is in series with the armature which has a resistance of 0.5 ohm.

(a) Outline the steps by which the motor regains equilibrium when this external resistance is suddenly removed, the load torque and field flux remaining constant.

(b) What is the developed torque in pound-feet?

(c) What is the final operating speed?

12. A 220-volt shunt motor is drawing an armature current of 25 amperes and is running at 800 rpm. $R_a = 0.4$. How many pound-feet of torque is it developing? If 1 ohm is added to the armature circuit, what will be the speed, for the same torque developed?

13. A 220-volt motor is drawing an armature current of 40 amperes and is running at 1500 rpm. $R_a = 0.35$. How many pound-feet of torque is it developing? If 2 ohms are added to the armature circuit, what will be the speed, for the same torque developed?

14. A 220-volt shunt motor is drawing an armature current of 30 amperes and is running at 900 rpm. Its R_a is 0.4 ohm.

(a) How much torque is it developing?

(b) How fast will it turn if its required torque is cut in half and 0.6 ohm is added to its armature circuit?

15. A shunt motor has been operating at 1200 rpm. and has been drawing an armature current of 40 amperes from 230-volt mains. Its armature resistance is 0.3 ohm. The voltage applied to the armature is now reduced to 150 volts, the field current and the load torque being held constant. What will be the new operating speed?

16. A shunt motor has been operating at 900 rpm. and has been drawing 200 amperes from 120-volt mains. Its armature resistance is 0.024 ohm. The voltage applied to the armature is reduced to 100 volts, the field current and the load torque being held constant. What will be the new operating speed?

17. The armature of a motor requires 50 amperes to develop a torque of 150 lb.-ft. at its normal speed. The applied voltage and the load are adjusted so that the motor develops the same horsepower at half the speed. What are the new values of torque and armature current? Assume that the field strength remains constant.

18. A motor which is running at a speed of 500 rpm. delivers 10 hp. at its pulley.

(a) What is the torque delivered by this motor?

(b) The pulley has a diameter of 15 in. What is the difference in tension in the two sides of the belt?

(c) The motor has an efficiency of 90% at this load. What is the power input to it in kilowatts?

(d) The charge for electricity is 3 cents per kilowatt-hour. The motor operates 8 hours each working day at a steady load of 10 hp. What will be the daily cost of energy?

19. A 230-volt shunt motor is rated at 10 hp. and 1150 rpm. with an armature current of 36.7 amperes. Assuming a constant line voltage, approximately how many pound-feet of load torque will be required to prevent the armature from rotating. How many times rated torque is this? What would happen to the armature in such a case?

20. A 7.5-hp. motor when delivering rated load takes a line current of 57.6 amperes at 115 volts and runs at 1525 rpm. $R_a = 0.15$; $I_f = 0.8$. What resistance must be inserted in series with the armature to cause this motor to develop a torque of 20 lb-ft. and run at a speed of 915 rpm.?

21. A 30-hp. motor when delivering rated load takes an armature current of 208 amperes at 120 volts and runs at 900 rpm. $R_a = 0.0245$; the field current is constant. What resistance must be inserted in series with the armature in order that the motor may develop a torque of 90.3 lb-ft. and run at 750 rpm.?

22. A shunt motor is rated at 7.5 hp., 230 volts, 1150 rpm. Its full-load armature current is 28 amperes, and its armature resistance is 0.4 ohm. The moment of inertia of its armature is 5.7 lb-ft.^{2} Assume that sufficient starting resistance is used to limit the starting current to 40 amperes, and that it starts without load and without appreciable friction. Calculate the initial acceleration in radians per second^2.

CHAPTER 5

VARIABLE-FLUX MOTORS

52. Shunt Motor Flux Change. An analysis of the transition period resulting from a change in the amount of flux in a shunt motor is more difficult than the transition periods previously discussed. Assume that a shunt motor has its field flux reduced by the addition of resistance to its field circuit. From an inspection of the torque equation, $T = c\Phi I_a$, a decrease in developed torque might be anticipated. But the assumed reduction in the value of Φ should produce a reduction in counter-emf. (since $E_g = K\Phi N$), thus permitting an increase in armature current and causing an increase in developed torque. Will one of these effects predominate, or will approximate neutralization occur?

The solution of an example with definite constants may be helpful. Consider a shunt motor whose armature resistance is 0.5 ohm, running idle at 1100 rpm., from 220-volt mains and drawing an armature current of 1.2 amperes. Its counter-emf. is evidently 219.4 volts. Assume that the field flux is now reduced to 90% of its original value. While the first small increment, say 1%, of this reduction is occurring, the speed may be assumed unchanged because of the steadying effect of the armature inertia, and the counter-emf. may then be computed on the basis of the flux change alone, with a value of 217.2 volts. The armature RI drop becomes $220 - 217.2$, or 2.8 volts, and the armature current will be 5.6 amperes. This represents an increase of about 360% in I_a, which is enough to more than compensate for the flux reduction and will result in a large increase in developed torque, with rapid acceleration. Additional increments of flux reduction are not likely to produce further decreases in counter-emf. because of the rapid increase in speed. In fact, as the motor regains equilibrium its armature current and counter-emf. come back almost to their original values, but a permanent speed increase occurs, the new speed being about 10/9 of the original speed, or 1220 rpm.

The transition may be outlined in general terms as follows:

1. The effect of a comparatively small flux reduction is felt more strongly by the counter-emf., which is decreased.

2. A comparatively large increase in armature current occurs.

3. The developed torque increases in spite of the flux reduction, so that it is no longer equal to the no-load retarding torque.

4. Acceleration occurs, and the speed increases.

5. The counter-emf. tends to return to its original value.

6. The armature current decreases from its peak value.

58

7. The developed torque decreases, tending to reach a value that will restore torque equilibrium.

8. The speed continues to increase, but at a slower and slower rate, to a new steady speed level.

9. At this level the values of armature current, developed torque and counter-emf. are practically the same as their original values, if the retarding torque has not been altered by the change in speed.

For the normal motor, whose armature circuit resistance is so small that most of the applied voltage is neutralized by counter-emf., the no-load speed may be considered without serious error to be inversely proportional to the field flux.

53. Effect of Flux Change on Loaded Motor. If a shunt motor is driving a constant-torque load when a flux reduction occurs, the transition period is quite similar to the no-load case. A temporary reduction in counter-emf. results in a very large increase in armature current, so that an accelerating torque appears. The speed rises rapidly to a higher level, the counter-emf. returns almost to its former value and a permanent increase in armature current occurs, such that $c\Phi_2 I_{a2} = c\Phi_1 I_{a1}$.

An analysis of the effect of a flux change on a loaded shunt motor whose armature circuit resistance is large will show that the change in speed is the reverse of the change noted for the normal motor. That is, a decrease in field strength will produce a lower instead of a higher speed. Furthermore, for a certain critical resistance of the armature circuit, changes in flux will have almost no effect on the speed.

54. Shunt Motor with Broken Field. If the field circuit of a shunt motor is broken while it is running idle with its armature supplied with normal voltage, it would seem that the developed torque would become zero and the motor would stop rotating. This, however, is not the case. The motor actually accelerates very rapidly and tends to reach a dangerously high speed. In such an event it is necessary to disconnect the armature from the supply mains as quickly as possible. The situation may be analyzed as follows:

1. The magnetic flux does not drop to zero when the field circuit is opened. A small amount, from 1 to 3% of the normal value, remains active in the magnetic circuit. This is called residual flux.

2. The counter-emf. drops to a very small value.

3. A large current rush occurs in the armature circuit — so large that a large torque is developed in spite of the weak field.

4. Rapid acceleration occurs.

5. The speed tends to reach a very high value in order that the counter-emf. may be restored to a high level. In most cases such a high speed will be necessary to restore equilibrium that the accompanying centrifugal force may damage the motor structure.

55. Series Motor. If the frame of a motor is provided with low-resistance field coils consisting of a few turns of heavy wire, and if these coils are connected in series with the armature so that they carry the armature current, the motor is called a series motor. The operating characteristics of such a motor will now be considered.

Like the shunt motor it has no counter-emf. at standstill and must be started with some protective resistance in the circuit to limit the starting current to a safe value. The starting current passes through the field coils on its way to the armature and produces a strong field flux which combines with the large current in the armature conductors to produce a powerful starting torque. Rapid acceleration occurs, accompanied by the production of a counter-emf. which begins to reduce the motor current. Equilibrium is reached at a speed such as will produce a counter-emf. sufficient to limit the motor current to the exact value needed to balance the load and friction torques.

If the load torque is now reduced, the speed and counter-emf. increase and both the current and flux decrease. Inspection of the developed torque equation, $T = c\Phi I_a$, shows that in the series motor a change of any definite amount in the developed torque can be accomplished by a smaller percentage change in the value of I_a than with the shunt motor, where Φ is practically constant.

Inspection of the speed equation,

$$N = \frac{V - (R_a + R_f)I_a}{K\Phi},$$

as modified for a series motor, shows that a given percentage change in the value of I_a, such as might be caused by a change in load, will be accompanied by a greater speed change than would occur in a shunt motor under similar operating conditions. This is due to the fact that the change in I_a is accompanied by a similar change in Φ.

If the load torque is removed from a series motor, the current needed is very small, the field flux also becomes small and the operating speed becomes so high that there is danger that the armature coils may be thrown out of their slots by the excessive centrifugal forces. Consequently series motors must always be geared or permanently coupled to their loads so that actual no-load conditions can never occur while the motor is connected to normal voltage mains.

56. The Compound Motor. The circuit diagram of a compound motor is shown in Fig. 36. Each pole supports two coils, a shunt coil of many turns and a series coil of few turns. The various shunt coils are connected together and are supplied with current from the line as in the shunt motor. The series coils are connected in series with the armature. The usual connections are such that the current direction in the series coil on any given field pole is the same as the direction of the current in the shunt coil on the same pole, so that the two coils assist each other in the production of flux. This is called the cumulative compound connection.

If the series coil terminals are interchanged so as to send the series coil current around the pole in the opposite direction to the shunt field current, the two coils are then trying to send fluxes in opposite directions. The actual field flux under these conditions will be set up by the difference between the two magnetizing forces of the coils. This arrangement is called the differential compound connection.

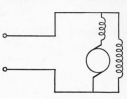

Fig. 36. Compound motor.

At no load, both types of compound motors behave just like the shunt motor, because the amount of armature current (which is also the series field current) required to produce the necessary torque is very small, and therefore the series coil effects are negligible. As load is added the speed and torque values begin to differ from those of a shunt motor. The speed-current curve of the cumulative compound motor slopes downward at a steeper angle than that of the shunt motor. This is due to the increase in flux produced by the series field.

The speed-current curve of the differential compound motor stays more nearly horizontal. On the basis of speed performance with light loads the latter motor would seem to excel, but it has one unfortunate feature which is of sufficient importance to bar it from almost every practical application. As increasing loads are placed on it, causing it to draw more armature current in order to produce sufficient torque, a point may be reached when the magnetic effect of the series field practically neutralizes the shunt field's influence and the motor passes into a period of instability during which it reverses in direction of rotation and draws a very large armature current. On account of this characteristic the differential connection is seldom used.

57. Motor Performance. To enable us to compare the performance of the various types of direct-current motors the speed-current and torque-current curves of each type are grouped together in Fig. 37. Notice that motors having the same speed and torque values at full-load armature current are selected for comparison.

The series motor is the only one in the group not having a definite and safe operating speed at no load. With regard to the no-load speeds of the two types of compound motors we must remember that their values relative to the full-load speed may be quite different from those indicated in Fig. 37, depending on the relative strengths of their series and shunt fields.

The differences between the torque-current curves of the various types of motors are not so marked as the differences between the speed-current relations.

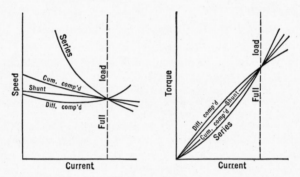

FIG. 37.   Motor performance curves.

58. Motor Applications. In order to make an intelligent choice of a particular type and size of motor for a particular job it is necessary to be familiar with the operating characteristics of the various kinds of motors and the specific power requirements of the proposed service. An analysis of the motor performance curves along the lines suggested in the preceding article should enable the student to obtain a fairly definite idea of the operating features and limitations of the various direct-current motors. The speed-torque characteristics of the countless loads handled by these motors are much more difficult to determine exactly, but in order to select a suitable motor for a given job the general nature of the speed-torque curve for the load must be considered, together with any additional facts that may have an influence on the size of motor selected. The motor whose speed and torque characteristics are most suitable for the load can then be selected.

Most of the industrial uses for motors can be classified as follows:

1. Constant-speed service, where it is desired to operate at an approximately constant speed over a wide range of torque values. Blowers, fans and factory line shafting are common examples of this type.

2. Multispeed service, where a number of different operating speed

levels may be desired, but where each speed should be held fairly constant regardless of load torque variations. Individual machine tools are usually of this type.

3. Periodic service, where the load comes on and off at fairly frequent intervals; or where considerable variation in speed for different load torques is permissible. Punch presses, rolling mills and freight elevators are examples of this class.

4. High starting torque, variable-speed service where great variations in speed for different load torques are permissible. Railway service, cranes and hoists are of this type.

The shunt motor is the best direct-current motor for class 1 jobs, and when equipped with field rheostat speed control is best for class 2 also. The cumulative compound motor handles class 3 jobs nicely, and the series motor is best suited to class 4.

SUGGESTED BIBLIOGRAPHY

1. Electric Drive Practice, Fox, McGraw-Hill Book Co., 1928.
2. Standard Handbook for Electrical Engineers, 6th edition, section 18.

PROBLEMS

1. The following data apply to a shunt motor. Fill in the blanks.

	V	I_a	R_a	rpm.	$T_{dev.}$	Flux
Old conditions	200	25	1.0	1000	100%	100%
New conditions	220	25	5.0	....	.....	85%

2. A 230-volt motor has a full-load speed of 1150 rpm. and an armature current of 108 amperes. $R_a = 0.107$. At no load the flux is 5% greater and the current is 5.5 amperes. What is the no-load speed?

3. A 220-volt motor has a no-load speed of 1200 rpm. The value of R_aI_a at no load is negligible. When fully loaded the armature carries 92 amperes and the field flux is decreased 6%. $R_a = 0.057$. What is the full-load speed?

4. A 220-volt motor has a no-load speed of 1200 rpm. The value of R_aI_a at no load is negligible. When fully loaded the armature carries 92 amperes and the field flux is increased 6%. $R_a = 0.057$. What is the full-load speed?

5. The following data apply to a shunt motor. Fill in the blanks.

	V	I_a	R_a	rpm.	$T_{dev.}$	Flux
Run A	220	25	1.0	1000	100%	100%
Run B	205	3	1.0	940	.....	.....

6. The following data apply to a shunt motor. Fill in the blanks.

	V	I_a	R_a	rpm.	$T_{dev.}$	Flux
Run A	220	30	0.9	1000	40.8 lb-ft.	100%
Run B	230	15	0.9	....	22.8 "	.....

7. A 220-volt shunt motor is drawing an armature current of 30 amperes and is running at 750 rpm. $R_a = 0.4$. How many pound-feet of torque is it developing?

What will be its speed if the load torque is held constant and the field flux is reduced to 80% of its former value?

8. A shunt motor has an armature circuit resistance sufficiently great to consume 75% of the constant impressed voltage, when working against a given constant load torque. What would happen to the speed of this motor if its field flux were reduced to 75% of its initial value?

9. A certain shunt motor has such a high armature circuit resistance that at low speeds practically all the applied voltage is consumed in RI drop. If the load torque is adjusted to be directly proportional to the speed, how then would the motor speed vary with the flux? With the voltage applied to the armature?

10. A shunt motor rated at 7.5 hp. at 230 volts takes an armature current of 28 amperes at rated load and is connected to a punch press through an intermediate gear which runs at a quarter the speed of the motor. $R_a = 0.4$ ohm. With no load except the idle press, the armature draws 4 amperes at 230 volts and runs at 1140 rpm. When the punch is operated the speed drops 20%. What is the armature current? Would a series or a compound motor give better performance than the shunt motor on this job?

11. A 230-volt shunt motor with an R_a of 0.3 ohm draws a no-load I_a of 1.5 amperes and runs at 1200 rpm. What will be the approximate value of the speed this motor will attempt to reach if its field circuit is broken, causing Φ to become 3% of its former value? Assume that the torque opposing rotation becomes four times as great as its initial value.

12. A series motor when taking currents of 20, 40 and 60 amperes from 600-volt mains runs at speeds of 1600, 1000 and 800 rpm. respectively. The resistance of the armature circuit (including the series field) is 0.5 ohm. What are the torques at 20 and 40 amperes in terms of the torque developed with 60 amperes?

13. A series motor, propelling a car up a long, uniform grade, takes a current of 100 amperes at 500 volts and runs at a speed of 100 rpm. The resistance of the armature and field together is 0.2 ohm. If the voltage is suddenly reduced to 140 volts, what is the speed at which the motor will run, assuming frictional resistances to remain constant?

14. A series motor's total resistance is 0.5 ohm. The line voltage is 550. At full load it takes 30 amperes and runs at 800 rpm. At reduced load it takes 15 amperes and runs at 1500 rpm. Find (a) the value of the developed torque at full load; (b) the value of the flux at reduced load as a percentage of its full-load value.

15. The following tabulated data apply to a certain series motor. Fill in the blanks.

Run No.	V	R	I	N	$T_{dev.}$	$K\Phi$
1	600	0.5	50	700	...	....
2	600	0.8	50	...	...	....
3	400	...	50	426	...	....
4	400	0.5	25	...	...	0.46

16. When an interurban car runs at full speed on level track its motor fluxes are so low as to be almost proportional to their ampere-turns. Series motors are used. To obtain higher speed the series fields can be shunted by resistors. When each series field is shunted by twice its own resistance, what will be the approximate percentage increase in speed, for the same torque developed?

17. A certain series motor is drawing 100 amperes from 500-volt mains and operating at 600 rpm. The motor resistances are: $R_a = 0.2$, $R_{series} = 0.1$. If the load torque remains constant, what will be the approximate speed of this motor when a 0.1-ohm resistor is shunted across the series field? Assume motor flux proportional to field amperes.

18. A certain type of streetcar weighing 15 tons is tested on level track. To propel it at a constant speed of 10 mph. or less requires a tractive effort (propelling force) of 150 lb. This car is to be started from rest and uniformly accelerated up a 3% grade so that it reaches a speed of 10 mph. in 10 seconds. What is the approximate tractive effort required?

19. A streetcar weighing 20 tons is to be moved up a long, uniform grade of 3% (3 ft. rise in 100 ft.) at a constant velocity of 20 mph. Four series motors are to be used.

(a) Determine the approximate horsepower needed in each motor.

(b) If the car wheel diameter is 24 in. and the gear ratio between motor shaft and car axle is 4 to 1, find the motor rpm.

(c) Find the approximate car current if the four motors are connected in parallel across 600 volts. Assume efficiency of motors and gearing to be 75%.

20. A machine is operating as a cumulative compound motor. How would you change:

(a) The direction of rotation, keeping the motor cumulative compound?

(b) The direction of rotation and at the same time change the motor to a differential compound?

(c) The kind of compounding, keeping the direction of rotation the same?

21. Given a cumulative compound motor with the following operating conditions. Fill in the blanks.

Run No.	V	R_a	I_a	N	Φ	$T_{dev.}$
A	220	0.3	2	1200	100%	....
B	190	0.5	40	....	125%	....

22. A compound motor runs at 1250 rpm. with $I_a = 42$ amperes, $R_a = 0.2$, $R_{se} = 0.05$, $V = 230$. What percentage change occurs in the flux if it runs at 1435 rpm. with $I_a = 32$ amperes and $V = 235$?

23. A compound motor has such constants that at full load the flux is 20% greater than the no-load flux and the resistance drop in the armature and series field is 5% of the applied voltage. What percentage of the no-load speed is the full-load speed?

24. A 230-volt compound motor has an R_a of 0.15, an I_a of 56 amperes and a speed of 1100 rpm.; it develops a torque of 79.5 lb-ft. With a reduced load it draws 30 amperes from 230-volt mains and develops a torque of 36.3 lb-ft. What will be its new speed? The series field resistance is included in R_a.

25. A 115-volt compound motor has a shunt coil strength of 4000 ampere-turns and a series coil strength of 1000 ampere-turns when the load is such as to make $I_a = 100$ amperes. What percentage change in shunt field circuit resistance will be necessary to keep the field flux the same if I_a becomes 150 amperes?

26. Given the following operating conditions applying to a differential compound motor. Fill in the blank space.

Run No.	V	R_a	I_a	N	Φ
A	230	0.3	2.2	1250	100%
B	225	0.3	35.	....	82%

CHAPTER 6

MOTOR STARTING AND SPEED CONTROL

59. The Starting Box. The armatures of shunt and compound motors of about 2-hp. rating and larger are provided with conductors of such large size and such low resistance that the value of the starting current, $I = V/R_a$, is dangerously large. This difficulty could, of course, be remedied by using high-resistance armature wire, but by so doing the motor efficiency would be made very low, and it would no longer operate at a fairly constant speed regardless of the amount of load.

A more satisfactory procedure utilizes a temporary protective resistance which may be inserted in the armature circuit at the instant of start, and may then be shunted or bridged out of the circuit a little at a time until the armature is finally connected directly to full line voltage. Such a device, when arranged for manual operation, is called a starting box. Most of the starting boxes now in use are of either the three-terminal or the four-terminal type. The circuit diagrams and operating features of these types will now be described.

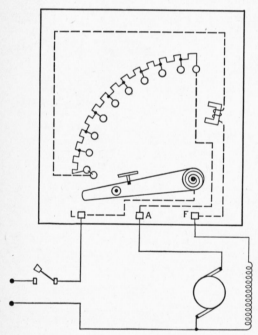

FIG. 38. Three-terminal starting box.

Figure 38 shows the internal connections of a three-terminal box, and the external connections needed to enable the box to perform its duty. It consists of (a) the protective resistance for the motor armature, with taps brought to contact studs; (b) the contact arm which sweeps over

66

the contact studs and bridges out the resistance sections, (c) the holding coil, which is an electromagnet connected in series with the motor field and is designed to hold the contact arm in the running position; (d) the spring which throws the contact arm to the off position in case of a failure of the power supply.

The motor field circuit is connected to full line voltage as soon as the arm is moved to the first stud, so that full field strength is available for the production of a large starting torque. It is an interesting problem to predict the motor behavior during the starting period if the field connection is transferred from the first to the last contact stud.

Figure 39 shows the internal and external connections of a four-terminal box. It has the same general features possessed by the three-terminal box, but differs in the method of supplying current to the holding coil, for which an entirely separate circuit is provided.

A comparative study of the two types of boxes shows that the three-terminal box is somewhat simpler, and is able to break the armature circuit and stop the motor in case of an interruption in the field circuit. The latter feature is not particularly important, however, because the line

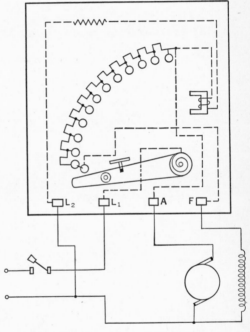

FIG. 39. Four-terminal starting box.

current in such a case would rise to such a high value that the motor fuses would open the supply circuit quickly and positively.

On the other hand, the four-terminal box is particularly suited for use with variable-speed shunt motors, where the operating speed is altered by changing the resistance of the shunt field circuit. The holding coil will be unaffected by a reduction in the value of the field current.

In Fig. 40 the external and internal circuits of the two types of boxes are shown in a schematic diagram which may be helpful in contrasting their operating features.

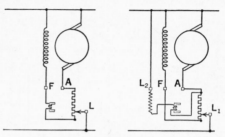

Fig. 40.   Starting box schematic diagrams.

60. Automatic Starters. The process of bridging out successive sections of a starting resistance so as to produce rapid and fairly uniform acceleration can be accomplished automatically, with results that are usually much better than with manual operation. The equipment necessary to do this is called an automatic starter.

There are three general types of automatic starters. They may be given the somewhat descriptive names of counter-emf., series-lockout and time-element starters.

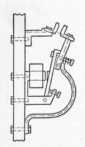

Fig. 41.   Counter-emf. contactor.

61. Counter-emf. Starter. Figure 41 shows one type of counter-emf. contactor designed to bridge out a section of a motor starting resistance. The heavy dashed line shows the path of the motor current. The magnet coil consists of many turns of fine wire and is usually designed to close the main contacts when the voltage applied to the coil becomes 70 to 90% of the motor's rated voltage. It is possible to calibrate this contactor to close at any desired voltage within reasonable limits by adjusting the length of the air gap in its magnetic circuit.

Figure 42 shows a simplified diagram of an automatic starter employing three counter-emf. contactors and a heavy-duty contactor of similar design used as a main line switch. The operation may be explained as follows: when the start button is pressed, the supply circuit for the coil of contactor L is completed and L closes, connecting the motor field to the line and the armature with its protective resistance R_1R_4 to the line also. An auxiliary contact S is mechanically linked with L so that it is closed simultaneously with L, thus by-passing the start button. As the motor accelerates, its rising counter-emf. increases the voltage between P and M. When this voltage reaches a predetermined value, say 40% of the line voltage, the coil of accelerating contactor 1 receives enough current to close its contacts, thus bridg-

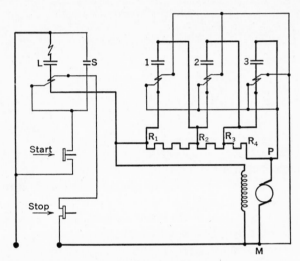

FIG. 42. Schematic diagram of automatic starter.

ing out section R_1R_2 of the starting resistance. Further acceleration and growth of counter-emf. occur until the voltage between P and M reaches, say, 70%, when contactor 2 closes. Contactor 3 may be adjusted to close at 90% of line voltage, which completes the starting operation.

62. Series-lockout Starter. A series-lockout starter employs the same kind of line contactor with push-button control, but differs in the type of accelerating contactor used. The accelerating contactor has a coil of heavy wire which is usually connected in series with the armature, and special design features are required to prevent premature operation which might short out the starting resistance at the first inrush of current.

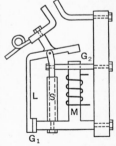

FIG. 43. Series-lockout contactor.

Figure 43 shows one type of series contactor which has a peculiar magnetic circuit. Suppose its coil to be connected in series with a motor armature. When the line contactor closes, the initial current rush is very large and the magnetic flux created in M reaches such a high value that the short return path S is overcrowded. A large proportion of the flux takes the path L and crosses the gap G_1, producing a strong attraction there which prevents the main gap G_2 from closing. As the motor current decreases, the number of flux lines taking the path L is reduced more rapidly than the quantity through S and the attraction at G_1 is no longer powerful enough to hold G_2 open. The main contacts then close and a section of the starting resistance is bridged out.

The purpose of the copper sleeve enclosing S is to introduce a time lag in the growth of flux through S as the motor current first builds up from zero, and thus prevent the main contacts from closing during the initial current rise.

For detailed circuits utilizing this and similar contactors the reader is referred to textbooks devoted to the special subject of motor control.

63. Time-element Starter. A time-element starter employs a number of contactors so designed that there is a definite time interval between the closing of one contactor and the operation of the next in the sequence. When contactors of this type are employed to short the various sections of a motor starting resistance the time required to accelerate the motor to normal speed becomes independent of the load.

In one type of time-element starter the closing of the line contactor by a push button energizes the motor field, closes the armature circuit through its starting resistance and applies line voltage to several accelerating contactors of the shunt- or high-resistance type. Each of these is provided with a dash pot as a time delay device. The dash pot usually consists of a piston operating in an oil-filled cylinder, and the time required for the piston to complete its travel can be adjusted by a valve in the by-pass pipe connected to the ends of the cylinder. By suitable adjustment of these valves the accelerating contactors can be made to close in the proper sequence, and to bridge the starting resistance sections at the desired time intervals.

In another type the closing of the line contactor completes the motor armature circuit through its protective resistance and at the same time starts a small auxiliary motor by which a camshaft is rotated slowly. The coils of the accelerating contactors will be energized in the proper succession and at the desired time intervals by cam-operated contacts.

64. Comparison of Accelerating Methods. Under the following conditions the counter-emf. type of contactor is considered to be the best for motor acceleration.

1. The motor to be started is small (less than 5 hp.) and is driving a small-inertia load, so that the counter-emf. will rise rapidly.

2. The supply voltage is not subject to severe fluctuations, say more than 10 to 15%.

3. The load torque is variable, and more rapid acceleration is desired when the motor is lightly loaded.

The conditions under which some form of series contactor is preferable are:

1. The motor to be started is large and is handling a high-inertia load.

2. Considerable variation of the supply voltage may be expected.

3. The load torque is variable, and more rapid acceleration is desired when the motor is lightly loaded.

Time-element accelerating contactors are particularly desirable for starting the several motors of a group used in a complex manufacturing operation where the quality of the product depends to some extent on accurate timing of the individual steps in the operation. One rolling unit of a steel mill, for example, requires numerous motors to drive the varied equipment used in the rolling process. For best results the acceleration of each motor must be accurately timed so that its performance will keep in step with the others of the group.

Many occasions arise when the best results will be obtained by using two or more different types of contactors in the same circuit.

65. Arc Suppression. All the contactors which have just been described are alike in one respect. When they open, the air gap thus introduced between the main contacts is comparatively short. Hence, if it becomes necessary to open a contactor while its contacts are carrying a heavy current, there is difficulty in extinguishing the arc which tends to persist across the gap. Of the various devices which have been employed to assist in extinguishing contactor arcs, two will be described briefly.

It is general practice to mount all contactors on vertical panels with the main contacts uppermost. The arc resulting from the interruption of a heavy current will then be able to swell upward naturally until its length becomes so great that the arc voltage is unable to sustain it. The prompt extinction of the arc can be assisted by mounting a boxlike chute above the contacts. The chute must be narrow, with side walls of fireproof insulating material, and should contain one or more transverse partitions so arranged that the swelling arc will strike against their edges. Scallops will thus be formed in the arc pattern which will materially hasten its suppression.

66. Magnetic Blowout. If an arc occurs in a region where there is a magnetic field, the field exerts a deflecting force on it just as if it were a metallic conductor carrying current. Since an arc stream has very little mass a large acceleration can be produced by a comparatively small force. A properly placed electromagnet can therefore assist in the rapid extinction of an arc by accelerating its upward movement from the contacts. Figure 44 shows the usual arrangement. The coil of the blowout magnet is connected in series with the main contacts, and must carry current in the indicated direction for the assumed direction of current in the arc.

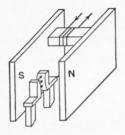   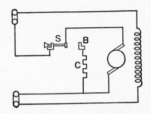

FIG. 44. Magnetic blowout.   FIG. 45. Dynamic braking circuit.

67. Dynamic Braking. In many industrial operations the driving motors must be started and stopped frequently. In such cases it is just as important to have rapid retardation as it is to have rapid acceleration. If the load is one with a large amount of inertia some form of retarding torque in addition to friction will be required.

A very simple and effective method of producing large amounts of retarding torque is known as dynamic braking. Figure 45 shows a shunt motor connected for normal operation. The starting resistance has been omitted for the sake of clarity. If gradual retardation is desired, switch S is opened. If rapid retardation is needed, S is thrown quickly to contact B. A circulating current whose initial value will be $E/(R_a + R_c)$ will flow through the low resistance C, impelled by E, the induced voltage of the armature. The direction of this current will be opposite to the direction of the current forced through the armature by the supply voltage while the machine was running as a motor. The magnetic field is unchanged. Therefore the torque produced by the interaction of the armature current and the magnetic field will be a retarding torque.

The initial value of the retarding torque thus produced will be very large if R_c is small. Since E varies with the speed of the armature the value of the retarding torque will not continue at its initial high level but will decrease rapidly and will become zero at standstill. Hence this method of producing a retarding torque cannot be utilized to create a holding torque.

68. Series Motor Starters. Starters for series motors may be either manually operated or automatic, and the general features of such starters when used with single motors are very similar to those already described. In some cases, however, a load is shared by two or more series motors which must be started and controlled as a unit. A special type of controller known as the series-parallel controller has been devised for this purpose. As arranged for two motors the first position of the controller handle places the motors in series with each other and with a series resistor. As the controller handle is advanced the amount of series resistance is reduced until each motor is finally supplied with half of the line voltage. If higher speeds are desired the controller is advanced more, causing a shift in the motor connections from a series to a parallel arrangement, with some resistance inserted again in the circuit. Further movement of the controller handle reduces this resistance until the final running position is reached, when the motors are in parallel across full line voltage. A schematic diagram of a typical series-parallel controller is shown in Fig. 46.

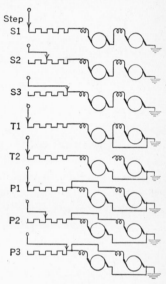

Fig. 46. Series-parallel controller.

A discussion of the circuit arrangements necessary for four or six motors to be controlled in this manner, or of the special schemes which may be adopted to bring about a smooth transfer from the series to the parallel arrangement without loss of torque, is beyond the scope of this book.

69. Speed Regulation. The term speed regulation is used to describe the amount of speed variation which occurs in so-called constant-speed motors. It is usually defined as the difference between no-load and rated-load speeds expressed as a percentage of rated-load speed, and refers to speed variations inherent in the motor rather than variations produced at the will of the operator. In general, the more resistance a shunt motor has in its armature circuit the poorer is its speed regulation when the mechanical load varies.

70. Speed Control — Field Rheostat. The term speed control is used in connection with devices for producing deliberate changes in the speed of a motor.

The simplest and most familiar arrangement is the field-rheostat method.   This method, as used with shunt and compound motors, requires a variable resistance to be inserted in series with the shunt field. Since the shunt field current of a motor is relatively small the field rheostat need not be bulky or expensive to produce the desired results, and the power converted to heat in the rheostat will usually be negligible. The variation in speed which can be produced by this method ranges from the normal value up to the highest safe operating speed.

71. Speed Control — Armature Rheostat.   The armature-rheostat method makes use of a heavy rheostat of sufficient current capacity to carry the motor armature current for long intervals without overheating.   For control purposes it is connected in series with the armature, and the operator secures different motor speeds by varying its resistance.   The speed variation which can be secured by such means ranges from normal down to standstill.   Thus it is evident that the armature rheostat is not a competitor of the field rheostat, but is instead a valuable supplement.   It should be noted, however, that the use of an armature rheostat to obtain low speeds is accompanied by several disadvantages.   There will be considerable loss of power in the rheostat; it is bulky and occupies considerable space, and causes the motor speed regulation to be very poor.

72. Speed Control — Variable Reluctance. A speed-control method of considerable interest is known as the variable-reluctance method.   Utilization of some kind of mechanical device for changing the effective air-gap length is necessary.

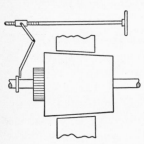

In the Reliance motor, shown diagrammatically in Fig. 47, variations in gap length are accomplished by turning a hand wheel projecting from the motor frame.   Rotation of this wheel shifts the armature parallel to its axis by means of a bell crank pressing against

FIG. 47.   Schematic diagram of Reliance motor.

a collar on the shaft.   The armature and the pole shoes are tapered slightly so that a comparatively small axial shift will have an appreciable effect on the gap length.   An increase in gap length increases its reluctance and reduces the flux, thereby increasing the speed.

Although the variable-reluctance type of motor is necessarily more costly than a standard motor equipped with field-rheostat control, the ratio of maximum to minimum speeds obtainable is greater and the speed regulation under varying load conditions is just as good.   It is particularly well suited to drive certain types of machine tools such as lathes and drill presses.

73. The Ward-Leonard System. The problem of speed control may be approached from another angle. Instead of varying the field current, the reluctance or the resistance of the armature circuit, the armature voltage may be varied at its source. Of the various systems utilizing this principle the Ward-Leonard has the most general interest.

Figure 48 shows the fundamental requirements of the Ward-Leonard system. The armature of the working motor is connected by heavy, low-resistance leads to the armature of a shunt generator. The field of the generator is connected in potentiometer style to a constant voltage supply. The generator is driven by a motor, gas engine or other source of mechanical power.

When the motor is to be operated the generator is first brought up to normal speed. Then its field excitation is slowly increased by moving the potentiometer slider to the left as shown in the figure. This raises the voltage produced by the generator from approximately zero to a value high enough to send a suitable amount of current through the armature of the working motor. Moving the slider still farther to the left increases the speed

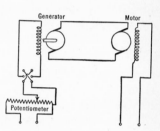

FIG. 48. Ward-Leonard system.

of the working motor. If reversed operation is desired the slider is moved as far to the right as it will go, the reversing switch is thrown to the other position and the slider is then advanced to the left until the desired speed level is reached.

Since the potentiometer and the generator field are both high-resistance circuits carrying comparatively small currents the potentiometer may be small in size and may be mounted some distance away from the machine, thus making remote control of the working motor possible.

As the first cost of the complete equipment is very high, a separate generator being required for each working motor, this sort of control is justified only for large motors operating under difficult conditions where the cheaper types of control would be inadequate.

SUGGESTED BIBLIOGRAPHY

1. Electric Motors, CROCKER and ARENDT, Van Nostrand, 2nd edition, 1914.
2. Controllers for Electric Motors, H. D. JAMES, Van Nostrand, 2nd edition, 1926.
3. Electric Railway Handbook, 2nd edition, sections 4 and 5.
4. Control of Electric Motors, HARWOOD, John Wiley & Sons, 1936.

PROBLEMS

1. A shunt motor is to be started from 200-volt mains. Its R_a is 1.0 ohm; its R_f is 100 ohms. A starting current of 40 amperes will be allowed.

(a) Compute the total resistance required in the starting box.

(b) If the shunt field connection is changed from the first to the last contact stud, calculate the initial value of the voltage applied to the field circuit when the handle is moved up to the first stud, and discuss briefly the probable result.

2. A 50-hp., 250-volt shunt motor has a full load I_a of 165 amperes. The full-load speed is 500 rpm. $R_a = 0.08$; $R_f = 30$ ohms. It is necessary to have 150% of full-load torque at the moment of starting. Find the total resistance required in the starting box. If this resistance is not removed from the armature circuit find the speed when full-load torque is demanded, and when half-load torque is demanded.

3. A shunt motor has the following constants: $V = 220$; $R_a = 0.8$; $N = 1000$ rpm.; $I_a = 22$ amperes. A starting current of 38 amperes will be permitted. Compute the number of ohms in the starting box and the resistance of each step.

4. A shunt motor has the following constants: $V = 220$; $R_a = 0.8$; $N = 1000$ rpm.; I_a full load $= 25$. Compute the number of ohms in the starting box and the resistance of each step. Allow I_a to have a maximum value of 45 amperes for the first step and 40 amperes for the remaining steps.

5. A 115-volt shunt motor is generating a counter-emf. of 108 volts when running at a speed of 800 rpm. and driving a high-inertia load. It is planned to stop the motor by the use of dynamic braking. A braking resistance of 2 ohms is to be used. $R_a = 0.5$. What current will be delivered to the resistor immediately after dynamic braking begins? How many pound-feet of retarding torque will be developed at this instant?

6. A dynamic braking resistor is to be designed for a shunt motor rated at 250 hp. When fully loaded it runs at 450 rpm. with a supply voltage of 230. $R_a = 0.0075$; $I_a = 880$. A dynamic braking torque of 3000 lb-ft. is desired at the beginning of the braking period. Determine the approximate resistance and current rating of the braking resistor needed.

7. A series motor has the following constants: $V = 600$; $I = 70$; $R = 0.55$; hp. $= 50$; rpm. $= 995$. A railway car is to be equipped with two of these motors, using series-parallel control.

(a) How much series resistance will be required to limit the starting current to 140 amperes with a 600-volt supply?

(b) With the motors delivering rated load torque what speed will they attain when the starting resistance is finally removed, with the motors still in series?

(c) How much resistance will be required to limit the motor current to 100 amperes immediately after the motors are shifted from the series to the parallel connection?

(d) Can the same resistance grids be utilized?

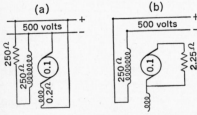

(a)   (b)

Prob. 8, Ch. 6.

8. A cumulative compound motor, connected as shown in (a), hoists a certain load at the rate of 50 ft. per min. when the armature current is 100 amperes. What is the maximum speed at which the load will descend if connections are made as shown in (b)? Frictional losses may be neglected.

CHAPTER 7

THE MAGNETIC CIRCUIT

74. Coulomb's Law. In Chapter 1 certain magnetic concepts were introduced and discussed briefly. It is the purpose of this chapter to discuss such additional concepts as are needed for a clear understanding of motor magnetic circuits.

The well-known experimental work of Coulomb in 1800 concerning force reactions between bar magnets resulted in a general statement regarding these forces which has become known as Coulomb's law. It may be stated as follows:

$$F = \frac{m_1 m_2}{\mu d^2},\tag{23}$$

where μ = a proportionality constant called the permeability of the medium.

m_1 = the pole strength of one magnet.
m_2 = the pole strength of the other magnet.
d = the distance between the poles.
F = the force, which acts along a straight line joining the poles and is a repulsion if the poles are alike and an attraction if they are unlike.

This equation can be used to form a definition of the unit pole. If two north poles of equal strength (their companion poles being far removed) exert a repulsive force of 1 dyne upon each other when placed 1 cm. apart in air, each is termed a unit pole.

75. Field Intensity. In Chapter 1 it was stated that one method of measuring the strength of a magnetic field is to determine its flux density by counting the number of flux lines piercing a unit area placed normal to the lines. Coulomb's law has become the basis of another method.

The direction of a magnetic field at any point is given by the direction in which a north test pole will tend to move if placed at that point in the field. If the test pole is of unit strength it will also measure the strength of the field. The force which a field exerts upon a unit test pole is called the intensity of the field at the point where the test pole is located, and is measured in dynes. Intensity is evidently a vector quantity, having both magnitude and direction. The usual symbol for magnetic field intensity is H.

Let a unit pole be placed d centimeters from a magnet pole of m units strength. Applying Coulomb's law, the expression for the force exerted upon the unit pole becomes $m/\mu d^2$ dynes. This therefore is the value of the intensity that a magnet of m units strength produces at a distance of d centimeters from it.

$$H = \frac{m}{\mu d^2} \text{ dynes per unit pole.} \qquad (24)$$

In 1931 by general agreement the name oersted was assigned to the unit of magnetic field intensity.

76. Flux Density. The term flux density as used in Chapter 1 is a vector quantity like field intensity except that it does not depend upon the medium. In other words, the flux density of the field at a distance of d centimeters from a magnet pole of m units strength is

$$B = \frac{m}{d^2}, \qquad (25)$$

and if the same system of units is continued,

$$B = \mu H. \qquad (26)$$

Instead of thinking of B as a number of units of force it is usual to consider it as the number of lines of flux piercing a square centimeter area placed normal to them. That is, if a magnet creates a force effect of H units at a given spot within its sphere of influence, the presence of that force sets up a " flow " of flux lines parallel to the force and therefore establishes at that spot a flux density of B lines per square centimeter.

77. Difference of Magnetic Potential. If a unit test pole is placed in a magnetic field of intensity H, and is compelled by it to move a distance dx centimeters in the direction of H, it is evident that work will have to be done by the magnetic field upon the test pole, and the amount will be $H\,dx$ ergs per unit pole.

Two names are commonly applied to this quantity $H\,dx$. If the terminals of this distance dx are points A and B, $H\,dx$ may be called the difference in magnetic potential between A and B, or the magneto-motive force (mmf.) from A to B.

If a unit test pole is placed in a magnetic field of intensity H, and moves from A to C, a distance dy centimeters perpendicular to the direction of H, it is evident that such motion does not represent any work done by H and therefore $H\,dy = 0$, and A and C are at the same magnetic potential.

A surface everywhere perpendicular to the direction of H is called an equipotential surface.

Let the points A, D in Fig. 49 be connected by any path lying in a magnetic field of intensity H, and let a unit pole be urged along that path by the action of H. As the unit pole traverses the small distance ds, the amount of work done upon it by the field $= H\, ds \cos \alpha$. The work done by the field in moving the unit pole over the entire path will be the line integral, $\int_{A}^{D} H\, ds \cos \alpha$, and this therefore is an expression for the magnetic difference of potential between A and D or the mmf. from A to D.

In Chapter 1 the magnetic effects of an electric current were briefly discussed. Suppose that a conductor carrying a current of I amperes is placed perpendicular to a small bundle of flux lines emerging from a unit pole. Let the length of the conductor be l and the flux density of the field where the conductor is lying be B lines per square centimeter. A force of $BlI/10$ dynes

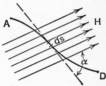

FIG. 49. Difference of magnetic potential.

will be exerted on the conductor, tending to move it perpendicular to the flux lines. If we allow the conductor to move a distance dx centimeters under the urge of this force, work amounting to $BlI\, dx/10$ ergs will be done. But $Bl\, dx$ can be replaced by ϕ, the flux cut by the conductor during its motion. Then the work done can be written as $\phi I/10$ ergs. These relations are not altered if the motion through the distance dx occurs to the unit pole instead of the conductor.

$$\text{Work done on the conductor} = \frac{\phi I}{10} \text{ ergs.} \qquad (27)$$

If the conductor length extends to infinity and if the distance dx is extended along a path which completely encircles the conductor, all the flux from the unit pole will cut the conductor. The same is true if a finite length of conductor is formed into a loop and the unit pole is made to pass through the loop and around to its starting point. But the total flux from a unit pole is 4π lines.* Therefore the work done on the conductor by the field of the unit pole is $4\pi I/10$ ergs, and this can be called the mmf. of the conductor.

$$\text{mmf.} = \frac{4\pi I}{10} \text{ ergs per unit pole,} \qquad (28)$$

for a single-turn coil carrying I amperes.

* The reader is urged to consult any of the books listed at the end of this chapter for proof of this statement and for other valuable material on magnetic fields which is necessarily omitted from this chapter.

78. Field Intensity of a Long Wire.   In deriving an expression for the field intensity in the vicinity of a long, straight wire carrying a steady current, let a point P be selected whose perpendicular distance from the wire is r centimeters.   The intensity H of the field at P due to the current in the wire will be directed along a tangent to a circle whose center is at the wire and whose radius is r.   The work done by a unit pole in making one complete circuit around the wire is $H \times 2\pi r$, where H is the value of the field intensity in dynes per unit pole.   But it has been shown that $4\pi I/10$ is an expression for the work done by a unit pole as it moves along a path which encircles a conductor carrying a current of I amperes. We may then write

$$H \times 2\pi r = \frac{4\pi I}{10},$$

or $$H = \frac{I}{5r} \text{ dynes per unit pole,} \tag{29}$$

as the expression for the field intensity of a long, straight wire.

79. Force between Two Parallel Wires. In Fig. 50, conductors M and N are r centimeters apart and are carrying equal currents in opposite directions.   The direction of the flux density at N of the field due to the current in M is indicated by the vector B_M and its value is μH_M. In the derivation of the equation for the field intensity of a long wire it was shown that $H_M = I/5r$.   Therefore

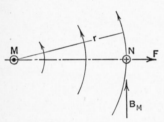

FIG. 50.   Force   between   two parallel wires.

$$B_M = \frac{\mu I}{5r}.$$

The force tending to move conductor N is $B_M Il \sin \theta/10$, so that

$$F = \frac{\mu I^2 l \sin \theta}{50r}.$$

This may be changed to read

$$F = \frac{\mu I^2}{50r} \text{ dynes per centimeter of length,} \tag{30}$$

since $\sin \theta$ is 1.

In a similar manner the force exerted on M by the field of the current in N can be shown to be equal to F but opposite in direction.   The two forces act along a line joining the wire centers and tend to spread the wires apart.

Two parallel wires carrying currents in the same direction will set up forces tending to draw them together.

80. Coil Magnetomotive Force. The path which the unit pole follows in its journey around the conductor need not be a circle, as assumed in Art. 78, for its direction at any point can be expressed in terms of a radial component (involving no work) and a tangential component in which work will be done by the pole.

If the unit pole encircles N wires each carrying I amperes, the value of mmf. will be N times as great;

$$\text{mmf.} = \frac{4\pi NI}{10} \text{ ergs per unit pole.} \tag{31}$$

Instead of using the name, ergs per unit pole, for this unit of mmf., a special name, the gilbert, is given to this quantity. Thus a coil of wire of N turns carrying I amperes is said to produce $4\pi NI/10$ gilberts of mmf.

A mmf. always tends to produce magnetic flux lines which link with or thread through the coil which is the source of the mmf., and thus form closed paths. The number of flux lines produced by a given mmf. depends upon the nature of the material in which the flux lines are located, and the geometry of that material. For example, if we imagine a centimeter cube of air located in a magnetic field of such intensity as will produce a mmf. of 1 gilbert between opposite faces of the cube, 1 maxwell of flux will be found traversing the cube. If the air-path length is changed to 0.5 cm. without changing the cross-section of the path or the mmf., the flux will be doubled. The same mmf. applied to an air path having a length of 1 cm. and a sectional area of 2 sq. cm. will likewise double the flux.

81. Reluctance. In general the ratio of the mmf. applied to a given material sample to the number of flux lines traversing the sample is called the reluctance of the sample. In symbols

$$\frac{\text{mmf.}}{\Phi} = \Re. \tag{32}$$

The reluctance of any given material sample depends upon the length and cross-section of the specimen and the permeability of the material. The equation which expresses this relationship is usually written:

$$\Re = \frac{l}{\mu A}, \tag{33}$$

where $\Re$ is given in gilberts per maxwell if l is in centimeters and A in square centimeters.   The value of μ is unity for air and other non-magnetic substances.

It will be recalled that in the motor the supply voltage is balanced by an equally large voltage consisting of the sum of the counter-emf. and the armature RI drop.   Likewise, if a lamp or a heating element is connected to a source of power, the supply voltage is balanced by an equally large RI drop.   The flow of current might be pictured as producing an opposition to the applied voltage and adjusting itself until that opposition just balances the supply voltage.   It is helpful to think the same of a magnetic circuit.   The mmf. produced by current in a coil of wire produces flux and the flux generates a counter-mmf., $\mathcal{R}\Phi$, which just balances the coil mmf.

If the magnetic circuit on which the coil is mounted is composed of several sections differing from each other in dimensions or material, the flux will adjust itself so that the sum of the counter-mmfs of the various sections will equal the coil mmf.

$$\text{Coil mmf.} = \frac{4\pi NI}{10} = \mathcal{R}_1\Phi + \mathcal{R}_2\Phi + \cdots + \mathcal{R}_n\Phi. \qquad (34)$$

82. Mmf. per Unit Length.   Consider a closed magnetic circuit linked with a coil of N turns carrying I amperes, and assume the entire circuit to be homogeneous in material and uniform in cross-section. Then

$$\text{Coil mmf.} = \frac{4\pi NI}{10} = \mathcal{R}\Phi.$$

Now

$$\mathcal{R}\Phi = \frac{l\Phi}{\mu A} = \frac{lB}{\mu},$$

and if we substitute this value of $\mathcal{R}\Phi$ in the preceding equation and divide both sides by l, we have

$$\frac{4\pi NI}{10l} = \text{gilberts per cm.} = \frac{B}{\mu}. \qquad (35)$$

This indicates that, since the counter-mmf. produced by the passage of flux through the given sample is the same for each unit length of path, the total coil mmf. may be thought of as a summation of the mmfs. of each unit length, and that the value of the coil mmf. per unit length of magnetic circuit may be found by dividing the total mmf. by the path length.   Conversely the total coil mmf. required to produce a desired flux in a magnetic circuit of the assumed type can be calculated if the mmf. per unit length can be determined.

A comparison of the units involved in equation 35 with those used in defining field intensity will show that mmf. per unit length of path is merely another name for field intensity.

83. The Ampere-turn. The gilbert is the accepted fundamental unit of magnetomotive force, but a derived unit, the ampere-turn, is preferred by most practicing engineers. The ampere-turn is the mmf. produced by a current of 1 ampere in a coil of 1 turn.

$$1 \text{ ampere-turn} = \frac{4\pi}{10} \text{ gilberts.} \tag{36}$$

Referring again to equation 35, the reader's attention is directed to the units involved. The mmf. is in gilberts, the length of path in centimeters, the flux density in lines per square centimeter and μ has a value of unity for air. Suppose that we wish to write a similar equation using the ampere-turn. It would take the form

$$\frac{\text{ampere-turns}}{\text{inch}} = K \frac{\text{lines}}{\text{square inch}},$$

and we must determine the value of K. The transfer of units is carried through as follows:

$$\frac{\text{ampere-turns}}{\text{inch}} \cdot \frac{4\pi}{10} \cdot \frac{1}{2.54} = \frac{\text{lines}}{\text{square inch}} \cdot \frac{1}{(2.54)^2}$$

or

$$\frac{\text{ampere-turns}}{\text{inch}} = 0.313 \frac{\text{lines}}{\text{square inch}}$$

for air and other non-magnetic substances.

In symbols:

$$\frac{NI}{l} = 0.313B. \tag{37}$$

For example, suppose that it is desired to find the ampere-turns required to produce an average flux density of 10,000 lines per square inch in an air gap 0.2 in. long, the rest of the magnetic circuit being of negligible reluctance.

$$\frac{NI}{l} = 3130, \quad \text{and} \quad NI = 626.$$

84. B-H Curves. The relationship between the ampere-turns per inch and the flux density in lines per square inch is not a constant if the material is magnetic. Since a large part of the magnetic circuit of a motor is iron or steel, it becomes very important to consider ways and means of determining this relationship.

The most satisfactory method for engineering purposes involves the determination and use of the so-called *B–H* curves. Samples of the

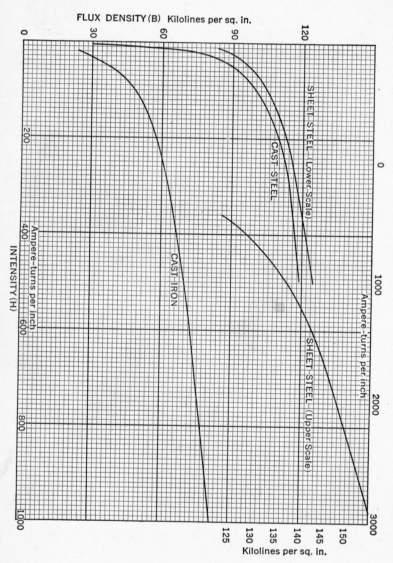

FIG. 51.   B-H curves.

various kinds of iron and steel entering into the construction of motors are prepared and placed in a special apparatus whereby they may be subjected to various values of ampere-turns and the corresponding flux values accurately measured. The average flux densities are then determined by dividing the flux values by the sectional areas of the samples; and the ampere-turns per inch corresponding to each density value are computed and plotted. The resulting curves may be referred to whenever any engineering calculations must be made concerning the design or predicted performance of motors built of these materials.

The *B–H* curves shown in Fig. 51 are obtained by tests on typical specimens of cast iron, cast steel and electrical sheet steel; and are used in the examples and problems of this book.

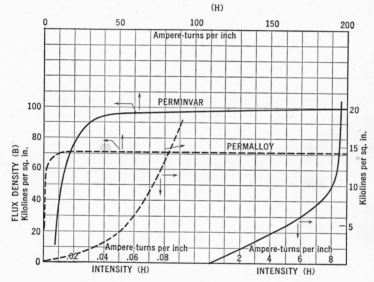

FIG. 52. B-H curves.

About 1923, new methods of manufacturing and heat treatment of nickel-iron alloys resulted in the production of Permalloy, a material which had very superior magnetic properties, particularly at low flux densities. This was followed in 1926 by the development of Hipernik, another nickel-iron alloy with somewhat similar properties; and in 1929 Perminvar, an alloy of nickel, cobalt and iron, was produced. These and similar alloys have been extensively used in the construction of telephone loading coils, instrument transformers and special relays, but their cost and their undesirable characteristics at high densities have precluded their more general use.

Typical *B–H* curves of these alloys are shown in Figs. 52 and 53.

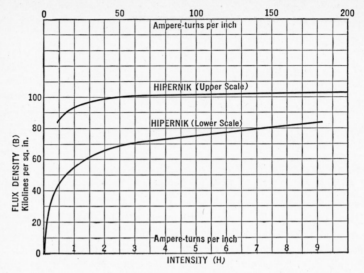

Fig. 53. B-H curves.

85. Series Magnetic Circuit:, Given Φ; to Find *NI*. The following example will illustrate the use of *B–H* curves in the solution of a simple series circuit.

In Fig. 54, *AA–BB–CC* is a closed circuit of cast steel in which 216,000 lines of flux are desired. Part *A* has a cross-section of 4 sq. in. and a length of 12 in. Part *B* has an area of 2 sq. in. and a length of 15 in. Part *C* has an area of 6 sq. in. and a length of 10 in.

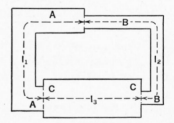

Fig. 54. Series magnetic circuit.

The densities can be computed easily:

$$B_A = 54,000; \quad B_B = 108,000; \quad B_C = 36,000.$$

Now by referring to the *B–H* curve for cast steel the value of the mmf. per unit length (*NI* per inch) corresponding to each of the density values can be determined. The data and results are summarized in the following table.

Part	Area	Length	B	H	NI
A	4	12	54,000	12	144
B	2	15	108,000	175	2625
C	6	10	36,000	8	80
					Total = 2849

The indicated total is the number of ampere-turns which must link with this magnetic circuit in order to produce 216,000 lines of flux.

If part C is cut and an air gap of length G is formed, a large increase in total ampere-turns will be found necessary if the same value of flux is desired in the magnetic circuit, because the air gap has a much greater reluctance than the cast steel which previously occupied the space. The NI values for parts A and B will be unchanged, but NI_C will be decreased slightly, owing to the reduction in the length of part C. H_G for the air gap is obtained by means of equation 37, and is then multiplied by the gap length and added to the other products to obtain the new value of NI.

Some thought must be given to selecting the proper value of average flux density in the air gap to be used in equation 37. From what has been said concerning magnetic fields in air the flux lines may be expected to flare out as they leave one face of the cast-steel section. This will cause a slight reduction in the average flux density, for the same number of lines will be spread out over a larger area. One method of approximating this effect is to increase both dimensions of the air-gap cross-section by the air-gap length, and use this increased area in calculating the average density. This gives good results in the typical motor magnetic circuit.

86. Series Magnetic Circuit: Given NI; to Find Φ. Consider the cast-steel circuit of Fig. 54 again, and assume that the number of ampere-turns linking the circuit is known. It is required to determine the flux that will be produced in the circuit. A straightforward solution of this problem is hindered by the fact that B and μ are interdependent, and neither one is known in this case.

The procedure to be followed may be called the "trial and error" method. A value of Φ for the circuit is assumed, and the density values B_A, B_B, B_C, B_{gap} are computed as in the previous example. The values of H for each part are then determined and the total NI found. If this sum is less than the number of ampere-turns actually available, a greater value of Φ must be assumed and a new set of calculations carried through. In this manner the correct flux value may be approached with any desired degree of accuracy if a sufficient number of trials is made.

87. Parallel Magnetic Circuit. Suppose that a cast-steel structure, proportioned about as shown in Fig. 55, has an exciting coil linking with its center section. How many ampere-turns must this coil supply in order to produce a flux of Φ lines in the center section, and in what ratio will the flux divide between the left-hand and right-hand branches? The parts will be designated A, B, C, from left to right. It is now necessary to assume values of Φ_A and Φ_C such that $\Phi_A + \Phi_C = \Phi_B$.

Then $B_A = \Phi_A/\text{sect. } A,$ $B_B = \Phi_B/\text{sect. } B,$ and $B_C = \Phi_C/\text{sect. } C.$ By referring to the $B\text{--}H$ curve for cast steel we can determine the values of H_A, H_B and H_C and multiply each by the proper length of path to obtain the NI drops for each part. The sum $(NI)_A + (NI)_B$ represents the counter-mmf. of one magnetic circuit, and this must equal $(NI)_C + (NI)_B$, the counter-mmf. of the other circuit,

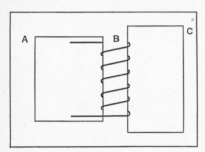

Fig. 55.   Series-parallel magnetic circuit.

which also must equal the ampere-turns generated in the coil. With ordinary luck the first computations will not result in the desired equality in NI drops for the right-hand and left-hand paths, and new values of Φ_A and Φ_C must be chosen, and the computations repeated.

If the value of the coil ampere-turns is known (see Fig. 55), and the fluxes in all the paths are unknown, a modification of the " trial-and-error " method just explained must be used. A value of Φ_B is assumed, and a reasonable assumption is also made regarding the proportions in which it divides between the branch circuits A and C. The densities resulting from these assumed values of Φ are computed, and H and NI are determined for each part. If $(NI)_A = (NI)_C$, and if $(NI)_A + (NI)_B =$ coil NI, the problem is solved. If not, new assumptions as to the quantity of flux and its distribution must be made and the computations repeated.

88. Motor Saturation Curve. Figure 56 shows a portion of the magnetic circuit of a typical four-pole motor. What procedure should be followed to find the number of field ampere-turns required to produce a definite value, Φ_g, of air-gap flux?

In order to make the problem definite, the following dimensions and data are given:

Part	Material	Area sq. in.	Length in.
1. Yoke	Cast steel	7.	12.
2. Pole..........	Sheet steel	13.	3.25, each
3. Gap..........	Air	15.	0.062, each
4. Teeth	Sheet steel	10.	1.25, each
5. Armature core	Sheet steel	9.	3.50

Assume that the value of Φ_g desired is 1,000,000 lines, meaning that this is the number of lines in the space between the armature surface and the face of one pole, which will contribute directly to the production of voltage and torque. The corresponding flux values in the remaining parts of one complete magnetic circuit must next be found.

The problem of determining exactly how these 1,000,000 lines will distribute themselves in the slots and teeth of the armature is a difficult one and is beyond the scope of this book. It is certain, however, that the great majority will enter the teeth immediately in order to reduce the length of travel in air. Assume that all the air-gap flux enters the teeth.

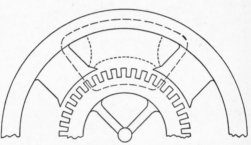

Fig. 56. Motor magnetic circuit.

Upon passing through the teeth to the armature core the lines will divide into two equal groups, one proceeding to the left and the other to the right. Hence the number of flux lines upon which the calculation of core density must be based will be $1/2\ \Phi_g$ or 500,000. Considering the right-hand path only, it is evident that these lines are augmented to 1,000,000 again as the second set of teeth and the second gap are traversed.

A considerable number of lines do not follow the proper path from pole to armature and then to pole again, but jump across from pole tip to pole tip as indicated by the dotted lines in the figure. Lines that avoid a useful path are called leakage flux lines, and a careful study of their probable number must be made whenever a new design is begun. Assume that in this case the leakage flux amounts to about 15% of the gap flux. Then the flux in the pole itself will be $1.15\Phi_y$ or 1,150,000.

When this flux reaches the yoke it divides again, so that the flux in the yoke between the poles will be about 575,000.

The next step is to determine the density in each part of the circuit. Then the corresponding values of H for each part can be obtained from the B–H curves, after which the NI drop in each part and the total NI can be computed. Each field coil will supply half of the NI required for the complete circuit. The results of these computations are tabulated below. Each item should be checked carefully.

PART	FLUX	DENSITY	H	NI
1. Yoke	575,000	82,200	31	370
2. Pole	1,150,000	88,500	20	130
3. Gap........	1,000,000	66,700	20,900	2590
4. Teeth	1,000,000	100,000	65	160
5. Core	500,000	55,500	5	20
			Total	3270
			NI per pole	1635

If seven or eight new values of Φ_g are now assumed, and the same procedure followed to obtain the ampere-turns per pole for each Φ_g, the final results may be represented graphically by plotting the values of Φ_g, the useful flux per pole, as ordinates and the corresponding ampere-turns per pole as abscissas. The graph showing the magnetic behavior of a particular magnetic circuit is called the saturation curve or the magnetization curve for that circuit, and is very useful in predicting the performance of the machine in service.

The saturation curve of a machine may also be obtained experimentally. The armature is turned at constant speed by a driving motor, and a voltmeter is connected to the brushes. The field coils are supplied with current from a separate source. Simultaneous readings of field current and armature voltage are obtained, varying the field current from zero to a high value, and the curve plotted from these readings is the saturation curve.

To show that this experimental curve has the same significance as the curve obtained from the B–H curves and design data, it is necessary merely to note the relationships between the abscissas and the ordinates of the two curves. The abscissa of any point on the experimental curve is the value of the current supplied to the field in amperes. If this is multiplied by the number of turns in a field coil (a constant for the machine), the result is the NI per pole for the machine, which is the abscissa value for the corresponding point on the calculated saturation curve. The ordinate of any point on the experimental curve is the value of voltage generated in the armature. If this is divided by KN (see equation 14) the result will be Φ_g, the useful flux per pole. In other words, since constant speed is maintained and there is no appreciable armature current to cause RI drop, the terminal voltage becomes proportional to the amount of gap flux being cut by the armature conductors.

89. Effects of Line Voltage Changes. One interesting use of the saturation curve is found in the prediction of the effects of changes in line voltage on the speed of a shunt motor. If the change in line voltage is rather small, say a 5% increase, and if the load torque remains constant, the speed will be practically unaffected by the voltage change. An inspection of the speed equation

$$N = \frac{V - RI}{K\Phi} \tag{22}$$

confirms this.

If, however, a large voltage change occurs, say a 25% increase, $K\Phi$ will not increase nearly this much, and we can expect a noticeable speed increase. In any case the flux values corresponding to the normal voltage and the new voltage can be obtained from the saturation curve and inserted successively in the speed equation, and the new speed can be computed easily. The result will be only approximately correct if the motor is heavily loaded, as armature reaction (flux production by the armature current) has not been taken into account.

90. Voltage of Self-induction. It will be recalled that the voltage induced in a conductor moving across a field and cutting flux at the rate of $d\Phi/dt$ lines per second is $d\Phi/10^8 dt$ volts. Faraday's classic set of experiments demonstrated that other ways of producing a time rate of change in the number of flux lines linking with a conductor are equally successful in the production of a voltage in the conductor. For example, the conductor may consist of a stationary loop of wire through which a number of magnetic lines are threading. If the number of lines thus linked with the conductor changes from instant to instant, a voltage is induced which is proportional to $d\Phi/dt$, the rate of change of these lines.

Figure 57 shows a single loop of wire connected to a battery through a current-regulating device. Assume that there are no other sources of magnetic flux in its vicinity, so that the flux linking with the loop will be zero when the loop current is zero. Now let the loop current grow at a uniform rate. Flux will appear in the loop simultaneously with the current, and the number of lines linking with the loop at any instant will be proportional to the current value at that instant. Since the flux threading the loop is undergoing a time rate of change, a generated voltage may be expected in the loop. This expectation is confirmed by experiment, and the direction of the induced. voltage is found to obey Lenz's law; that is, it opposes the flow of the current which produces it.

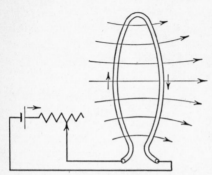

FIG. 57.   Voltage of self-induction.

That this voltage of self-induction, as it is called, should be opposed to the applied voltage seems perfectly logical, for, if it were not so opposed, the net voltage in the circuit would increase, which would speed up the flux change and cause more induced voltage. This cumulative action would result in complete destruction of the loop — a ridiculous conclusion.

If the loop current is made to decrease at a steady rate by means of the current regulator, a voltage of self-induction will appear again while the current and flux are changing. This time the induced voltage tends to prevent the current from decreasing.

A circuit so shaped that a considerable amount of flux is produced by a flow of current in it is said to be an inductive circuit.

91. Coefficient of Self-induction. The average voltage induced in a single turn of wire through which a changing flux is passing has already been expressed as

$$e = \frac{\Phi}{10^8 t} \text{ volts.}$$

If there are N turns linking this flux the voltage will be

$$e = \frac{N\Phi}{10^8 t}.$$

Let

$$\Phi = \frac{\text{mmf.}}{\Re} = \frac{4\pi NI}{10\Re},$$

and substitute in the voltage equation, obtaining

$$e = \frac{4\pi N^2 I}{10^9 \Re t}. \tag{38}$$

If the reluctance of the magnetic circuit is constant we may write

$$e = L\frac{I}{t},\tag{39}$$

where L replaces the quantity $4\pi N^2/10^9\mathfrak{R}$ and is called the coefficient of self-induction. Coils containing no iron will have a constant reluctance and a constant L. In motor field coils, however, L may acquire quite a range of values, depending on the amount of saturation.

Equation 39 is used to define the unit of self-inductance. If a coil develops a counter-emf. of 1 volt when the rate of current change in it is 1 ampere per second, the coil is said to have an inductance of 1 henry.

92. Rise of Current in an Inductive Circuit. If a coil having a considerable amount of inductance is suddenly connected to a constant supply voltage, V, the current does not rise instantly to the value V/R because as soon as the current begins to increase a counter-voltage, $L(di/dt)$, is produced which opposes the increasing current.

Figure 58 shows a typical current-time curve for an air-core coil. If another ordinate scale is chosen to represent voltage and its units adjusted so that the distance OY equals the applied voltage, then the ordinate AP of the curve at

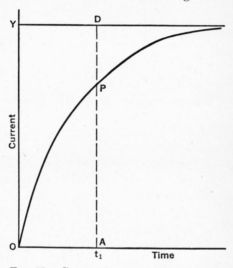

FIG. 58. Current rise in inductive circuit.

any time t must be Ri volts, where R is the coil resistance and i is the coil current at that instant. The remaining distance PD represents the counter-voltage being generated in the coil by the changing current.

The complete equation for the voltage conditions in the coil at any instant can be stated as follows:

$$V = Ri + L\frac{di}{dt}.\tag{40}$$

At the closing of the switch, $i = 0$, $Ri = 0$ and $V = L(di/dt)$, so that the initial rate of current increase will be $di/dt = V/L$. After the current begins to build up, the rate of increase continually grows less and finally $di/dt = 0$ and $V = RI$.

In order to solve equation 40 for the value of i let us rearrange it in the form

$$\frac{di}{\dfrac{V - Ri}{L}} = dt.$$

Multiplying numerator and denominator by $-R/L$, we have

$$\frac{-\dfrac{R}{L} di}{-\dfrac{R}{L}\left(\dfrac{V - Ri}{L}\right)} = dt,$$

which, when integrated becomes

$$-\frac{L}{R} \log\left(\frac{V - Ri}{L}\right) = t + \log C.$$

From a study of the initial conditions we find

$$\log C = -\frac{L}{R} \log \frac{V}{L}.$$

Making this substitution,

$$-\frac{L}{R} \log\left(\frac{V - Ri}{L}\right) = t - \frac{L}{R} \log \frac{V}{L},$$

or

$$\log \frac{\dfrac{V - Ri}{L}}{\dfrac{V}{L}} = -\frac{R}{L} t,$$

$$\frac{V - Ri}{V} = e^{-\frac{R}{L} t},$$

$$i = \frac{V}{R}\left(1 - e^{-\frac{R}{L} t}\right). \tag{41}$$

In this equation e is the Napierian base. It will be evident that the value of R/L determines the rate of increase of current, and that theoretically the current never reaches its final value V/R. It will be evident also that, when $t = L/R$,

$$i = \frac{V}{R} (1 - e^{-1}),$$

$$= 0.632 \frac{V}{R}.$$

The ratio L/R of a coil is sometimes called the time constant of the coil.

93. Decay of Current in an Inductive Circuit. If an air-core coil which has been drawing current from a constant supply voltage is suddenly short-circuited and the supply voltage is disconnected at the same time, the current in the coil does not drop to zero instantly but

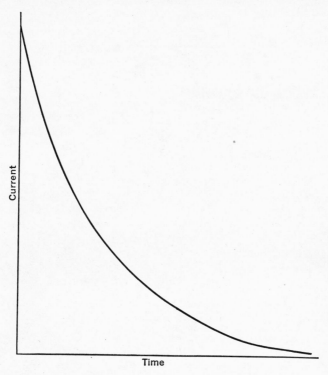

Fig. 59. Current decay in inductive circuit.

follows some such curve as Fig. 59 shows. As soon as the current begins to decrease a voltage of self-induction is produced which opposes the decrease. If the voltage equation for this circuit is written as it applies to these new conditions we will have

$$0 = Ri + L\frac{di}{dt}.$$

Rearranging and dividing by R,

$$i = -\frac{L}{R}\frac{di}{dt}.$$

Rearranging again,

$$\frac{di}{i} = -\frac{R}{L}dt,$$

$$\log i = -\frac{R}{L}t + \log C,$$

$$i = Ce^{-\frac{R}{L}t}.$$

But $i = V/R$ when $t = 0$.
Therefore

$$C = \frac{V}{R} = I,$$

and

$$i = Ie^{-\frac{R}{L}t}, \tag{42}$$

in which I is the original current value which existed before the short circuit was applied, and the other symbols have the same meaning as in equation 41.

94. Energy Storage in a Magnetic Field. If every term of equation 40 is multiplied by ($i\,dt$), some interesting facts will become evident.

$$Vi\,dt = Ri^2\,dt + Li\,di \tag{43}$$

In this equation, $Vi\,dt$ = energy supplied to the circuit in the time dt.
$Ri^2\,dt$ = energy transformed into heat.
$Li\,di$ = energy stored in the magnetic field.

If in the term expressing the energy stored in the magnetic field the value of i is substituted from equation 41 and the expression integrated between the limits of 0 and ∞ for t, the total magnetic energy storage becomes

$$W = \tfrac{1}{2}LI^2 \text{ joules.} \tag{44}$$

Since $i = 0$ when $t = 0$, and $i = I$ when $t = \infty$, this same result may be obtained more simply by a change of variable, permitting the integration of the expression $Li\,di$ between the limits $i = 0$ and $i = I$.

If L is large the amount of energy stored in the magnetic field may be considerable and may become a source of danger under certain conditions. Suppose that the current which such a coil has been carrying is suddenly reduced to zero by opening the switch connecting it to the supply circuit. The counter-voltage, $L(di/dt)$, will become very large, often ten or fifteen times the voltage of the original supply circuit, and the stored energy of the coil will dissipate itself in the form of an arc across the switch blades, or through the coil insulation.

If it becomes necessary to open an inductive circuit frequently, it is good practice to shunt a resistance across the circuit before disconnecting it from the line. The stored energy can then dissipate itself slowly by sending current through the resistance and the induced voltage does not reach such high values. Such resistances, called field discharge resistors, are frequently connected across the shunt field circuits of shunt motors equipped with automatic starters.

95. Pull of Magnets. It has been shown that the expression for the energy storage in a magnetic field is

$$W = \tfrac{1}{2}LI^2. \tag{44}$$

In dealing with a magnetic circuit having an air gap it is very convenient at times to have another expression for magnetic energy storage in terms of the average flux density in the air gap. This can be derived as follows: From equations 38 and 33 we find

$$L = \frac{4\pi N^2}{10^9 \mathcal{R}} = \frac{4\pi N^2 \mu A}{10^9 l}.$$

Substituting this value of L in equation 44

$$W = \frac{2\pi N^2 I^2 \mu A}{10^9 l}. \tag{44a}$$

From equation 32

$$\Phi = \frac{\text{mmf.}}{\mathcal{R}} = \frac{4\pi N I \mu A}{10 l},$$

$$B = \frac{\Phi}{A} = \frac{4\pi N I \mu}{10 l},$$

then

$$B^2 = \frac{16\pi^2 N^2 I^2 \mu^2}{100 l^2}.$$

Now if both numerator and denominator of equation 44a are multiplied by $8\pi\mu l$, we obtain

$$W = \frac{16\pi^2 N^2 I^2 \mu^2 l A}{10^9 l^2 8\pi\mu},$$

and from the expression just developed for B^2

$$W = \frac{B^2 l A}{10^7 8\pi\mu}. \tag{45}$$

Although it is not known just where or how this storage of energy is accomplished it is usually assumed that it is stored in the magnetic field.

If the magnetic circuit is a composite one it seems reasonable to assume that the energy storage will be distributed about as the mmf. drop is distributed, which in a circuit with an air gap means that nearly all the energy storage will occur in the gap and may be thought of as distributed throughout the volume of the gap.

If equation 45 is taken to be the energy storage in the gap and l and A are the air-gap length and area respectively, the energy storage per unit volume of air gap will be

$$W_g = \frac{B^2}{10^7 8\pi\mu} \text{ joules or } \frac{B^2}{8\pi\mu} \text{ ergs,}$$

and this reduces to

$$W_g = \frac{B^2}{8\pi} \text{ ergs per cu. cm.,} \qquad (46)$$

since $\mu = 1$ for air.

When the various properties of magnetic fields and lines of force were listed it was said that magnetic lines in air seem to be in a state of tension and if the surfaces bounding the gap are movable they will tend to be drawn together. Now it has been stated that an air gap in a magnetic circuit contains most of the stored energy associated with the circuit. If the gap is allowed to shorten itself in response to the tension of the lines of force, the work necessary to accomplish this motion must come from the stored energy in the gap. If the gap is forcibly lengthened the energy storage will be increased.

Inspection of equation 45 indicates that a change in l by a very small amount, Δl, will produce a proportional change in the energy stored, if Δl is so small that no appreciable change in the value of B will be produced.

Let
$$\Delta W = \frac{B^2 A \, \Delta l}{8\pi} \text{ ergs, in air,}$$
$$= P \, \Delta l,$$

where P is the gap tension in dynes. Therefore P may be written

$$P = \frac{B^2 A}{8\pi} \text{ dynes,} \qquad (47)$$

which is a very useful relationship for lifting magnets.

SUGGESTED BIBLIOGRAPHY

1. Electric and Magnetic Fields, ATTWOOD. John Wiley & Sons, 1932.
2. Standard Handbook for Electrical Engineers, McGraw-Hill Book Co., 6th edition, sections 2 and 4.
3. Handbook of Engineering Fundamentals, ESHBACH. John Wiley & Sons, 1936.

PROBLEMS

1. A north pole of 10 units strength and a south pole of 20 units strength are located 10 cm. apart. Find the magnitude and direction of the force exerted upon a unit test pole placed at A.

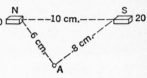

2. What is the magnetic field intensity at a point 15 cm. away from a long, straight wire carrying 20 amperes? What is the value of the intensity 30 cm. away?

Prob. 1, Ch. 7.

3. A cast-iron ring with a circular cross-section 2 in. in diameter has a mean radius of 10 in. How many ampere-turns are required to produce a total flux of 120,000 maxwells in this magnetic circuit?

4. A cast-iron ring with a circular cross-section 2 in. in diameter has a mean radius of 10 in. The ring has been cut through by a saw, forming an air gap 0.5 in. in length. How many ampere-turns are required to produce a total flux of 90,000 maxwells in this magnetic circuit, and how many additional ampere-turns are required to increase this flux by 50%? Neglect fringing and leakage fluxes.

5. A coil of 200 turns is wound in one layer on a cast-steel annular ring which has a mean diameter of 5 in. and a circular cross-section of 0.8 sq. in. An air gap of 0.09-in. length has been cut in the ring. Find the ampere-turns required to produce flux densities of 40, 60, 80, 100, 110 kilolines per square inch, and plot a curve of total flux against amperes excitation.

6. A coil of 200 turns of No. 14 wire is wound on a wooden annular ring which has a mean diameter of 5 in. and a circular cross-section of 1 sq. in. Find (*a*) the flux density in the core when the coil carries 4 amperes; (*b*) the flux density if the wooden ring is replaced by a cast-steel ring of the same dimensions and the coil is supplied with 4 amperes.

7. A cast-steel ring with a mean radius of 10 in. has a circular cross-section 2 in. in diameter. There are 6900 ampere-turns on this circuit. Find the flux density and the total flux.

8. A cast-iron ring with a mean radius of 10 in. has a circular cross-section 2 in. in diameter. The ring has been cut, making an air gap 0.5 in. in length. There are 24,000 ampere-turns on this circuit. Find the flux density and the total flux. Neglect fringing and leakage fluxes.

9. Two iron magnetic circuits loop through a common coil. Each circuit has a mean length of 40 in. One is of cast iron 1 sq. in. in section; the other is of cast steel 2 sq. in. in section. Find how many ampere-turns are required to produce a total flux of 248,000 lines through the coil.

10. Two magnetic circuits have the same mean path length, 30 in., and loop through the same energizing coil. Circuit A is cast iron, 1 sq. in. section; B is cast steel, 2 sq. in. section. B has a 0.1-in. air gap cut in it. Find the flux in A when the B section has an average flux density of 90,000 lines per sq. in. Neglect fringing.

11. Given a cast-steel part as shown; determine the average flux density in the air gap, and in the neck, and the average mmf. drop across each in ampere-turns per inch.

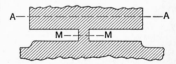

Section $A–A$ = 2.25 sq. in.

Section $M–M$ = 0.25 sq. in.

Flux density at $A–A$ = 13,350 lines per sq. in.

Prob. 11, Ch. 7.

12.

Part	Length in.	Area sq. in.	Material
A	20	3	Cast steel
B	10	3	Cast iron
C	10	1	Cast steel

B has a flux density of 60,000 lines per sq. in.   What current is required if the coil has 1000 turns?

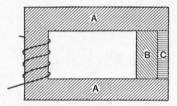

Prob. 12, Ch. 7.

13. In the magnetic circuit shown, find the coil ampere-turns required to produce a density of 60,000 lines per sq. in. in the air gap.   Neglect leakage and fringing fluxes.

A	Cast steel	10 in. long,	4 sq. in. section.
B	" "	24 " "	2 " " "
C	" "	8 " "	5 " " "
D	" "	10 " "	4 " " "
Air gap		0.1 " "	4 " " "

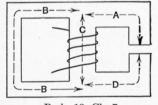

Prob. 13, Ch. 7.

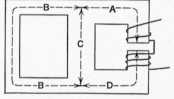

Prob. 14, Ch. 7.

14. In the magnetic circuit shown, find the coil ampere-turns required to produce a density of 35,000 lines per sq. in. in part B.   Neglect leakage and fringing fluxes.

Air-gap length 0.05 in.; 4 sq. in. section.   The other parts of the magnetic circuit have the same materials and dimensions as in Problem 13.

15. In the magnetic circuit shown the coil is supplying 3000 ampere-turns.   Find the sectional area of the sheet-steel bridge, D, which will cause the air-gap density at G to have an average value of 45,000 lines per sq. in.

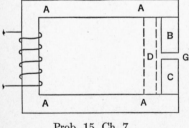

Prob. 15, Ch. 7.

Part	Material	Length in.	Area sq. in.
A	Cast steel	14	2
B	Cast steel	2	2
C	Cast steel	2	2
Gap	Air	0.1	2.2
D	Sheet steel	4.1	...

16. The accompanying figure is a simplified diagram of a reverse-current relay. The cast-steel path $ABCD$ has a length of 10 in. and a sectional area of 0.5 sq. in. The cast-steel plunger EF is 1.7 in. long and 0.5 sq. in. in section. The air gap G is 0.15 in. long and 0.5 sq. in. in section. The rod K is non-magnetic. Coil 1 has 200 turns and 5 amperes; coil 2 has 10,000 turns and 0.1 ampere.

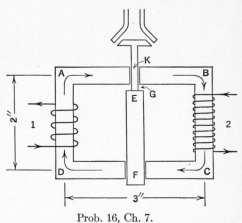

(a) With the current and flux directions as shown find the flux in $ABCD$ and the flux density in EF.

(b) If the current in coil 1 has the same value but is reversed in direction, what will be the average flux density in the air gap G?

Prob. 16, Ch. 7.

17. If coil 1 in the figure of Problem 16 carries 2 amperes in the opposite direction to that indicated in the figure, what will be the approximate air-gap density? The other circuit constants are unchanged.

18. Repeat the calculations of Problem 16 with Hipernik substituted for cast steel and with the turns of coils 1 and 2 reduced to 40 and 2000 respectively.

19. A certain 100-hp., 625-volt compound motor is designed to operate at 1050 rpm. at no load. The armature has 78 slots with 18 conductors per slot. There are 6 parallel paths in the armature winding, and the total armature winding resistance is 0.078 ohm. The machine has 6 poles. The interpole winding (connected in series with the armature) has a resistance of 0.026 ohm. The series field has 17 turns per pole and a total resistance of 0.032 ohm. The shunt field has 2900 turns per pole.

Name of Part	Magnetic Circuit Dimensions			
	Number in Circuit	Material	Length in.	Section Area sq. in.
1. Yoke..........	1	Cast steel	16.5	14
2. Pole..........	2	Sheet steel	6.8	31
3. Air gap........	2	Air	0.13	44
4. Teeth.........	2 sets	Sheet steel	1.89	25
5. Armature core..	1	Sheet steel	6.0	15

Assume a leakage coefficient of 1.15. Neglect fringing. Plot the magnetization curve of this machine, using air-gap flux per pole as ordinates, and ampere-turns per pole as abscissas.

20. Basing your calculations on the data of Problem 19:

(a) Determine how many ampere-turns per pole are required if the machine runs at 1050 rpm., with the armature current approximately zero, and a line voltage of 625.

(b) The machine is operated as a shunt motor on 625-volt mains, and the shunt field is adjusted so that the speed with zero armature current is 1050 rpm. With armature currents as abscissas, plot curves of developed torque and speed. Neglect the effect of armature reaction.

(c) The machine is operated as a cumulative compound motor on 625-volt mains, and the shunt field is adjusted so that the speed with zero armature current is 1050 rpm. Plot torque-current and speed-current curves as above.

(d) Same conditions as (c), except the differential compound connection is used.

(e) The shunt and series field coils are removed from the poles, and a new set of series coils with 47 turns per pole and a total resistance of 0.082 ohm is placed in position. The machine is then operated as a straight series motor on 625-volt mains. Plot the torque-current and speed-current curves.

21. How fast would the compound motor of Problem 20 run at no load if the supply voltage of both field and armature circuits is reduced to 500 volts?

22. The motor of Problem 20 is operating as a cumulative compound motor from 700-volt supply mains. $I_a = 150$ amperes. What must be the total resistance of the shunt field circuit in order to make the motor operate at 1015 rpm.?

23. The straight series arrangement of Problem 20 is used. What will be its operating speed under the following conditions: $V = 500$, $I_a = 150$. The series field is shunted by a resistor of 0.164 ohm, so that only a fraction of the armature current enters the field coils.

24. The motor of Problem 20 is operating as a series motor connected to 600-volt mains. It draws 100 amperes. What is its speed? If it later draws 125 amperes from 575-volt mains what must be the armature torque developed?

25. The motor of Problem 20 is operating as a shunt motor connected to 550-volt mains. The shunt field circuit resistance is 395 ohms. What value of I_a will be required to produce a developed torque of 100 lb-ft.?

26. The motor of Problem 20 is operating as a cumulative compound motor from 600-volt supply mains. Its shunt field circuit resistance is 600 ohms, and its armature current is 100 amperes. Find the operating speed.

27. The motor of Problem 20 is operating as a cumulative compound motor connected to 500-volt mains. The shunt field resistance is 395 ohms. What value of I_a will be required to produce a developed torque of 200 lb-ft.? Use " trial-and-error " method.

28. A 250-hp. compound motor is connected to 230-volt mains. It has 6 poles, 600 armature conductors and 6 parallel paths in the armature winding. The series coil on each pole has 1.5 turns. At full load, $I_a = 880$ amperes, the counter-emf. = 217.5 volts and the speed is 450 rpm. The characteristic magnetization curve applies to this motor if one ordinate unit $= 2 \times 10^6$ lines of air-gap flux and one abscissa unit $= 4000$ ampere-turns per pole.

(a) Determine the ampere-turns per pole at full load.

(b) Determine the approximate no-load speed.

(c) Determine the approximate no-load speed if the voltage applied to the field and armature becomes 150 volts.

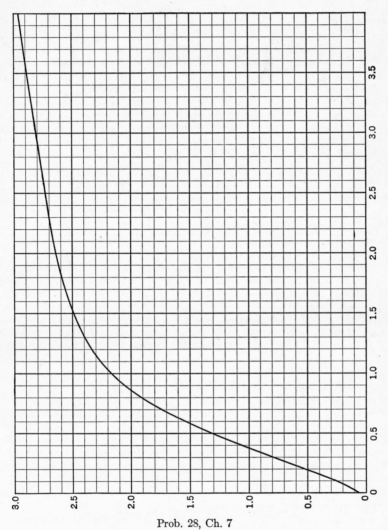

Prob. 28, Ch. 7
Characteristic magnetization curve.

29. The motor of Problem 28 has its series coils reversed, thus making it differential compound. What torque will be developed in its armature when $I_a = 500$ amperes and $V = 230$ volts?

30. The motor of Problem 28 has its shunt and series coils removed and new series coils installed. Each series coil has 6 turns. The combined resistance of armature and field is now 0.02 ohm. $V = 230$ volts.

(a) What will be the motor speed when $I_a = 600$ amperes?

(b) What torque will it produce when $I_a = 700$ amperes?

31. Two similar shunt motors are mechanically coupled together, and their armatures are connected in series across 220-volt mains. At no load and with normal field excitation the line voltage is equally divided between them, and they run at 1200 rpm. If the field strength of one motor is increased 30%, at what speed do they run? What is the voltage across each armature? Assume that the armature resistances are negligible.

32. Two identically similar shunt machines are mounted on a common base and their shafts are mechanically coupled together. Their armatures are connected in series across a 230-volt line. The resistance of each armature is 0.04 ohm. The field windings are separate, each being connected to the 230-volt line through its own rheostat. When the fields are equally excited to their normal values the set runs at no load at a speed of 1100 rpm. Evidently under these conditions the two armatures divide the line voltage equally. Such a set is called a " balancer set " and is often used to change a two-wire to a three-wire distribution system.

(a) If the flux of one machine is increased 20%, what will be the speed of the set, and what will be the voltage across each armature?

(b) If the flux of the second machine be now decreased 20%, what will be the speed of the set, and the voltage across each armature?

33. Two shunt motors have their fields connected in parallel and their armatures in series across the supply line. The armatures are mechanically coupled to each other and to the load, which they drive at 1000 rpm. The residual flux is 10% of the normal flux, and armature resistance is negligible.

(a) At what speed will the load be driven if one of the motors has its armature short-circuited?

(b) Assuming, again, the normal operation, what would be the speed should the field of one of the motors be broken?

34. A voltage of 100 volts is suddenly applied to a field coil having a resistance of 50 ohms; t seconds after the application of this voltage the current is 1.2 amperes.

(a) What is the voltage of self-induction at this instant?

(b) What is the heat loss in watts at this instant?

(c) What is the rate of energy storage, in watts, in the magnetic field at this instant?

35. An air-core inductance is connected to a direct-current supply of 110 volts. $L = 0.58$ henry; $R = 13.5$ ohms. What will be the value of the current 0.01 second after the switch is closed? How long will it take for the current to build up to half its final value?

36. An air-core inductance coil has been drawing current from a direct-current supply. $L = 0.54$ henry; $R = 12$ ohms. This coil is suddenly short-circuited and the supply voltage is disconnected. What percentage of the original current will be found in the coil 0.02 second after the supply switch is opened?

37. A coil having an inductance of 10 henrys and a resistance of 25 ohms is connected to a 115-volt line. What must be the value of the discharge resistor used with this coil so that the voltage across the coil terminals, upon breaking the circuit, shall not exceed 230 volts?

38. Find the approximate pull in pounds exerted by a lifting magnet whose air-gap density is 10,000 lines per square centimeter, and whose lifting area is 10 sq. cm.

CHAPTER 8

GENERATOR CHARACTERISTICS

96. Nature of Generated Voltage. Figure 60a shows a crude arrangement by which voltage may be generated in a conductor. The slot in which the conductor lies is parallel to the axis of rotation and the motion is perpendicular to the flux lines so that the most favorable conditions

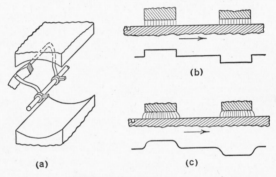

(a)   (b)   (c)

FIG. 60. Voltage generated by one conductor.

for the generation of voltage are secured. The ends of the conductor are connected to two slip rings mounted on and insulated from the shaft, and the generated voltage may be measured by connecting a voltmeter to the two brushes.

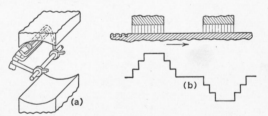

(a)   (b)

FIG. 61. Voltage generated by three conductors.

If the flux under each pole is assumed to exhibit no fringing effect the resulting voltage wave will be somewhat as shown in developed form in Fig. 60b, while Fig. 60c shows the effect of fringing. Notice that in each case the amplitude of the voltage wave is small and that the voltage is zero during most of the rotational period.

If the armature is constructed as a cylindrical shell dovetailed to a supporting spider which is integral with the shaft it is possible for several conductors to be connected in series by means of wires on the inner surface of the shell as represented in Fig. 61a. From the resulting voltage wave (Fig. 61b) it is evident that an increase in the amplitude and the spread of the voltage wave has been secured.

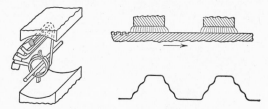

FIG. 62. Voltage rectified by a commutator.

By substituting a two-part commutator for the slip rings the alternating voltage is transformed into a pulsating, unidirectional voltage as shown in Fig. 62.

The arrangement illustrated in Fig. 63 doubles the amplitude of the coil voltage with only a small increase in length of wire. The return conductors are no longer shielded from the magnetic field by being placed

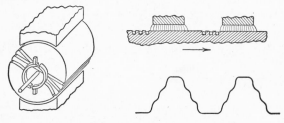

FIG. 63. Rectified voltage of 6-conductor coil.

within the armature shell, but are located on the armature surface. A three-turn coil wound in this way will have six active coil sides contributing to the coil voltage.

Finally there is the more practical arrangement shown in Fig. 64a. Each of the six symmetrically spaced slots contains two insulated conductors, connected in pairs by end connections, and each pair terminates at two adjacent commutator bars. In order to appreciate the advantages of this construction it is necessary to examine the connection pattern carefully. Starting at the upper brush, conductors 10, 9, 8, 7, 6 and

5 form one path to the lower brush, and the other path includes 11, 12, 1, 2, 3 and 4. In order to predict the value of the total generated voltage it is necessary to find the contribution of each conductor and study the way in which it varies with the armature position.

Let Fig. 64b represent the air gap under one pole and assume that the flux is so distributed that a conductor passing the pole center generates 6 volts and that the voltage it produces in other positions is about as indicated in the table immediately below the figure. A tabulation of the voltages generated by each conductor at the instant pictured in Fig. 64a can now be drawn up.

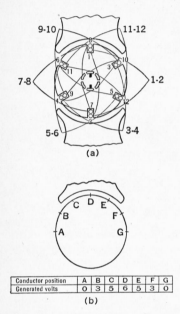

(a)

(b)

Fig. 64. Voltage of 12-conductor drum winding.

Conductor position	A	B	C	D	E	F	G
Generated volts	0	3	5	6	5	3	0

Conductor number	10	9	8	7	6	5	Total
Conductor position	F	F	D	D	B	B	
Generated volts	3	3	6	6	3	3	24

A similar tabulation can be made for the other path.

Conductor number	11	12	1	2	3	4	Total
Conductor position	B	B	D	D	F	F	
Generated volts	3	3	6	6	3	3	24

Now imagine the armature to turn 30° in a clockwise direction. Conductors 10 and 9 will be short-circuited by the upper brush and 3 and 4 by the lower brush, leaving 8, 7, 6 and 5 still active in one group and 11, 12, 1 and 2 in the other. The voltages will be

Conductor number	10	9	8	7	6	5	Total
Conductor position	G	A	E	E	C	C	
Generated volts	0	0	5	5	5	5	20

and

Conductor number	11	12	1	2	3	4	Total
Conductor position	C	C	E	E	G	A	
Generated volts	5	5	5	5	0	0	20

When the armature turns 30° further the conditions of the original position will be duplicated. Conductors 8, 7, 6, 5, 4 and 3 will be found in one path and 9, 10, 11, 12, 1 and 2 will be in the other, and the voltage generated in each group will be 24. It is evident from an inspection of the voltage wave of this machine, Fig. 65, that a great improvement has been effected in the smoothness of the generated voltage.

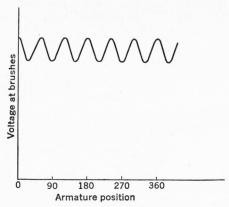

FIG. 65. Voltage wave of 12-conductor winding.

97. Generated Voltage Equations. From the preceding discussion it is evident that the generated voltages of the individual armature conductors vary continually in magnitude and change periodically in direction, but that they are interconnected in such a way that the sum of the voltages in each armature group has a fairly steady value. When the term " generated voltage " is used it is this steady summation value which is meant.

In Chapter 4 the generation of voltage in a motor armature was discussed. It was then called counter-emf., and was observed to play an important part in maintaining torque equilibrium. Generated voltage as used in this chapter refers to exactly the same phenomenon.

Equations 13 and 14, developed for the analysis of motor performance, are reproduced here for convenience.

$$E_g = \frac{10^{-8}}{60} \times \frac{pZ}{m} \times \Phi N, \tag{13}$$

$$E_g = K\Phi N. \tag{14}$$

98. Requirements for Generator Operation. In order to make a dynamo function as a generator it is necessary to drive its armature with a motive power unit such as a steam engine or an electric motor; and the field coils of the generator must be supplied with current in order to produce the necessary flux. Although equation 14 indicates that changes in generator voltage may be produced by varying either the speed or the field current, in many cases the nature of the prime mover is such that a fairly definite speed level must be maintained for best results. Variations in generated voltage must then be secured by varying the field current alone.

99. Terminal Voltage. The voltage which is indicated by a suitable voltmeter connected to the brushes of the generator is called the terminal voltage of the generator. It agrees in value with the generated voltage if the machine is unloaded, that is, if no current is being drawn from the armature. If a receiving circuit is connected to the armature terminals and current is drawn from the generator, the terminal voltage becomes less than the generated voltage, since a portion of the generated voltage is now required to balance the armature RI drop.

The equation relating these quantities may be written

$$E = V + R_a I_a, \tag{48}$$

in which E is the generated voltage.

V is the terminal voltage.

$R_a I_a$ is the voltage drop in the armature.

Note that this equation is really the familiar equation for the motor armature circuit with the algebraic sign of the RI term changed.

100. Production of Counter-torque. The amount of torque which the prime mover must supply to the generator shaft is very small as long as the current output is zero, even though the generator is producing a large voltage. It must merely be sufficient to overcome the counter-torques of bearing and brush friction, windage and the iron or magnetic losses.

As soon as a receiving circuit is connected to the armature terminals the resulting current in the armature conductors reacts with the field flux to create a torque which, by application of the direction rule illustrated in Fig. 6, is found to be a counter-torque. The prime mover is forced to produce more torque in order to maintain the desired speed of rotation.

In a loaded motor the applied voltage and the counter-emf. are opposite and almost equal to each other, differing only by the amount of the armature RI drop. In a loaded generator the driving torque and the counter-torque produced by its current are opposite and almost equal to each other, differing only by the amount of torque represented by the frictional and magnetic losses.

101. Types of Generators. Generators, like motors, are usually classified with reference to the method of providing field excitation: the shunt, the series, the cumulative compound and the differential compound generator. In addition there are a few types designed for special purposes, such as the Rosenberg and the diverter-pole generators. These will be discussed in Chapter 14.

There are two varieties of shunt generators. If the shunt field circuit is supplied with current from a separate power supply the generator is called a separately excited shunt generator. If the generator field circuit is connected to its own armature terminals the machine is called a self-excited shunt generator.

102. Separately Excited Shunt Generator.* The relationship between armature current output and terminal voltage for a typical separately excited shunt generator is shown in Fig. 66a, and the generator connections required for an experimental determination of this curve are shown in Fig. 66b. The driving speed and the shunt field current are held constant during the test.

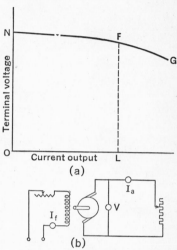

FIG. 66. Separately excited generator.

When the receiving circuit is open the armature current is zero and the terminal voltage is represented by the intercept ON. As the resistance of the receiving circuit is reduced the armature current increases and the terminal voltage decreases. At rated or full-load current, which is taken to be OL on the graph, the terminal voltage will be LF, and the curve NFG is usually called the external characteristic curve.

The curve NFG is reproduced in Fig. 67 so that the causes of its downward trend may be discussed more conveniently. Inspection of equation 14 indicates that, under the operating conditions specified in the preceding paragraph (constant field current and constant speed), the generated voltage may be expected to remain constant as represented by the line NPR. Actually, however, the generated voltage will follow some such curve as NAB, owing

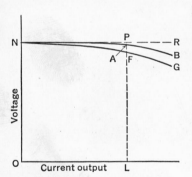

FIG. 67. Characteristics of separately excited generator.

* See Appendix for additional material on generator characteristics.

to a certain amount of demagnetizing action set up by the current in the armature. This effect of the armature current is usually negligible until values of one-half to three-fourths of rated current are reached, but it becomes increasingly important at heavier loads. The flow of current through the armature creates a drop in voltage (R_aI_a), which still further reduces the voltage available at the terminals. For any load current such as OL the ideal value of the generated voltage is LP; the reduction in voltage due to the demagnetizing action of the armature current is PA; the armature RI drop is AF; and the terminal voltage of the machine is LF.

If the resistance of the receiving circuit is reduced to zero, thus short-circuiting the generator, the resulting current output will be dangerously large. There is also the possibility that an arc will flash around the commutator from the positive to the negative brush at the instant the short circuit occurs. It is advisable to protect this type of generator from severe overloads, as it has no self-protective characteristics.

103. Self-excited Shunt Generator. Before discussing the external characteristic of a self-excited shunt generator it is necessary to consider the process by which the generator is able to build up and maintain a terminal voltage at no load. The first requisite is a magnetic circuit with the property of retaining a small amount of magnetism long after the exciting current in its field coils has been reduced to zero. Most generators of this type retain from 2 to 3% of their normal magnetic strength after being shut down, and the flux so retained is called residual flux. If the armature is rotated at normal speed a voltage amounting to 2 or 3% of the normal value will be generated by the cutting of the residual flux alone.

104. Building-up Process. If the shunt field circuit is now connected to the armature terminals a small current will flow through the field. The initial value of this current will be e/R_f, where e is the residual voltage and R_f is the resistance of the field circuit from terminal to terminal. If this initial current flows through the field coils in the proper direction to strengthen the residual flux, the armature conductors will generate more voltage, which will cause the field current to increase, and a further increase in generated voltage will occur. Saturation effects, however, become noticeable as the field current and flux reach high values. Equal increments of increase in field current are no longer able to produce such large increments of flux, and a condition of equilibrium is soon reached at which the generated voltage just equals the voltage needed to drive the required current through the field circuit.

In Fig. 68 the building-up process is expressed by graphical means. The straight line OPM represents the voltage-current relation in the field circuit, and is usually called the shunt field resistance line. Its equation is of the form $y = R_f x$, where x is the shunt field current in amperes, R_f is the resistance of the shunt field circuit in ohms and y is the field voltage drop. The curved line FQM is the saturation curve of the generator plotted for its rated speed. For a selected value of x such as OD the ordinate DQ is the voltage being generated in the armature at rated speed, while the ordinate DP is that fraction of the generated voltage needed to force the field current OD through the field circuit.

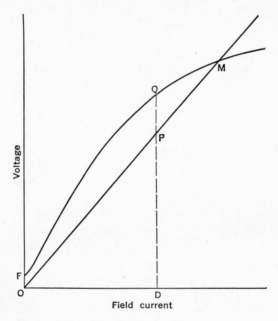

FIG. 68. Building-up process.

Let any ordinate of the saturation curve be Y and let the corresponding ordinate of the shunt field resistance line be y. At the beginning of the building-up process $x = 0$, $y = 0$ and $Y = OF$, the voltage due to the residual flux. With the closing of the field circuit, x begins to have steadily increasing finite values, and for each value of x the corresponding value of Y is greater than y, until finally point M is reached where $Y = y$ and x becomes constant. Where Y is but little greater than y, as in the region near F and again near M, the field current changes slowly; but where Y is much greater than y, as in the vicinity of P, the field current changes rapidly.

A somewhat different view of the building-up process may be obtained by considering it as an example of the rise of current in an inductive circuit. In Chapter 7 it was shown that the voltage conditions in such a circuit might be expressed by the equation

$$V = Ri + L\frac{di}{dt}.$$

A restatement making use of the symbols employed in the preceding paragraph will read:

$$Y = R_f x + L\frac{dx}{dt}.$$

At the start, $R_f x = 0$ and $Y = OF = L(dx/dt)$. Thus the initial rate of field current growth is equal to the residual voltage divided by the inductance of the field. The subsequent rate depends upon the value of $Y - y$. When the field current has reached the value OD, the field voltage drop (y) will be equal to DP; the generated voltage (Y) will be DQ and the voltage $(L[dx/dt])$ available to produce further increases in field current will be PQ.

The procedure by which a self-excited generator may be made to build up a voltage at its terminals may now be summarized.

1. Residual magnetism, if not already present, must be established by a temporary connection of the field windings to an external power supply.

2. The armature must be driven at a suitable speed.

3. The field circuit must be connected to the armature terminals in such a way that current begins to pass through it in the proper direction to strengthen the residual magnetism.

4. The field rheostat should be turned to the position of minimum resistance until the building-up process is well under way. Sufficient resistance may then be inserted to prevent the final voltage from exceeding the desired value.

The no-load terminal voltage of a self-excited generator operating under specified speed and field resistance conditions may be predicted by an easy graphical method.

1. Draw the saturation curve of the machine for the specified speed, plotting generated voltage vertically and field current horizontally.

2. Draw the shunt field resistance line with the same voltage and current scales, and with its slope equal to the specified field circuit resistance.

3. Observe the coordinates of the point of intersection of the saturation curve and the shunt field resistance line. The ordinate of this point is the no-load terminal voltage to be expected under the specified conditions.

105. Effect of Changes in Field Resistance. If, with a no-load terminal voltage as indicated by the point of intersection, M, Fig. 69, the resistance of the field circuit is increased, a reduction in terminal voltage will occur. To predict the new value of this voltage it is necessary to draw a new field resistance line whose slope is equal to R_2, the new resistance of the shunt field circuit. The point N where the new line cuts the saturation curve determines the new terminal voltage. If the shunt field resistance is still further increased, a critical value may be reached

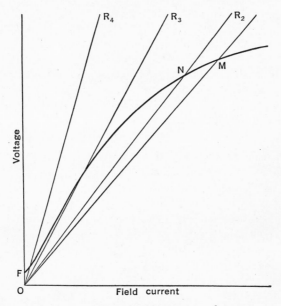

Fig. 69.   Effect of field resistance change.

for which the terminal voltage will undergo large variations in value if the operating conditions are disturbed slightly, as by a speed fluctuation. The critical position of the shunt field resistance line is shown at R_3, where it practically coincides with the lower part of the saturation curve. For all values of field resistance greater than R_3, such as represented by the line R_4, it is impossible to maintain a terminal voltage much above the residual value.

From this discussion it should be evident that any attempt to build up the voltage of a self-excited generator will be unsuccessful if the shunt field resistance is greater than the critical value. If the resistance is equal to or only slightly less than the critical value the build-up will be sluggish and uncertain. For positive, prompt results it is advisable to reduce the field-circuit resistance to the minimum until the building-up process is nearly completed and then add resistance if necessary to bring the terminal voltage to a specified value.

106. Effect of Changes in Speed. If the speed of a self-excited generator is increased and no change is made in the resistance of its field circuit the value of the no-load terminal voltage will be increased by a somewhat larger percentage than the percentage speed change. Similarly a given amount of speed decrease will be accompanied by a larger decrease in terminal voltage. The cause of this behavior will be evident when it is recalled that an increase, of say 10%, in the speed will tend to

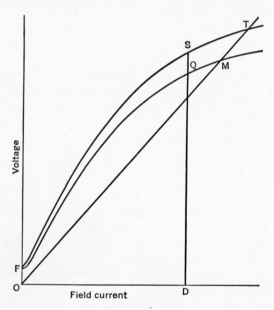

Fig. 70.   Effect of speed change.

generate 10% more voltage; but any increase in generated voltage has a direct effect on the field circuit in the form of an increase in field current, and more flux will be generated which will carry the voltage up to a still higher level.

In Fig. 70 a graphical method is shown by which a fairly accurate prediction of the effect of a speed change upon the no-load terminal voltage can be made.   The curve FQM is the saturation curve of the machine plotted for rated speed, the line OM is the shunt field resistance line and the ordinate of M is the no-load terminal voltage.   If it is desired to predict the terminal voltage which the machine will produce with a 10% increase in speed a new saturation curve must be constructed by erecting a number of ordinates to the present curve FQM and increasing the length of each by 10%. The new curve FST can then be drawn through the points so determined. The point of intersection, T, of this new curve with the extension of the shunt field resistance line will indicate the value of the terminal voltage to be expected at the new speed.

Just as, for a given speed, there is a critical value of shunt field circuit resistance beyond which the machine cannot be made to build up, so, for a given field resistance, there is a critical speed below which the building-up process cannot be successful.

107. Factors Affecting Building-up. A summary of the factors which influence the voltage build-up in a self-excited generator is presented below.

1. There must be sufficient residual magnetism to give a reliable start to the building up of voltage.

2. The field circuit resistance must be at or near its minimum value, so that the build-up when once started will be rapid and certain.

3. The field coil on each pole must be so connected as to carry current in the proper direction. That is, the feeble current forced through the field by the residual voltage must exert a strengthening effect upon the residual flux.

A machine which has been functioning properly as a self-excited generator will not build up if its direction of rotation is reversed. A small reversed voltage will be induced in the armature by the residual flux, and the resulting field current tends to weaken the residual flux.

If the direction of rotation is left as it was originally and the connections of the field circuit to the brushes are interchanged, the machine will likewise fail to build up, owing to the bucking action of the reversed field current on the residual flux.

108. External Characteristic Curve. The external characteristic curve for a typical self-excited generator driven at constant speed and with constant field circuit resistance is shown in Fig. 71, together with the connections required for an experimental determination of this curve. The terminal voltage decreases more rapidly with increasing current output than it does in a separately excited generator. In addition to the voltage drops due to the demagnetizing action of the armature current and to armature resistance, a drop is produced by the gradual decrease in the voltage applied to the field circuit.

For a given current output, OL, the voltage drop, PA, is due to the armature demagnetizing action; the drop AC is due to the decrease in field current, and CF is due to armature resistance. The ordinate LF, therefore, is the terminal voltage, and LC is the generated voltage $(K\Phi N)$.

As the load circuit resistance is reduced in order to draw more current from the generator the terminal voltage decreases so rapidly as the current increases that a critical point, M, is soon reached at which the current output is a maximum.   Attempts to draw more current by making still further reductions in load resistance result in decreases of both current and voltage.   The critical load is usually far beyond the safe operating range of the generator.

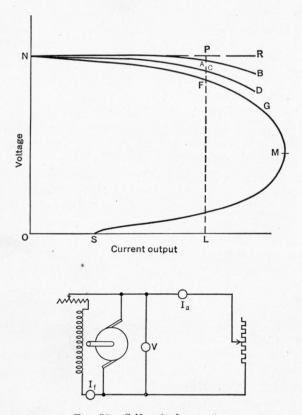

FIG. 71.   Self-excited generator.

The following analysis will explain the peculiar shape of this part of the external characteristic curve.   Let the load current I be thought of as equal to V/R, where V is the terminal voltage of the generator and R is the resistance of the load.   Let R be reduced by an amount r.   The new load current

$$I_1 = \frac{V - v}{R - r},$$

where v is the amount of voltage reduction due to the three factors just listed. When we reach the critical load M, no matter how much the increment r is or how rapidly it is subtracted, the resulting increment, v, has a greater reducing effect on the value of the numerator of the ratio than the increment r has on the denominator, and I therefore becomes less than before.

The short-circuit current of this type of generator has a comparatively small value, since V and I_f are then zero and the only voltage available to force a current through the armature circuit is that due to the residual flux.

109. Prediction of External Characteristic Curve.* Several graphical methods have been devised for predicting the external characteristic curve of a self-excited generator. One of the simplest of these makes use of the saturation curve, the shunt field resistance line and the measured resistance of the armature. It has already been shown that M, Fig. 68, indicates the no-load terminal voltage for the assumed speed and field resistance conditions. M likewise represents the generated voltage at no load without appreciable error. If current is drawn from the generator its terminal voltage is pulled down to a lower value and an IR drop occurs in the armature. Suppose that the terminal voltage for a given current output becomes DP volts. The field current must be OD amperes, capable of generating DQ volts. The intercept QP can be interpreted as the difference between the generated voltage and the terminal voltage for the given load. QP must therefore equal $R_a I_a$.

This method for obtaining points on the external characteristic curve for the machine may be summarized as follows:

1. Assume a value for the output current.

2. Multiply the measured armature resistance by the assumed current, thus obtaining the value of the RI drop which will occur in the armature with the assumed current.

3. Pick this value of voltage from the voltage scale of Fig. 68 by means of a pair of dividers, or a compass, and find by trial where it just fits as a vertical intercept between the saturation curve and the shunt field resistance line. The junction of the intercept and the resistance line will be the terminal voltage of the machine corresponding to the assumed current output.

If this process is repeated for a suitable number of assumed current values, a sufficient number of points on the characteristic curve may be obtained to determine its trend.

* See Appendix for additional material on generator characteristics.

The principal objection to this method is the neglect of the flux-producing action of the armature current. The points predicted for large current outputs will be quite inaccurate for this reason.

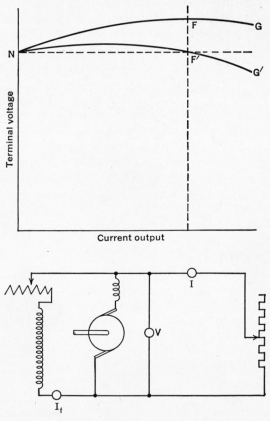

Fig. 72. Compound generator.

110. Compound Generator.

If series coils are added to the poles of a shunt generator and are connected in series with the armature so that the armature current tends to increase the air-gap flux, the machine is called a cumulative compound generator, or briefly a compound generator.

In practice the compound generator may have its shunt field either separately excited or self-excited, depending on its particular operating requirements. If self-excited, the shunt field circuit may be connected in either of two ways, with little difference in its operating characteristics.

(a) Directly to the armature terminals (short-shunt connection).

(b) Across the combination of armature and series field (long-shunt connection).

At no load the series field coils are inactive. When a compound generator delivers current to a load circuit, the terminal voltage is not reduced as rapidly as was observed for the two types of shunt generators already discussed. In fact, sufficient series coil turns may be provided to cause the terminal voltage to increase as the load current increases.

Figure 72 shows typical external characteristic curves for two compound generators, and the connections required to obtain them experimentally. The curve NFG is typical of a compound generator with series coils strong enough to produce quite a large increase in gap flux as the current output increases. This causes a correspondingly large increase in generated voltage, so that, after the reductions caused by armature RI drop and the demagnetizing action of the armature current are subtracted, the terminal voltage for full-load current is greater than the no-load voltage. Such a generator is said to be over-compounded.

The curve $NF'G'$ is typical of a compound generator with a smaller number of series turns. As the load increases, the series ampere-turns increase the gap flux and the generated voltage is increased, but by an amount that is just sufficient to make the full-load voltage equal to the no-load value. Such a generator is said to be flat-compounded.

The amount of compounding is quite often expressed in percentage as follows:

$$\text{Percentage of compounding} = \frac{\text{Full-load volts} - \text{No-load volts}}{\text{No-load volts}} \times 100.$$

111. Determination of Series Turns. The procedure required in converting a shunt generator into a compound generator with a definite percentage of compounding can be explained by means of an example.

A separately excited shunt generator, whose field coils have 3000 turns each, is tested at no load, and it is found that a field current of 0.575 ampere is needed to produce a terminal voltage of 230 at 1200 rpm. Its rated load of 20 amperes is then added and the field rheostat is adjusted until the voltage becomes the desired value, say 250 volts. The new shunt field current is found to be 0.875 ampere.

It is evident that an increase in field current of 0.3 is needed to produce the desired amount of compounding. This is equivalent to 900 ampere-turns per pole. To accomplish the same result by keeping the shunt field constant and using series coils to produce the additional excitation will require coils having 45 turns.

$$\text{Series coil turns} = \frac{900 \text{ ampere-turns}}{20 \text{ amperes}} = 45.$$

A sufficiently large wire size must be selected for the series coils to carry the full armature current without overheating or without producing excessive voltage drop.

112. Adjustment of Compounding. Compound generators are usually provided with more series turns than are necessary to meet the requirements of the machine's voltage rating, and a device called a series field diverter is added to the machine, enabling the operator to adjust the amount of compounding by trial to suit the exact needs of the circuit which is being supplied with current. The diverter consists of an adjustable low-resistance shunt connected in parallel with the series field winding so that the armature current is divided, part passing through the series field and part through the diverter. The lower its resistance the less will be the series field current for a given load, and the smaller will be the compounding effect.

Another means of changing the percentage of compounding is available to the operator if the prime mover can be operated safely and conveniently at various speeds. Suppose that a certain generator rated at 230 volts no load does not show enough compounding effect to be satisfactory, when driven at its rated speed of 1000 rpm. If the speed is raised to 1200 the no-load voltage can be brought back to 230 again by adding resistance to the shunt field circuit. When full load is placed on the machine the series field contributes just as many ampere-turns as it did for full load at 1000 rpm. Since the percentage increase in ampere-turns is greater and the initial saturation of the magnetic circuit is less, the ratio of full-load flux to no-load flux will be greater and the percentage of compounding will be increased.

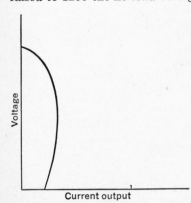

Current output

Fig. 73. Differential-compound generator.

113. Differential Compound Generator. If the series field connections of an over-compounded or a flat-compounded generator are reversed, an external characteristic similar to Fig. 73 may be expected. Such a machine is called a differential compound generator. The rapid decrease in voltage and the narrow range to the value of the output current are evidently due to the demagnetizing action of the series ampere-turns.

114. Series Generator. A generator whose field poles are provided with low-resistance coils connected in series with the armature is called a series generator. It is decidedly different from other types of generators in the shape of its external characteristic curve. At no load (open circuit) the field current is necessarily zero and the only voltage appearing at the armature terminals is that due to the residual flux.

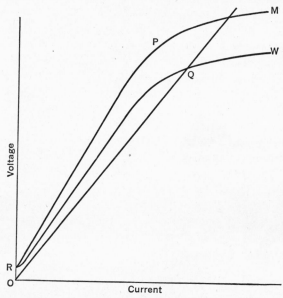

FIG. 74. Series generator.

If the receiving circuit is closed and is made sufficiently low in resistance the residual voltage will send an appreciable current through the load circuit, and, if this current passes through the series coils in the proper direction to strengthen the residual flux, the terminal voltage and load current will increase together until a point of equilibrium is reached.

Figure 74 shows the saturation curve and the external characteristic curve for a typical series generator. OR is the value of the residual voltage, RPM is the saturation curve and RQW is the external characteristic curve. The straight line OQ may be called the load resistance line. The abscissa of any point on it represents a definite value of load current, I, and the corresponding ordinate is the voltage, V, which must be applied to the load circuit of resistance R in order to produce the current I. The equation of the line is evidently $V = RI$.

Q is the point of equilibrium at which the generator will continue to operate until some change is made in R or in the speed of the generator.

Notice the similarity between the building up of a series generator with a given load circuit resistance, and the building up of a self-excited shunt generator with a given field circuit resistance.

115. Voltage Regulation. An important characteristic of a generator is the steadiness of its terminal voltage as its current output fluctuates owing to changes in load circuit resistance. The normal tendency of such a generator is to show a reduction in voltage as the current output increases. A generator in which the voltage change is small for large changes in current is said to have good voltage regulation.

Voltage regulation is usually expressed in percentage as follows:

$$\text{Percentage regulation} = \frac{\text{No-load voltage} - \text{Full-load voltage}}{\text{Full-load voltage}} \times 100.$$

The term is correctly applied if restricted to voltage changes accompanying gradual current changes; it does not cover the behavior of the generator under very rapid fluctuations in current.

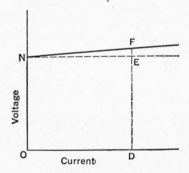

FIG. 75.   Battery characteristic.

116. Load Characteristic. The graphical representation of the relationship between the current supplied to a load and the voltage applied to the load terminals may be called the load characteristic. Thus the straight line OQ, Fig. 74, is the characteristic of a resistance load, the slope of the line being the value of the resistance in ohms. If a battery developing a constant voltage and having a constant internal resistance is considered as a load, its characteristic may be represented by the line NF, Fig. 75. A voltage DF is required to force a current of OD amperes through it against the back voltage DE and the internal resistance drop EF.

In a similar manner the load characteristics of various combinations of resistances and batteries may be drawn. A load consisting of a resistance in parallel with a battery will have a characteristic represented by the line SS', Fig. 76. The characteristic of the resistance alone is OR, and of the battery alone is NB. In order to determine a point on the combined characteristic, the current Vc which a selected voltage OV will force through the resistance is added to the current Vd sent through the battery by the same voltage, giving the value Vf for the current drawn by the combination at voltage OV. By determining in this way the points corresponding to at least two selected voltages the straight line SS' may be drawn.

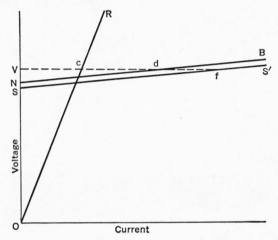

FIG. 76. Battery and resistance load.

A thorough understanding of the principles of load characteristics leads the way to the graphical prediction of the voltage and current which will be supplied by a generator to a specific load. It is merely necessary to draw the characteristic of the load in question on the same sheet and with the same scale values as the external characteristic of the generator, and note the values of the volts and amperes indicated by the point of intersection.

117. Generator Applications. The self-excited shunt generator will give satisfactory service with nearly all types of commercial loads that do not require very close voltage regulation. It can be used for such varied duties as charging storage batteries, driving motors and supplying current to heating devices; and it has the advantage of being a complete, self-contained unit which can be used in isolated locations, or where the cost of providing separate excitation would be excessive.

The separately excited shunt generator generally has better voltage regulation than the self-excited machine, making it more suitable as a source of current for incandescent lamps. In addition it has voltage stability, even at voltage levels much below normal. This feature makes it valuable as a power source for testing laboratories.

The characteristics of the compound generator make it particularly suitable for loads requiring close voltage regulation. For a load located so near to the generator that the voltage drop in the connecting wires is negligible the generator can be adjusted to produce flat-compounding. Variations in load current will then have no appreciable effect on the terminal voltage.

If the line connecting the generator to the load has sufficient resistance to cause a disturbing voltage drop, an over-compounded generator should be used with the amount of compounding adjusted to compensate for the line drop and produce a practically constant voltage at the load.

The external characteristic of the differential compound generator is such as to make it unsuitable for general use. It can be made to deliver a fairly constant current to a storage battery when driven at varying speeds, as by a wind motor or by belt connection to a railway car axle, but special generators are usually available which perform better under these conditions.

The series generator is likewise unsuitable for most generator applications. The series motors of direct-current locomotives may be converted into generators under certain conditions in order to produce regenerative braking on the down grades. Series generators may be utilized as voltage boosters in certain types of distribution systems, particularly in railway service. This application will be discussed in Chapter 14.

SUGGESTED BIBLIOGRAPHY

1. Principles of Direct Current Machines, LANGSDORF, 4th edition, McGraw-Hill Book Co.
2. Experimental Electrical Engineering, Vol. I, KARAPETOFF-DENNISON, 4th edition, John Wiley & Sons, 1933.

PROBLEMS

1. A 2.5-kw., 125-volt shunt generator has an armature resistance of 0.3 ohm, and the demagnetizing action of the armature current is negligible. How much must the flux be increased as the load is increased from no load to full load in order to maintain constant terminal voltage?

2. Find the torque which suddenly opposes rotation in a generator when its armature is called upon to deliver 300 amperes, if at zero load 120 volts is generated between armature terminals at a speed of 400 rpm. Assume constant flux.

PROBLEMS

3. A belted generator is running at 440 rpm. The voltage between brushes is 550 volts when the armature, whose resistance is 0.0375 ohm, is delivering 400 amperes. What is the pull on the belt due to the current in the armature if the pulley diameter is 40 in.?

4. Replot the saturation curve of Problem 19, Chapter 7, using NI per pole as abscissas, and volts generated at 1000 rpm. as ordinates.

5. The machine of Problem 19, Chapter 7, is driven as a shunt generator at 1200 rpm. The shunt field has a total resistance of 167 ohms and is separately excited from 230-volt mains, giving an excitation of 4000 ampere-turns per pole. Compute the no-load terminal voltage.

6. Given the machine of Problem 5. What will be the no-load terminal voltage at 1500 rpm., with the same excitation? At 800 rpm.?

7. A certain self-excited shunt generator when running at 1000 rpm. has 100 volts at the terminals at no load. When the speed is reduced to 800 rpm., the voltage drops to 64. What has been the percentage change in field current? In flux? If the speed is increased to 1250 rpm. the voltage is 140. What is the percentage change in flux from that at 1000 rpm.? If the field resistance is 100 ohms, what additional resistance must be placed in the field circuit to reduce the no-load terminal voltage to 100 when the speed is 1250 rpm.?

8. The machine of Problem 5 is reconnected as a self-excited shunt generator with a total shunt field resistance of 350 ohms. What will be the value of the no-load terminal voltage if the generator is driven at 1000 rpm.?

9. What will be the no-load terminal voltage of the machine described in Problem 8 if the shunt field resistance is increased to 400 ohms, the speed remaining at 1000 rpm.?

10. Suppose the driving speed of the generator in Problem 9 to be reduced to 800 rpm. What will be the no-load terminal voltage if the shunt field resistance is 400 ohms?

11. The machine of Problem 5 is operated as a separately excited shunt generator at 1000 rpm., and is supplied with a constant field current of 2 amperes. Determine the approximate terminal voltage which the machine will maintain when it delivers 50 amperes to a receiving circuit.

12. Suppose that the external characteristic curve of a certain self-excited shunt generator is available. Show by a sketch a graphical method by which the approximate current which this generator will deliver to a load of constant resistance, R_x, may be predicted.

13. The machine of Problem 5 is connected as a self-excited shunt generator and is operated at 1000 rpm. The shunt field resistance is held constant at 350 ohms. The resistance of the armature and interpoles is 0.104 ohm. Determine by a graphical method the approximate value of the terminal voltage when the machine delivers 200 amperes to a receiving circuit.

14. The machine of Problem 28, Chapter 7, is to be used as a shunt generator. It will be driven at 500 rpm. and supplied with a shunt field current of 4 amperes. Each shunt field coil has 1000 turns. What will be its no-load terminal voltage?

15. What will be the no-load terminal voltage of the machine of Problem 14 if it is operated as a self-excited shunt generator at a speed of 520 rpm., and has a shunt field resistance of 57.5 ohms?

16. What will be the no-load terminal voltage of the machine of Problem 15 if the speed is increased to 600 rpm., with the same shunt field resistance?

17. The machine of Problem 28, Chapter 7, is to be used as a cumulative compound generator. The shunt field will be separately excited from 230-volt mains, and its resistance is 57.5 ohms. What will be the value of the terminal voltage when the current output is 300 amperes and the speed is 500 rpm.?

18. If a compound generator is adjusted to be flat-compounded when the speed is 1200 rpm., will it be over- or under-compounded if the speed is changed to 1000 rpm., and the shunt field rheostat is adjusted to give the same terminal voltage at no load? Explain with the aid of a diagram how you reached your conclusion.

19. The machine of Problem 5 is connected as a cumulative compound generator with the shunt field current held constant at 1 ampere. Determine the approximate terminal voltage when the current output is 100 amperes. The series field has 17 turns per pole and a resistance of 0.032 ohm, and the speed is 1000 rpm.

20. The characteristic magnetization curve applies to a certain 500 kw., 500-volt, 6-pole compound generator if one abscissa unit = 15 amperes of shunt field current, and one ordinate unit = 200 volts generated at 1200 rpm. Resistances are: armature, 0.02 ohm; interpoles, 0.005 ohm; series field, 0.003 ohm; shunt field, 17 ohms. Series field turns, 4 per pole.

With the speed maintained at 1200 rpm.: (a) how much resistance must be added in the shunt field circuit to generate 500 volts at no load; (b) if with this adjustment the compounding is such that the terminal voltage is again 500 when $I_a = 1000$ amperes, approximately how many turns has the shunt field coil? (This machine is connected as in Fig. 72, and the demagnetizing action of the armature current is assumed to be negligible.)

21. The characteristic magnetization curve applies to a compound generator if one abscissa unit = 1 ampere of shunt field current and one ordinate unit = 100 volts at 1200 rpm. This machine is to be operated as a compound motor from 220-volt mains. $R_f = 100$, $R_a = 0.05$, $R_{series} = 0.08$.

(a) What will be the no-load speed?

(b) What must be the value of the ratio shunt turns/series turns on each field pole if the speed is 900 rpm. when $I_a = 100$ amperes?

22. The characteristic magnetization curve applies to a certain series generator if one abscissa unit = 20 amperes, and one ordinate unit = 100 volts generated at 750 rpm. $R_a = 0.3$. $R_f = 0.1$. This machine is operated as a series motor from a 230-volt line. When the current is 20 amperes the developed torque is 40.7 lb-ft. Find the speed and developed torque when the current becomes 35 amperes.

23. The machine of Problem 22 is driven as a series generator at 600 rpm. What will be the approximate current delivered to a constant-resistance load of 4.9 ohms? (The flux-producing action of the armature current is negligible.)

24. Given the following data on a shunt generator:

Speed = 500 rpm. (constant).	I_f at no load = 8.
R_a = 0.08 ohm.	I_f at full load = 10.
I_a at full load = 165.	V at no load = 230.
Shunt coil turns per pole = 900.	V at full load = 250.

It is desired to convert this machine to a compound generator. How many turns per pole will be required to produce the same increase in voltage with the shunt field current held constant at 8 amperes?

CHAPTER 9

ARMATURE WINDINGS

118. Winding Essentials. In the preceding discussions of motor and generator performance it has been taken for granted that the armature conductors are so connected to each other and to the commutator that additive force and voltage effects are produced. That is, the currents in the conductors under each pole are so directed that the small deflecting forces exerted on the individual conductors by the poles add up to a large total for the entire armature. Similarly the voltages induced in the individual conductors combine to form the total counter-emf. if the machine is functioning as a motor, or the total generated voltage if the machine is a generator. The subject of armature windings deals with the various methods of interconnecting the armature conductors so that the desired force and voltage effects will be produced efficiently and economically.

All armature windings (except rare types such as the homopolar winding) are alike in three respects.

(a) The armature conductors are arranged in polar groups. All the conductors lying under a north pole, for example, are carrying current in one direction, while the conductors under an adjacent pole (a south pole) will be carrying current in the opposite direction.

(b) The number of conductors in each polar group remains practically constant as the armature turns, but individual conductors are continually being transferred from one group to the next as they pass out from under one pole and approach the next.

(c) A reversal of the current direction in each conductor necessarily accompanies its transfer from one group to the next.

There is no fundamental difference between a motor armature winding and a generator armature winding.

119. Closed-circuit Drum Winding. The earliest type of practical winding for constant voltage motors and generators was known as the Gramme ring winding. Since this type of winding is of historical interest only, it is not discussed here. The interested student may consult any of the more comprehensive textbooks for descriptive details.

Modern windings are of the so-called drum type, meaning that the

129

entire winding is placed in slots cut in the outer surface of a cylindrical drum-shaped armature. A simple example of a drum winding will now be described. Figure 77a shows an eight-slot armature for a two-pole machine. It is assumed that a sixteen-conductor winding is to be

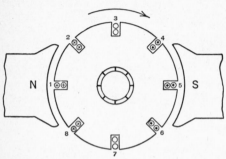

FIG. 77a.   Armature with 8 slots, 16 conductors.

installed. The slots are numbered consecutively for convenience, and the individual conductors are designated by the slot number followed by T or B, depending upon whether the conductor occupies the top or the bottom position in the slot. For the assumed polarity and direction of rotation the induced voltages in the conductors at this instant are as indicated.

From an inspection of the indicated voltage directions it is evident that conductor $1T$ may be connected at the far end of the armature to any of the conductors in slots 4, 5, or 6 with a resulting gain in voltage. For reasons which will appear later let the connection be made to $5B$ and let the near end of $5B$ be connected to $2T$ by way of commutator bar A. Figure 77b shows this portion of the connections, which may be considered as the winding pattern; this pattern is repeated systematically until all the armature conductors are connected. Thus $2T$ is connected at the far end to $6B$, and the near

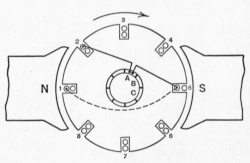

FIG. 77b.   Winding pattern.

end of $6B$ is carried to commutator bar B. From B the connection goes to $3T$, then $7B$, bar C, and so on.

The completed winding is shown in Fig. 78. Particular attention should be given to the following facts concerning this winding.

1. A closed electrical circuit has been formed. This may easily be verified by starting at any convenient conductor and tracing through the complete winding connections.

2. The conductors in slots 3 and 7 are not generating voltage, because their positions at this instant are such that no cutting of flux occurs.

.3. The remaining conductors are all generating voltages, but the algebraic sum of these voltages around the complete armature circuit is zero.

4. The conductors in that part of the winding between bars G and B produce a summation voltage which is equal to that produced by the conductors in the part between F and C. Each of these groups contains six conductors whose voltages add arithmetically.

5. If a brush is placed in contact with the commutator at F–G, and another brush is placed at B–C, a definite voltage will be maintained between these points of contact, and an external circuit connected to these brushes will draw current from both portions of the winding.

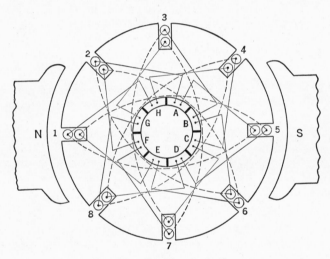

Fig. 78. Completed winding.

120. Four-pole Lap Winding. Figure 79a shows a twelve-slot armature installed in a four-pole frame. As in the two-pole winding, Fig. 78, the first step consists in the selection of a suitable winding pattern. The conductors in slots 3, 4, 5, 11, 10 and 9 are eligible to be paired with 1T, since they all lie under poles of opposite polarity. Conductor 4B is chosen and the near-end connection made to 2T by way of bar A. This winding pattern (shown in heavy lines) is repeated systematically, resulting in the complete winding of Fig. 79a. Figure 79b shows the same winding in the form of a developed diagram. This method of representing armature windings is particularly helpful when the number of slots is large.

As in the two-pole winding, it is advisable to note as many facts as possible concerning the results achieved by this arrangement. Several are listed below.

1. All the armature conductors are generating voltage at this instant.

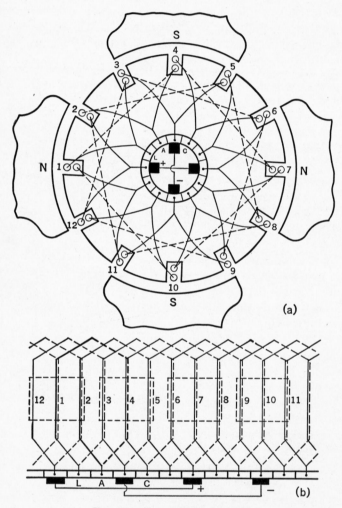

FIG. 79. Four-pole lap winding.

2. After a 15° rotation occurs, the conductors in slots 2, 5, 8 and 11 will become inactive temporarily.

3. After an additional 15° rotation they will again be active, but they will have changed their polar group membership.

4. Four brushes are needed to utilize all parts of the winding. Two will be positive and two negative.

5. The active conductors are grouped in four paths in parallel between the positive and negative brush sets.

6. In tracing the winding a forward progression from $1T$ to $4B$ is followed by a backward connection to $2T$ by way of the commutator and another forward jump to $5B$, then back to $3T$, and so on. This overlapping characteristic gives rise to the name lap winding, which is applied to windings of this type.

121. Form-wound Elements. A considerable saving in the labor of assembling armature windings may be effected by the use of form-wound elements. For example, in preparing to wind the twelve-slot armature of Fig. 79a, a piece of wire may be secured of sufficient length so that when shaped as shown in Fig. 80a the sides will fit exactly in the spaces intended for conductors $1T$ and $4B$, and the ends will be brought close together so that they may be soldered to adjacent commutator bars. A second piece shaped exactly like this one may be placed in the spaces for $2T$ and $5B$, and ten additional pieces will fill all the slots completely.

Armature winding elements may often be shaped by hand, but if large conductor sectional areas are specified in the design the elements must be " pulled " to the proper shape by machines.

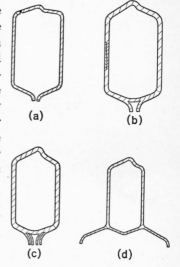

(a)   (b)

(c)   (d)

Fig. 80. Typical winding elements.

The winding elements of most armatures must be formed of several turns, each properly insulated and with an additional layer of insulation wrapped around the complete bundle. In this way the number of active conductors contributing voltage to the brushes may be multiplied. Figure 80b shows a two-turn winding element.

The windings shown in Figs. 78 and 79 require as many commutator bars as slots. For safe generation of higher voltages designers often specify twice as many commutator bars as there are slots. This necessitates the use of a two-coil winding element, such as is shown in Fig. 80c.

Figure 80d shows a two-turn winding element with the ends spread apart to permit attachment to two widely separated commutator bars.

This is the type of winding element required for wave or series windings, to be described later.

122. Winding Terms. Before proceeding further with the discussion of armature windings it seems advisable to define and explain some of the terms commonly used.

Pole pitch: The center-to-center distance between adjacent poles, measured along the surface of the armature and usually expressed as the number of slots covered. Thus the pole pitch in Fig. 78 is 4 slots; in Fig. 79 it is 3 slots. It may be a fractional number.

Coil pitch: The span of a winding element, or the number of slots traversed in counting from one side of the element to the other. In Fig. 78 the coil pitch is 4 slots; in Fig. 79 it is 3 slots.

Back pitch: A term synonymous with coil pitch.

Front pitch: The distance (expressed in slot numbers) between two element sides that are joined to the same commutator bar. Thus the front pitch in Fig. 78 is -3 slots (from $5B$ to $2T$), and in Fig. 79 it is -2 slots. The minus sign merely serves as a reminder that in the windings so far described the front pitch is stepped off in the opposite direction to the back or coil pitch.

Commutator pitch: The rate of advancement around the commutator (measured in number of bars) in progressing from one winding element to the next. In the windings so far described (and in the great majority of lap windings) the commutator pitch is one bar.

Full-pitch winding: The windings of Figs. 78 and 79 are full-pitch windings. That is, the coil pitch is exactly equal to the pole pitch.

Fractional-pitch windings or chorded windings: Those in which the coil pitch is made somewhat less than the pole pitch.

Random-wound element: A multi-turn winding element threaded turn by turn into the proper armature slots. The armatures of very small motors are likely to have partially enclosed slots and must be random-wound, as form-wound coils could not be passed through the slot openings.

Skewed slots: Armatures of small motors frequently have their laminations stacked in such a way that the slots are not parallel to the axis of rotation but make a small angle with that axis. Such armatures are said to have skewed slots.

It has been found that this method of assembling the laminations tends to reduce the noise normally accompanying the magnetic pulsations produced by the passage of the teeth under the poles.

123. Four-pole Wave Winding. In tracing through the windings previously described, any given winding element is connected by way of a commutator bar to a second element located under the same pair of poles, and usually in slots that are adjacent to those occupied by the first. This in turn is connected to a third element likewise under the same poles, and a gradual progression around the armature results. This procedure is typical of all lap windings.

Suppose that a radically different winding order is tried. In preparing to wind the thirteen-slot armature shown in Fig. 81, a back pitch of three slots will be tried, and the first winding element will consist of $1T$ and $4B$. Instead of going back to $2T$ by way of a suitable commutator bar the connection will be carried ahead to the element $7T$–$10B$ by way of bar A. This element is located under the other pair of poles in practically the same position as the first element, and its voltage will add properly to that of the first. Proceed in a similar manner to element $13T$–$3B$ by way of bar G and then to $6T$–$9B$ by

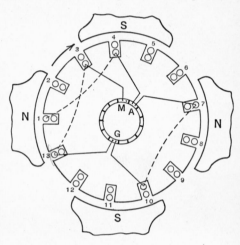

Fig. 81. Wave-winding pattern.

way of bar M. The complete winding is shown in Fig. 82a and is repeated in developed form in Fig. 82b.

The following facts concerning this winding should be noted.

1. Thirteen winding elements are used. They are of the type shown in Fig. 80d, all having the same back pitch and connected to the commutator in exactly the same way.

2. The number of commutator bars is the same as the number of slots, just as was observed in the lap windings already described.

3. The connection returns to the element adjacent to the starting point after passing through one element under the opposite pair of poles.

4. Two winding elements are connected in series between adjacent commutator bars, whereas in the lap winding a single winding element is terminated on adjacent bars.

5. There are two paths in parallel between positive and negative brush sets containing all the armature conductors except those that

are temporarily non-productive owing to their position halfway
between the poles.

6. One positive brush and one negative brush are sufficient for the
entire winding. Two additional brushes may be used if it seems
desirable to lower the brush current density.

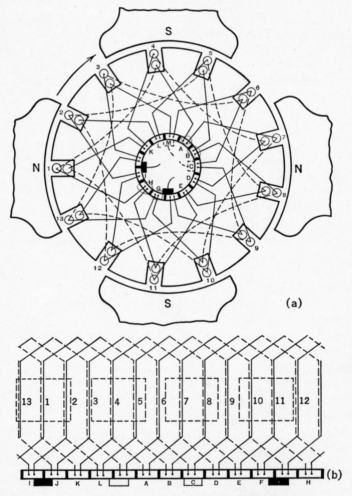

Fig. 82.   Completed wave winding.

124. General Rules for Lap Windings.   With the preceding examples
of simple lap and wave windings in mind it is possible to proceed to a
study of the general rules governing the assembly of lap and wave windings.   Lap windings will be considered first.

1. **Choice of back pitch.** For best results the back pitch should be made equal to or slightly less than the pole pitch. If the back pitch is exactly equal to the pole pitch the voltages generated by the two sides of each winding element add most effectively, since the sides reach the center lines of adjacent poles at the same instant.

If a fractional back pitch considerably less than the pole pitch is used there will be an appreciable saving in the amount of copper needed to form the winding elements, owing to shorter end connections. However, certain objectionable features accompany the use of extreme fractional pitches, which are considered by most engineers to outweigh by far the saving in copper. In the first place it brings about an appreciable reduction in the average voltage generated by each winding element, since there will be certain positions of the element for which the voltages generated in the element sides are in opposition. It has been pretty well established that the flux-producing action of the armature current (armature reaction) is particularly disturbing in this kind of winding. Commutation also is affected adversely.

The objections to a fractional pitch winding that are listed here do not apply to fractional pitches that are only slightly less than the pole pitch. If the pole pitch is, say, 10 1/2 slots or more, a back pitch differing from the pole pitch by one-half slot or even one slot will be just as satisfactory as a full pitch, and the slight saving in copper may well justify its use.

For further discussion of commutation and armature reaction as affected by armature winding details the reader is referred to later chapters.

It will be observed that the back pitch of the winding elements used in both lap and wave windings has been so adjusted that when one side of an element is installed in the *bottom* of a slot the other side just fits in the *top* of a slot similarly located under the next pole. The principal purposes of this procedure are:

(a) To produce symmetry in the winding.

(b) To eliminate confusion in the selection of winding elements at the beginning of the actual assembly of the winding.

The only alternative would necessitate " pulling " half of the winding elements to fit the span between the bottoms of two slots a pole pitch apart and spreading the sides of the remaining elements a little farther apart so as to fit in the tops of the same slots.

2. **Choice of front pitch.** The front pitch of a simple lap winding must be one slot less, or one slot greater, than the back pitch. In the

lap windings already shown, as in the great majority of lap windings, the front pitch is one slot less than the back pitch. This produces a clockwise " creep " or advancement of the winding as viewed from the commutator end, and such windings may be termed progressive lap windings.

If a front pitch one slot greater than the back pitch is chosen, a slight increase in the length of end connection leads is necessary; these leads overlap rather awkwardly and no special performance benefits are secured, so there is little justification for this choice. A lap winding with the front pitch greater than the back pitch " creeps " counter-clockwise and hence may be termed a retrogressive lap winding.

3. Commutator pitch. The commutator pitch is one bar for the great majority of lap windings. Obviously it must be a progressive pitch if the winding is a progressive winding.

The selection of bar A as the connecting link between the first and second winding elements in the two lap-winding examples is purely an arbitrary one. Its location, however, is such that the lead wires joining it to the two elements will be about equal in length, and this is sufficient reason for its selection. Once the first bar has been selected the order of connection to the remaining bars is definitely fixed for a given type of winding.

4. Number and location of brushes. Lap windings require as many brushes as there are poles. If there is danger that the armature current may be so large as to produce an excessive current density in each brush the axial length of the commutator may be increased and one or more brushes may be mounted alongside each of the brushes that would normally be required.

The brushes must be so located as to bridge across or short-circuit the commutator bars connected to the inactive winding elements when the sides of these elements are approximately halfway between the main poles. With the usual method of bringing the lead wires down to the commutator this places each brush in or very close to a plane passing through the pole center line.

125. General Rules for Wave Windings. In the two-layer lap windings which have been considered the number of armature slots has not been a limiting factor in the choice of winding pitches. In wave windings, however, there is a definite relationship between the number of slots and the winding pitches, so that it becomes impossible to install wave windings in some armatures without introducing a certain amount of winding dissymmetry.

1. Selection of back pitch. The fundamental considerations involved in the selection of the back pitch are the same as for lap windings. The span of the winding element should be equal to the pole pitch, or differ from it by a very small amount.

2. Selection of front pitch. It will be evident from an inspection of Fig. 82a that the winding pattern, which is repeated without variation in tracing through the entire winding, covers a section of the armature which is equal to the sum of the back pitch and the front pitch. The span of this winding pattern must be so related to the total number of slots that it is possible to use it once for each pair of poles and terminate at a slot immediately adjacent to the starting point. If the front pitch cannot be adjusted to meet this requirement a simple wave winding cannot be installed without employing various compromise measures, to be considered later.

The required relationship between winding pitches and slots for a simple wave winding may be summarized as follows:

$$(Y_b + Y_f)\frac{p}{2} = S \pm 1, \tag{49}$$

where Y_b = back pitch, in slots.
Y_f = front pitch, in slots.
p = number of poles.
S = number of slots in armature.

As an illustration, consider the feasibility of providing a 69-slot, 8-pole machine with a simple wave winding. The pole pitch is 8 5/8, so the most likely choice for Y_b is 9. If $Y_f = 8$, the left-hand side of equation 49 becomes 68, which is $S - 1$. This accordingly is a workable arrangement, and the winding will be retrogressive.

A back pitch of 9 and a front pitch of 10 prove feasible for a 6-pole, 56-slot machine as the equation may be balanced with $S + 1$ on the right-hand side. The winding will be progressive.

A 6-pole machine with 48 slots cannot be provided with a simple wave winding unless a compromise scheme is permissible.

3. Determination of commutator pitch. The selection of the first bar is governed by the same consideration as in lap windings: convenient location in an approximately central position between the two element sides which are connected to it. Once the first bar has been chosen the order of connection to the remaining bars is fixed.

In Fig. 81 bar A is chosen because of its convenient location relative to the element sides in slots 4 and 7. The selection of bar G rather than F or H for the next commutator connection is determined by the necessity of keeping in exact step with the winding element connections. It is evident that the winding pitches are such that one complete passage around the armature terminates at the slot immediately behind the starting point. Similarly one complete passage around the commutator must terminate at bar M if A is the starting point, and this passage must consist of two " jumps " of equal length, to correspond to the two jumps of the winding pattern. Bar G is therefore the required point for the connection.

In general terms, for the progress around the commutator to keep in step with the progress around the armature it is necessary to use a commutator pitch of the same number of bars as the number of slots in the winding pattern. This makes the commutator pitch equal to the sum of the back pitch and the front pitch.

4. Number and location of brushes. Wave windings require two brushes, regardless of the number of poles. Additional brushes may be used if it seems desirable to reduce the brush current density, but the general effectiveness of the winding is not increased thereby.

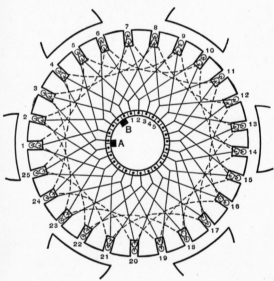

As in lap windings the proper position of the brushes is determined by the location of the commutator bars connected to the inactive elements. With the usual method of bringing the leads down to the commutator this places each brush in or very close to a plane passing through the pole center line.

FIG. 83.   Six-pole wave winding.

126. Wave Winding Paths. Figure 83 shows a simple wave winding for a 6-pole machine with 25 slots. Since two bars are in contact with brush A at this instant it appears that there are four winding paths leading away from brush A. A careful trace of the winding connections reveals, however, that two of these four paths are the beginning and end of a group of 3 winding elements that are temporarily inactive and are being short-circuited by this brush. The other two paths are long, one containing 10 elements and the other containing 9 elements; and both terminate at brush B. This accounts for a total of 22 elements. The remaining three are to be found in an inactive group which is being short-circuited at this instant by brush B.

The fact that the numbers of active elements in the two long paths are unequal at this instant has no special significance, because an instant later the commutator will have turned to a new position where the inequality will be reversed.

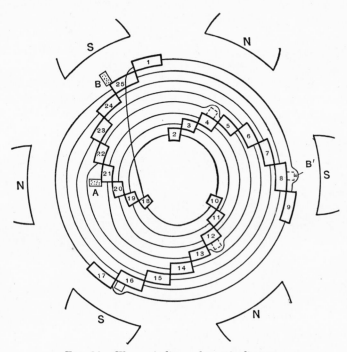

FIG. 84. Wave winding, schematic diagram.

After further consideration of the simple wave windings shown in Figs. 82a and 83 the following facts concerning the winding paths should be evident.

1. There are always two and only two long paths (containing active elements) between the positive and negative brushes.

2. Each time a brush overlaps two commutator bars a portion of one long path is taken out of active duty and forms a local path which is short-circuited by the brush.

In Fig. 84 the wave winding of Fig. 83 is reproduced in a schematic form. The numbered blocks represent commutator bars and the curved lines arranged in spiral fashion are the winding elements.   The grouping of the winding elements in two long paths in parallel between brushes A and B is clearly shown.

The brushes shown in dotted outline indicate places where additional brushes may be located.   The diagram shows, more clearly perhaps than the conventional one, the reason why these additional brushes are superfluous, except from the standpoint of brush current density, as already mentioned.   For example, B' if installed would have the same polarity as B, and it would be separated from B by just one inactive winding element, so that its presence would contribute practically nothing to the effectiveness of the winding.

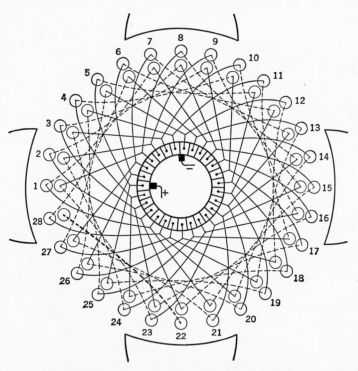

Fig. 85.   Wave winding with dummy coil.

127. Dummy Elements.   The most convenient expedient which may be employed to fit a wave winding to an armature with an improper number of slots is the use of one or more dummy elements.   As an illustration a 28-slot armature for a 4-pole machine will be selected.   An application of equation 49 gives 14 1/2 or 13 1/2 as the sum of the back and front pitches, whereas the sum must be a whole number to make a wave winding possible. However, a satisfactory winding can be formed with 27 winding elements connected to a 27-bar commutator. The twenty-eighth element will be installed, for if it were omitted the armature would be dynamically unbalanced. But its ends will be taped and left unconnected to the commutator. The connections may be made as shown in Fig. 85, in which the dummy element lies in slots 22 and 28. It will be observed that the back pitch is 6, and the front pitch is alternately 7 and 8 to allow for the extra slot. The commutator pitch is 13 bars, and the winding is retrogressive.

128. Multiplex Windings. Suppose that a 40-slot, 4-pole machine is to be provided with a lap winding. The pole pitch is 10, which will also be a suitable value for the back pitch. As an experiment let the winding connections be confined to the odd-numbered slots and commutator

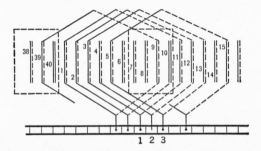

Fig. 86. Duplex winding pattern.

bars. That is, element $1T$–$11B$ (Fig. 86) will be connected to element $3T$–$13B$ via bar 1; then to element $5T$–$15B$ via bar 3, etc. This winding will eventually close on itself, completely filling all the odd-numbered slots and using all the odd commutator bars. A fresh start can now be made with the element $2T$–$12B$, connecting it to $4T$–$14B$ via bar 2, and an exact duplicate of the first winding can be placed in the even-numbered slots. An armature wound in this way, with two interlaced simple lap windings, is said to have a duplex lap winding.

Duplex wave windings may be installed in armatures having a suitable number of slots. As a test for suitability, equation 49 may be applied if the right-hand side is written $S \pm 2$ instead of $S \pm 1$.

Figure 87 shows a duplex wave winding for a 29-slot, 6-pole machine. A trace of the winding connections will disclose that after 5 complete passages around the armature (during which 15 winding elements are traversed) the winding does not close by returning to $1T$, as might be expected from the statements in the preceding paragraph, but continues on through the second half of the winding. This characteristic of a duplex winding is described by the term "singly reentrant." Hence the complete title for Fig. 87 should be " A singly reentrant, duplex wave winding." The winding which is shown in part in Fig. 86 is a doubly reentrant duplex lap winding.

Duplex windings are characterized by having twice as many paths in parallel between the positive and negative brushes as simple windings. Relatively thick brushes are required, so that both sections of the winding are always in contact with the brushes.

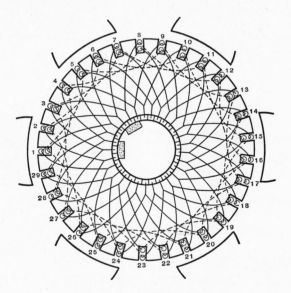

Fɪɢ. 87.   Duplex wave winding.

Duplex windings are particularly adapted to machines of low voltage and heavy current rating. With many paths from which current may be drawn, the current per path can be kept at a moderate value.

It is often possible to install triplex and quadruplex windings in large armatures, but their use is rarely justified.

129. Multi-coil Elements. All the windings which have been described have had the number of commutator bars equal to the number of slots (except certain wave windings requiring dummy elements). Conflicting factors frequently arise, however, in the preliminary design of motors and generators, which make it desirable to have the number of commutator bars considerably greater than the number of slots. For reasons beyond the scope of this book standard machines are likely to have from 7 to 15 slots per pole, and yet the bar-to-bar voltage at the commutator must be kept between the limits of 6 to 15 volts. A 230-volt machine may require 30 to 35 commutator bars per pole, and its armature slots per pole may be one-third to one-half of this number. Such a situation calls for the use of multi-coil winding elements.

A typical two-coil winding element is shown in Fig. 80c. This is suitable for a lap winding with twice as many commutator bars as slots. Its span or back pitch is governed by the same requirements as the one-coil element. Figure 88 illustrates the method of making the commutator connections. The terminals A–A belong to one coil and B–B to the other.

Two-coil or three-coil winding elements may also be employed in wave windings. As an example a 29-slot armature for a 4-pole machine will be chosen. It is desired to install a simple wave winding in this armature, using an 87-bar commutator and 3-coil winding elements. It will be helpful to imagine each slot divided into three subslots by partitions, thus forming 87 small slots.

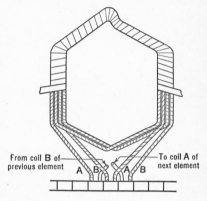

From coil B of previous element

To coil A of next element

FIG. 88. Two-coil element connections.

The pole pitch is 87/4 or 21 3/4 small slots. It will be advisable to choose a back pitch of 21 small slots, as that will permit the use of winding elements with a span of exactly 7 large slots.

The commutator pitch will be (87 − 1)/2 or 43, if a retrogressive winding is desired. Since the sum of the back and front pitches must equal the commutator pitch, the necessary front pitch for this winding will be 43 − 21, or 22 small slots.

130. Equalizer Connections. A simple lap winding for an 8-pole machine with 32 slots is shown in Fig. 89. This machine has 4 positive brushes, electrically connected by heavy copper leads, and 4 negative brushes similarly connected. There are 8 parallel paths in the armature winding between the two brush groups. The elements forming any one of the paths are concentrated under two adjacent poles, and the total voltage generated in this path will be dependent upon the amount of air-gap flux under these two poles.

It may seem from a superficial study of this machine that there is perfect structural symmetry and hence the flux values under all the poles will be identical. This ideal condition is practically impossible to attain. Slight differences in air-gap length, polar alignment or uniformity of lamination assembly are almost certain to exist in sufficient degree to produce noticeable differences in the reluctances of the various magnetic paths. These in turn will bring about differences in the amount of air-gap flux under the various poles. Since the total voltage generated in each armature path is dependent upon the amount of air-gap flux under the two poles associated with this path we may expect that the voltage in some of the paths will be greater than in others, and wasteful circulating currents will be produced in the winding.

A typical circulating current path will be described. Current may emerge from the winding at a positive brush touching one of the higher-

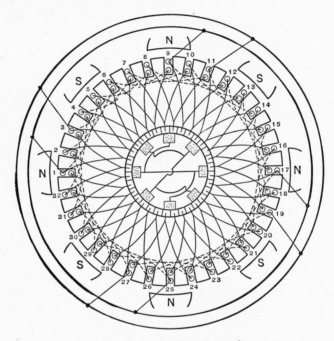

Fig. 89. Lap winding with equalizers.

voltage paths, flow through this brush and across a connecting jumper to some other positive brush touching a path of lower voltage, and reenter the winding at this point. It will then continue through the winding elements comprising the lower-voltage path and on into the path of higher voltage until it reaches its starting point.

The addition of this circulating current to the normal load current of the armature is likely to overheat the armature and produce such high current densities in some of the brushes that severe sparking will occur. It is very important therefore to discover a satisfactory method for reducing the circulating current to a negligible amount if lap windings are to be employed. Fortunately such a method has been developed.

Special interconnections called equalizer connections may be installed to accomplish the desired result.

In order to facilitate the proper installation of equalizer connections it is desirable to have the number of armature slots a multiple of the number of pairs of poles. Referring to Fig. 89 again, it will be evident that, no matter where slot 1 may be, slots 9, 17 and 25 are each in an exactly similar position and, under the ideal condition of equal polar fluxes, will be generating exactly the same voltage. A suitable ring or jumper may be mounted at the pulley end of the armature, and the winding elements in these slots may be connected to it. A similar ring may be used to join the winding elements in slots 3, 11, 19 and 27 as indicated. In like manner additional rings may be installed until every fourth or fifth winding element is provided with an equalizer connection.

Most of the circulating current due to unbalanced polar fluxes will now be diverted from the brush paths and will flow from the points of high potential to the points of low potential through the equalizer connections. Furthermore, the equalizer current is a true alternating current, and it produces some corrective ampere-turns in that part of the winding through which it flows which tend to reduce the flux inequality that is the original cause of the circulating current.

More recent machine designs make provision for equalizer connections at the commutator end of the armature. Some saving in copper is thus effected, and it is easier to support and insulate the equalizer properly.

Multipolar machines equipped with wave-wound armatures do not require equalizer connections. Each path of a wave winding is composed of an equal number of winding elements equally distributed under all the poles. Magnetic unbalance may exist; but it is unable to produce voltage unbalance in the winding paths.

131. Frogleg Winding. The frogleg winding, so called because of the peculiar shape of the winding elements, has been devised particularly for very large armatures operating under very severe service conditions. A two-coil winding element is used. One of the coils has its ends brought to adjacent commutator bars and is part of a standard lap winding. The ends of the other coil are spread approximately two pole pitches apart and are connected to the commutator as in a standard wave winding.

Since the same commutator serves both windings it is evident that this arrangement is possible only for certain armatures with the proper number of slots and commutator bars.

No equalizers are installed for the lap-wound coils, as it has been found that the wave-wound coils have powerful corrective effects on the flux unbalance and really serve as equalizers for the lap winding.

132. Winding-element Insulation. The conductors forming an armature winding element must be carefully insulated since it is usually a tedious and expensive task to uncover and repair a damaged element once the machine has been placed in service. Experience has shown that it is better engineering practice to use several thin layers of different insulating materials than to apply a single thick layer of one material.

The slots are usually lined with fish paper, which is the trade name for a special type of rag paper treated with zinc chloride during manufacture. It is usually impregnated with paraffin or varnish to add moisture-resistant properties.

If random-wound elements are required for a low-voltage machine, copper wire with a coating of enamel for insulation may be threaded into the proper slots (which have been lined with fish paper) and in many cases no additional insulation will be needed.

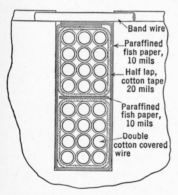

FIG. 90.   Typical slot section.

Form-wound elements for larger machines are likely to contain double-cotton-covered wire, with a wrapping of cotton tape around the complete element. Such an element is usually moisture-proofed by impregnation with varnish. Elements designed for armatures of large current rating are usually formed of strips of copper of rectangular cross-section, wrapped with cotton tape or varnished cambric.

Figure 90 shows a slot cross-section typical of a 230-volt machine.*

133. Comparison of Lap and Wave Windings. The principal characteristics of lap and wave windings may now be summarized for comparison purposes.

In lap windings a relatively small fraction of the total number of armature conductors are in series in one path. There are at least as many paths as there are poles. Equalizers are needed to reduce circulating current to a minimum.

In wave windings a large fraction (one-half, in simple windings) of the armature conductors are in series in one path. Simple windings will have two paths in parallel between armature terminals. Two brushes

* From " Fundamentals of Electrical Design," A. D. Moore, McGraw-Hill Book Co., 1927, with the author's permission.

are required in all cases; more brushes may be added to reduce brush current density. Equalizers are not required.

From this summary we may conclude that lap windings are ideally suited to machines of low voltage and large current output, such as a battery-charging generator. Wave windings are best suited to high-voltage, low-current machines. Most large motors for industrial use, and all series railway motors, are wave-wound.

PROBLEMS

1. Draw the diagram for a simple lap winding for an 8-pole machine with 40 slots and 40 winding elements. Show position of brushes.

2. Draw the diagram for a simple wave winding for an 8-pole machine with 61 slots and 61 winding elements. Show position of brushes.

3. Draw the winding diagram for a simple lap winding with 38 slots, 38 winding elements and 4 poles. Show position of brushes.

4. State suitable pitches for the following windings, and explain how you selected them.

(a) A simple wave winding for a machine with 8 poles, 49 slots.

(b) A duplex lap winding for a machine with 4 poles, 42 slots.

5. Draw the winding diagram for a simple wave winding with 34 slots and winding elements, and 4 poles.

6. Specify winding pitches and show the winding pattern for a duplex lap winding. The machine has 6 poles, 74 slots and 74 winding elements.

7. Indicate by a suitable winding table the connection order for a simple wave winding with 47 slots, 47 winding elements and 6 poles.

8. Specify winding pitches and show the winding pattern for a duplex wave winding to be installed in a 64-slot, 6-pole machine.

9. Draw the diagram for a duplex lap winding for a 4-pole machine with 32 slots and 32 winding elements. Show position of brushes.

10. State suitable pitches and show the winding pattern for a simple lap winding to be installed in a 6-pole machine with 56 slots. Three-coil winding elements are to be used.

11. State suitable pitches and show a portion of the winding connections for a simple wave winding to be installed in a 6-pole machine with 35 slots. Two-coil winding elements are to be used, requiring the use of 70 commutator bars.

12. What will be the approximate change in resistance of the armature of a 4-pole machine if the winding connections are changed from simple lap to simple wave?

13. What will be the approximate change in resistance of the armature of a 6-pole machine if the winding connections are changed from a duplex wave to a simple lap?

14. If the armature of a certain 4-pole machine generates 220 volts when running at 750 rpm., and it is lap wound, what will be the generated voltage at the same speed and with the same flux if the armature is reconnected to form a wave winding? What will be the relative values of armature current needed to develop the same torque?

15. A certain 4-pole, 230-volt shunt motor has a wave winding, and its four field coils are connected in series across the supply line. How can the armature and field coil connections be changed so as to produce the same speed and polar flux if connected to 115-volt mains?

16. Given the following data concerning a 4-pole generator: $E = 230$ volts; rpm. $= 900$; $\Phi = 2.5 \times 10^6$; $S = 51$ slots. A two-layer winding (with 51 winding elements) is required. Select a suitable type of winding; specify the pitches and the number of turns per winding element.

17. A 41-slot armature for a 6-pole machine is to be provided with a simple wave winding. State suitable pitches. Each winding element will have a resistance of 0.0011 ohm. Compute the resistance of the complete winding.

18. A shunt motor has an armature resistance of 0.4 ohm and runs at 1500 rpm., with the armature drawing 20 amperes from 115-volt mains. If the armature be rewound with twice as many turns of wire having one-half as much cross-sectional area, at what speed will the motor run when the armature takes 10 amperes from 115-volt mains, the field excitation remaining unchanged?

19. Suppose that we take any shunt motor and rewind every field and armature coil with twice the number of turns of wire of half the cross-sectional area, and then operate the machine on doubled line voltage. What change occurs in the no-load speed? In the maximum torque that can be developd without overheating any part?

20. A certain generator has its armature rewound with coils of exactly the same shape and outside dimensions as before, filling the same slots and connected in the same way to the commutator. But the wire used has one-half the diameter of that which was on the armature before.

(*a*) Using the same field and speed, how many times is the generator voltage increased?

(*b*) How much is the armature resistance increased?

(*c*) How much must the current output be reduced to avoid heating any coil at a greater rate than before rewinding?

CHAPTER 10

LOSSES AND EFFICIENCY

134. Transformers of Power. Motors and generators may be considered as transformers of power. A motor receives electrical power from its supply mains and converts it to mechanical torque and speed. The mechanical power supplied to a generator by its prime mover is changed to volts and amperes.

As in other familiar conversion processes there are some by-products which apparently serve no useful purpose and hence are called waste products or losses. Not all the electrical power supplied to a motor reappears at the shaft as mechanical power output; a considerable portion of it is changed in one way or another into heat. A generator likewise is unable to deliver in electrical form the exact equivalent of the mechanical power supplied to it.

The principal power losses will be classified in various ways and discussed individually, and the accepted methods of measuring them will be described briefly.

135. Classification of Losses. The list of important sources of power loss in motors and generators contains eight items, which may be classified in three groups, as follows:

1. Mechanical losses.
   (a) Bearing friction loss.
   (b) Windage, or air resistance loss.
   (c) Commutator friction loss.
2. Copper or RI^2 losses.
   (a) Shunt field copper loss.
   (b) Armature circuit copper loss.
   (c) Brush contact loss.
3. Core or iron losses.
   (a) Hysteresis loss.
   (b) Eddy-current loss.

A different classification scheme based on the manner in which the losses vary with load will be presented later in this chapter.

136. Bearing Friction Loss. It has been well established that bearing friction varies with the projected area of contact, the rubbing velocity and the type and condition of the lubricant. It is unaffected

151

by variations in contact pressure if the oil film between the contact surfaces is maintained. An empirical combination of these factors believed to be quite accurate for moderate-speed machines with standard sleeve bearings is shown in equation 50.

$$\text{Bearing friction loss} = 0.81A \left(\frac{V}{100}\right)^{\frac{3}{2}} \text{watts,} \qquad (50)$$

where V = the rubbing velocity, in feet per minute.

A = the projected area of the bearing, in square inches.

(By projected area is meant the product of the shaft diameter and the bearing length.)

137. Windage Loss. The envelope of air surrounding the armature offers resistance to its rotation, and the power required to overcome this resistance is called the windage loss.

Windage is negligible at slow armature speeds, but becomes important when the peripheral velocity reaches values of 5000 to 6000 feet per minute. It is an exponential function of the velocity, the exponent having values from 2 to 3.

Windage is often deliberately increased by the designer for the purpose of directing cooling air currents around and through the armature. This is usually accomplished by radial fins attached to the armature.

The combined windage and bearing friction loss can be measured accurately. It is impracticable, however, to isolate and measure the windage loss because of the difficulty of separating it from the bearing friction loss. Special frames could, of course, be built which would permit driving the armature first in a vacuum and then in air at various speeds, and the difference between the two corresponding power requirements at each speed could properly be considered as the windage loss.

138. Commutator Friction Loss. The frictional drag of the brushes on the commutator accounts for a small power loss. A convenient expression for its value may easily be derived.

Assume:

Coefficient of friction of carbon against copper .   = 0.28
Brush pressure, in pounds . . . .   = 2.0
Total brush contact area, square inches . . . .   = A
Commutator diameter, inches . . . .   = d
Commutator speed, rpm.   = N

The equation for the commutator friction loss in watts may be evolved as follows:

$$\text{Tangential force, } F = 2.0 \times A \times 0.28,$$
$$= 0.56A \text{ lb.}$$

Lever arm, R $\quad = \dfrac{d}{24}$ ft.

Torque, T $\quad = 0.56A \times \dfrac{d}{24}$,

$\quad\quad\quad\quad\quad = 0.0233Ad$ lb-ft.

Power, hp. $\quad = \dfrac{NT}{5250}$,

$\quad\quad\quad\quad\quad = 4.44 \times 10^{-6}AdN$ hp.

Power, watts $\quad = 3.31 \times 10^{-3}AdN.$ $\qquad$ (51)

Since

$$N = \frac{12V}{\pi d},$$

where V = the tangential velocity of the commutator, in feet per minute, the expression for the commutator friction loss may be altered to read:

$$\text{Loss, in watts} = 3.31 \times 10^{-3}A\,\frac{12V}{\pi},$$

$$= 12.65 \times 10^{-3}AV. \qquad (52)$$

The values of brush pressure and friction coefficient used in deriving the equation given above are somewhat larger than will be found in many of the modern machines. A conventional allowance of $8.0 \times 10^{-3}AV$ is suggested in the Standardization Rules of the A.I.E.E. This latter figure doubtless represents more nearly average conditions.

139. Shunt Field Copper Loss. It is an obvious fact that power is expended in building up the air-gap flux when the field circuit is first connected to its supply source, but after the flux reaches a steady value all the power consumed in the shunt field circuit is used to force the field current through the circuit in opposition to the ohmic resistance of the current path. The power so consumed appears as heat in the field windings and is called the shunt field copper loss.

If the operating conditions of the machine are such as to require frequent use of a rheostat in the shunt field circuit the power expended as copper loss in the rheostat is included in the shunt field copper loss.

140. Armature Copper Loss. From the power transformation viewpoint the armature of a motor or generator is the most important part of the machine. In it occurs the power transformation for which the entire machine is designed.

Most of the electrical power entering the armature of a motor is converted to mechanical speed and torque.   The small remainder is utilized in overcoming the ohmic resistance of the armature winding, and is transformed into heat in the winding.   This particular power item is called the armature copper loss or heat loss.

In like manner a small portion of the electrical power produced in a generator armature is converted to heat within the armature winding and therefore is not available for delivery to the receiving circuit.

Any auxiliary windings carrying the armature current will likewise experience copper losses which may logically be included with the copper loss of the armature winding proper.   Hence, if the machine has series field coils, interpole coils or pole-face windings, their copper losses should be added to and considered part of the armature copper losses.

141. Brush Contact Loss.   A carbon brush apparently in firm contact with a moving commutator is actually separated from it by a film of air which serves as a surprisingly effective barrier considering its extreme thinness.   The resistance of the air film under each brush and the resistance of the brush itself constitute sources of power loss which are relatively small, but yet are of sufficient importance to justify consideration here.   The equivalent resistance of the air film and all the brushes is called the brush contact resistance of the machine, and the power expended in overcoming this resistance is the brush contact loss.

The exact nature of the phenomena accompanying the flow of current from brush to commutator is not yet clearly understood.   It is known that brush contact resistance depends upon at least five factors, of which the most important from the operating standpoint is brush current density.   An approximately inverse relationship exists between brush contact resistance and current density so that the brush contact voltage drop is quite constant over a wide range of current values.

Tests made on many machines of various types and ratings likewise indicate a remarkable uniformity in the value of the contact voltage drop, a total drop of 2 volts being approximated in almost every case. Hence this value is recommended in the A.I.E.E. Standardization Rules to be used in routine predictions of brush contact loss.

The other factors affecting brush contact resistance are the brush temperature, the brush pressure, the rubbing velocity and the condition of the commutator surface.   For information on these less important items the reader is referred to the articles listed in the bibliography at the end of Chapter 12.

142. Hysteresis Loss.   The general nature of magnetic hysteresis loss and the factors affecting its value are discussed briefly in the Appendix.   It will be shown that magnetic hysteresis occurs in certain parts of direct-current machines, and the various ways in which hysteresis loss affects machine operation will also be stated.

Figure 91 shows part of the magnetic circuit of a generator, with clockwise rotation and normal air-gap flux assumed. To prevent confusion the armature conductors are omitted from the diagram. At the instant shown, tooth 1 is passing the center of a north pole and may be thought of as having south polarity produced in it by magnetic induction. When it reaches a similar position under the adjacent south pole its own polarity will evidently be reversed and its arrival under the next north pole will be accompanied by a return to the south polarity it first possessed. This tooth is thus carried through a miniature hysteresis loop and must be the source of a small hysteresis power loss. As the remain-

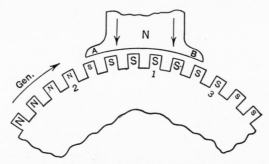

FIG. 91. Hysteresis effect.

ing teeth experience the same magnetic cycle the total hysteresis loss for all the teeth may amount to quite an appreciable item.

If a small unit volume of the armature core is studied for evidence of hysteresis loss it will be noticed that a periodic flux rotation occurs within the unit volume. The production of a modified form of hysteresis loop may therefore be expected, accompanied by a hysteresis power loss which becomes of some importance when totaled for the complete armature core.

A third and still smaller source of hysteresis loss is found in the pole face. The alternate passage of tooth and slot through the air-gap flux under the pole creates pulsations and ripples in the flux of the pole face. Even the very slight periodic variation in the flux density at any point in the pole face produced by these ripples is sufficient to cause hysteresis effects.

Magnetic materials carrying an alternating or pulsating flux usually show evidence of heat production. From the preceding paragraphs it is apparent that hysteresis loss may be held responsible for a large share of the heat so produced. It is believed that a periodic magnetic flux reversal causes a periodic shift in the molecular pattern of the material and that this displacement of the molecules is accompanied by friction which produces heat.

Another characteristic of hysteresis is of interest. A portion of the counter- or retarding torque of a motor or generator is attributed to the hysteresis loss. As evidence that the magnetic losses, of which hysteresis is a part, do produce a counter-torque, note that the power required to turn the armature of a generator is greater with the field excited than it is with no field current.

To obtain an understanding of this phenomenon refer again to Fig. 91. Since the armature is carefully located so as to have the air gap under the main poles as nearly equal as possible, balanced attractive forces with no tangential components are expected between the poles and the armature. But the retention of even a small amount of residual magnetism in the teeth approaching and leaving a pole produces dissymmetry in the pattern of the air-gap flux under the pole. The teeth coming up to a north pole will still have north polarity, and the teeth leaving the pole will retain some of their south polarity. This will bring about repulsive forces between the approaching teeth (such as tooth 2) and the pole, while there will be attractive forces between the pole and the departing teeth (such as tooth 3). The tangential components of these forces are all opposite to the direction of rotation, so that more driving torque is required than would be necessary if the hysteresis loss were absent.

143. Eddy-current Loss. Part of a motor magnetic circuit is shown in Fig. 92. The current direction in the armature conductors under a north pole will be as indicated in order to secure clockwise rotation as a motor. The voltage generated in each conductor by its passage through the field is, of course, opposite to the indicated current direction and becomes a part of the motor counter-emf. Unfortunately, however, the generation of voltage in the rotating armature is not restricted to the copper conductors in the slots but occurs in the teeth, the armature core itself and to some extent in the pole face.

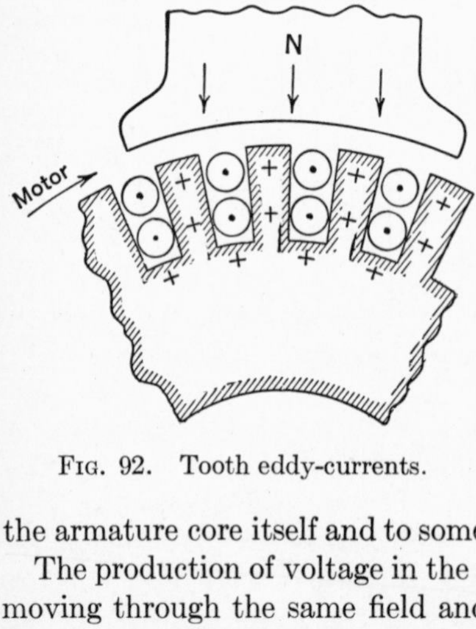

FIG. 92.   Tooth eddy-currents.

The production of voltage in the teeth is easily understood. They are moving through the same field and with the same velocity as the conductors; hence the generated voltage in a tooth, per inch of axial length, is the same as in the adjacent conductors.   The crosses in Fig. 92 indicating the direction of the voltage induced in the teeth and core may likewise represent the current resulting from this voltage.   Current produced in this way in conducting material of comparatively large volume affording a multiplicity of return paths is generally termed eddy current.

By application of the familiar force rules, the torque resulting from the linkage of the main field flux with the eddy current in the teeth may be shown to be a counter-torque tending to retard the rotation of the armature.

Naturally the unrestricted flow of eddy current through the armature iron will be accompanied by the production of a considerable amount of heat, and it becomes necessary to modify the armature design in such a way that eddy current will be reduced to a minimum without detracting from the strength and magnetic effectiveness of the armature. Modern armatures are never made of solid steel but are formed of thin steel sheets or laminations packed firmly together.   This method of construction not only is the most effective means of reducing eddy current but also tends to lower the cost of production.

The effect of armature lamination on the magnitude of eddy current can be understood with the help of Fig. 93.   The insulating property of the oxide film on the surface of each lamination is sufficient to prevent much transfer of eddy current from one lamination to the next.   The voltage generated in the outer edge of one lamination produces a localized eddy current whose path may be assumed to be as suggested by the dashed line in Fig. 93.

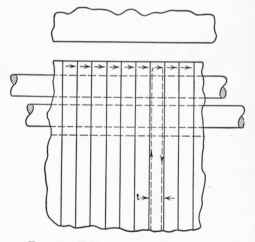

FIG. 93.   Eddy-current in laminations.

Now if new laminations of half the thickness are substituted for those shown in the figure the voltage per lamination will, of course, be cut in half; but the eddy current will be reduced by a much greater amount because the effective resistance of the current path does not shrink much with the reduction in thickness.   Hence the use of very thin laminations will reduce the eddy-current loss in the armature iron to an extremely small quantity.

In order to build up an expression for the power loss due to eddy current it is helpful to make several simplifying assumptions, none of which will cause serious error in the result. These will be mentioned as the derivation proceeds. A portion of Fig. 93 has been enlarged as shown in Fig. 94. For simplicity it is assumed that the machine has two poles, that the armature laminations are circular disks keyed to the shaft and that the eddy-current path is as shown by the arrows in the shaded edge of the lamination. If the top edge of the lamination is considered as a conductor cutting the polar flux, the induced voltage may be written:

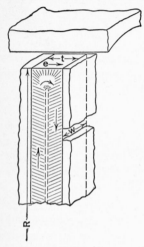

$$e = kBtv \quad \text{volts (see equation 5),}$$

where t = lamination thickness in centimeters, and the other symbols have previously been defined.

Substituting $R\omega$ for v,

$$e = kBtR\omega,$$

where R = armature radius, in centimeters.

Fig. 94.   Enlarged view of lamination.

ω = armature angular velocity, in radians per second.

It is assumed that the eddy current produced by this voltage is confined by the surface oxide film to the lamination where the voltage originates, and that the flux changes in the armature iron do not occur at a sufficiently rapid rate to generate appreciable inductive voltages.   The current may then be expressed by Ohm's law:

$$i = \frac{e}{r}.$$

The resistance, r, of the eddy-current path $= \rho l / A$, where

ρ = a constant for a given material and temperature.

l = length of eddy-current path, in centimeters.

A = sectional area of path, in square centimeters.

The path length, l, is approximately equal to $2t + 2R$. Since R is very large compared to t, $l \approx 2R$.

The sectional area, $A \approx (t/2)w$.

Therefore
$$r \approx \frac{\rho 2R}{\dfrac{tw}{2}} \approx \frac{\rho 4R}{tw}.$$

The eddy-current power loss $= ei = e^2/r$. But

$$\frac{e^2}{r} \approx \frac{(kBtR\omega)^2}{\underbrace{\rho 4R}_{tw}} \approx KB^2t^2\omega^2 Rtw,$$

and the product Rtw is a measure of the volume of the lamination. Hence the power loss per unit volume,

$$\text{Eddy-current loss per cubic centimeter} \approx KB^2t^2\omega^2. \qquad (53)$$

The indication that eddy-current loss is approximately proportional to the square of the lamination thickness is justification for the general practice of using armature laminations as thin as 0.014 in.

The production of flux ripples in the pole face by the rapid rotation of the armature, which was discussed briefly in the preceding article, will also be accompanied by whirling eddies of alternating current in the pole face. To limit the production of heat by these eddies to a moderate amount it becomes necessary to laminate the pole face.

144. Measurement of Losses. Some of the power losses which have been discussed can be conveniently isolated and their individual values can be measured under various operating conditions. Groups may be formed of the others, and measurements of the power loss of each group can be taken. The possible extent and kind of grouping depend upon the use to be made of the measurements.

If the variation of the several losses with load is to be investigated they may be formed into three groups.

Group A. The copper losses, requiring simple resistance measurements for their determination. The method may be outlined as follows:

Shunt field. Measure its resistance at a known temperature. If this temperature differs much from the operating temperature attained when the machine has been running for several hours, a correction factor must be applied to the resistance measurement. See Art. 13, Chapter 1. Include the field rheostat resistance in this measurement if the machine normally operates with one. Multiply the corrected resistance by the field current squared to obtain the shunt field copper loss in watts. Under normal operating conditions this loss will usually be unaffected by load changes.

Armature. The resistance of the armature must be determined. If the familiar drop-of-potential method is used a steady current of suitable magnitude should be passed through the armature, utilizing its main brushes for the purpose. The voltage drop produced by this current should be measured by placing one voltmeter lead on a commutator bar which is in contact with a positive brush and the other lead on a bar in contact with a negative brush. The contact resistance of the main brushes is thus eliminated from the measurement. As in the shunt field measurement a temperature correction may be required to bring the measured resistance up to the " hot " value.

To obtain the armature copper loss in watts at any load multiply the square of the armature current corresponding to the given load by the corrected armature resistance. As the load and the armature current are closely proportional, variations in load will produce great changes in the armature copper loss.

Other armature circuit losses. If the machine has series field coils, interpole coils or other auxiliary coils as a normal part of its armature circuit the copper loss of each in watts may be computed by multiplying its resistance by the square of the current it is carrying. These losses undergo the same variation with load that is a characteristic of the armature copper loss. A temperature correction may be applied if necessary.

Group B. The brush contact loss. This loss is seldom actually measured in routine testing, as it is usually a small item and can be quite accurately estimated for a wide range of loads. The conventional method requires the assumption of a constant 2-volt drop at the brush contacts. Hence:

$$\text{Brush contact loss in watts} \approx 2I_a.$$

Group C. The rotational losses, composed of the five items: bearing friction, windage, brush friction, hysteresis and eddy current. Evidence has already been presented which indicates that each of these losses is characterized by the production of a countertorque, and this common feature can be made the basis for several methods of obtaining the power loss of the entire group.

Perhaps the simplest method requires the machine to be operated as an unloaded shunt motor from a supply circuit of the proper voltage to produce normal speed and normal field current. The armature current, applied voltage and speed are measured while the motor is idling. Since the power output is zero the armature power input must be consumed entirely by the various losses, which are the five of Group C plus the armature copper and brush contact losses. By computing the last two losses and subtracting them from the armature input the amount of the Group C loss can be determined.

Experimental studies of the Group C loss indicate that it is approximately proportional to speed. From the no-load determination at a known speed it is possible therefore to compute the rotational losses of shunt or compound machines quite accurately at various loads and speeds. The speed range of a series motor is so great that it is better practice to measure its rotational losses at a sufficient number of speeds to enable a curve of rotational losses vs. speed to be plotted.

145. Calibrated Motor Method. This method of measuring the Group C or rotational losses is particularly advantageous when a more or less complete separation of the components of the group loss is

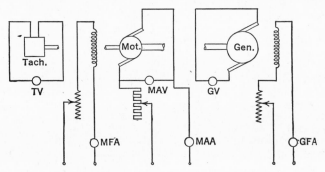

Fig. 95.   Losses by calibrated motor method.

desired. The machine to be tested is driven as an idle generator by a much smaller motor whose curve of output vs. armature power input has been determined at the speed selected for this test. Figure 95 shows the arrangement of apparatus. The operating conditions may be easily adjusted to suit a variety of test requirements.

For example, if the brushes of the test machine are lifted and its field is unexcited the power drawn from the driving motor is merely the amount needed for bearing friction and windage, and this can be determined by reading the instruments indicating the driving motor input and then referring to its calibration curve for the corresponding power output. If the brushes are lowered and similar readings taken the increase in the power requirement over the preceding test is the amount needed for brush friction. A third run at the same speed, with the field of the generator excited to the normal value, will show an additional power demand, representing the iron losses (hysteresis and eddy current).

The same arrangement of apparatus may be used for the separation of the hysteresis loss from the eddy-current loss, and for investigation of the variation of these and other rotational losses with speed. Detailed instructions for such tests may be found in the numerous handbooks and laboratory manuals especially devoted to experimental procedure.

146. Retardation Method. A third method of measuring rotational losses which is frequently used in testing large machines is known as the retardation method. Like the previous method it is effective as a means of separating the component losses as well as determining the amount of the whole group.

The machine to be tested is brought up to its highest safe speed, either by operating it as a motor or by driving it by an auxiliary motor. The source of driving torque is then disconnected suddenly and the machine is allowed to coast to standstill. During this retardation period frequent readings of instantaneous speed and elapsed time are taken and the speed-time or retardation curve is plotted.

The kinetic energy stored in the rotating armature is gradually dissipated by the rotational losses, and the rate at which this energy is dissipated at any instant is equal to the value of the rotational power loss at that instant. Since power is proportional to the product of speed and torque (equation 21), the rotational power loss at any instant during the retardation period may be written

$$P_R = CnT_R, \tag{54}$$

where n = rpm. at the instant considered.

T_R = total friction, windage and iron-loss torque at the same instant.

Since torque equals moment of inertia times angular acceleration, and acceleration is the rate of change of angular velocity, we may write

$$T_R = J\alpha = C_1 \frac{dn}{dt}, \tag{55}$$

where C_1 is a constant combining the moment of inertia with the proper conversion factor, and dn/dt is the rate of speed change at the instant considered.

Therefore

$$P_R = C_2 n \frac{dn}{dt}. \tag{56}$$

In other words, the product of the speed at any instant during the retardation process and the slope of the retardation curve at the same instant is proportional to the machine's rotational loss at that instant.

For the purpose of separating the rotational losses by this method additional retardation runs are required: one with the brushes lifted, and several with the field excitation at fractional values of the normal.

The references listed at the end of the chapter contain excellent discussions of the practical methods of measuring instantaneous speeds and evaluating the constant C_2.

147. Motor Efficiency. The ratio of the useful mechanical power output of a motor to its electrical power input is called the efficiency. It is usually expressed in percentage, and naturally must be computed with the output and input expressed in the same kind of power unit.

The greatest difficulty associated with the determination of efficiency by a direct load test is found in providing a suitable mechanical load which can be accurately adjusted and measured. Small motors are frequently loaded by some form of friction brake which produces a measurable load torque. The necessity of cooling the brake and the difficulty of producing a smooth, steady load make this method quite undesirable. Various forms of portable eddy-current brakes are available which are better for the purpose, but their weight and cost are objectionable. It is doubtful whether either of these devices can be used satisfactorily on motors of more than 10-hp. rating.

Of the various kinds of apparatus designed for loading motors perhaps the best two are the electric dynamometer and the calibrated generator. The usual form of dynamometer is a direct-current machine with an armature of standard construction which may be coupled to the machine under test. The frame, instead of being fastened rigidly to a bedplate, is supported on bearings concentric with the armature shaft bearings so that it may be rotated through a small angle. When the armature is driven by the test motor the voltage thus generated is applied to an adjustable resistance and the resulting current produces a counter-torque which serves as a load torque for the driving motor. At the same time the reaction between the armature of the dynamometer and its frame creates an equal and opposite torque tending to rotate the frame. This tendency is resisted by the pressure of a spring scale against a horizontal lever arm attached to the frame, and the amount of turning effort can thus be measured. Increases in load torque may be produced by increasing the dynamometer field excitation or by reducing the resistance connected to its armature.

A calibrated generator is a standard generator whose efficiency and loss curves have been determined accurately at the speeds required for the test. When driven by the machine to be tested it is usually supplied with a rheostatic load and the power delivered to this adjustable resistance is varied over the desired range and carefully measured. The generator input (which, of course, is the test motor output) is then determined by reference to its efficiency curve.

148. Efficiency by Method of Losses. The efficiency expression, output/input, may be changed to read:

$$\text{Efficiency} = \frac{\text{Input} - \Sigma \text{ losses}}{\text{Input}}. \tag{57}$$

This form suggests the possibility of calculating the efficiency of a motor without resorting to a direct load test, if data are available for computing the losses corresponding to a given input. As pointed out in Art. 144, the data required for this purpose are comparatively simple and easily obtained. The armature and field circuit resistances are needed for the calculation of the copper losses, and the rotational loss may be obtained by running the machine as a motor at no load and measuring the armature power input.

EXAMPLE: The following resistance measurements were secured on a compound motor (with interpoles), which had attained normal operating temperature.

Armature,   0.31 ohm.   Series field,   0.002 ohm.
Interpole coils, 0.09 ohm.   Shunt field (with rheostat), 470. ohms.

A no-load test showed an armature input of 1.5 amperes at 222 volts and 1650 rpm.

Determine the output, input and efficiency of this motor when its load is such as to require an armature current of 25 amperes from 230-volt mains.

$$\text{Shunt field current} = \frac{230}{470} = 0.49 \text{ ampere}$$

Shunt field copper loss = 230 × 0.49   = 113 watts
(If the expression $R_f I_f^2$ is used the same
result is obtained.)
Armature copper loss = 0.31 × (25)²   = 193 "
Series field copper loss = 0.002 × (25)²·   = 1.2 "
Interpole copper loss = 0.09 × (25)²   = 56. "
Brush contact loss = 2 × 25   = 50. "
Armature no-load input = 222 × 1.5   = 333. "
    Correction for brush contact and RI^2 = 4. "
Rotational loss at 1650 rpm.   = 329. "
    Correction for speed change, assuming a
    5% reduction in speed   = 16. "
    Corrected rotational loss   = 313.
                           Σ losses = 726 "
Input = 230 (25 + 0.49)   = 5863 "
                           Σ losses = 726 "
                           Output = 5137 "

$$\text{Efficiency} = \frac{5137}{5863} = 87.7\%.$$

Although the above example includes a correction of the rotational loss for a change in speed it is common practice to consider the rotational loss as constant in shunt and compound motors, as comparatively little change in the speed of these motors is associated with variations in load. Correction for the no-load brush contact and armature RI^2 losses is likewise unnecessary in most cases.

If other values of armature current are assumed and the losses recomputed a series of points on the curve of efficiency vs. armature current can be determined and plotted, and the current value corresponding to maximum efficiency can be found.

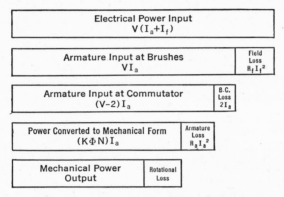

FIG. 96. Distribution of motor losses.

For obtaining the efficiency of large machines the method of losses has two important advantages over the direct load test:

A. The method of losses is more economical. The only power consumed is the small amount required to operate the motor at no load, and to measure its resistances.

B. It is usually more accurate, since the observational and instrumental errors affect the determination of the losses only, and as the losses are but a small part of the input the effect of these errors on the ratio of output to input is negligible.

The chart shown in Fig. 96 illustrates the successive stages by which the electrical input of a shunt motor is transformed into mechanical power output at the pulley.

149. Efficiency of a Generator. The efficiency of a generator may be obtained by direct load test, using an electric dynamometer or a calibrated driving motor to produce the driving torque. Simultaneous measurements of power output and input can be taken and the efficiency curve easily determined.

For large machines the direct load method has the disadvantages that were noted in the preceding article and the method of losses is preferable.

To facilitate the use of the method of losses the efficiency expression may be written:

$$\text{Efficiency} = \frac{\text{Output}}{\text{Input}} = \frac{\text{Output}}{\text{Output} + \Sigma \text{ losses}}, \qquad (58)$$

thus making it possible to use electrical measurements exclusively. An output current may be assumed and the losses corresponding to this current may be calculated by the methods already discussed. The efficiency can then be determined by means of equation 58. By repeating this process for other current values it is possible to determine the complete efficiency curve.

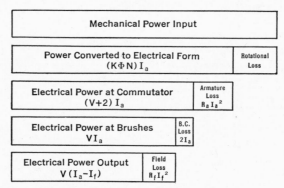

FIG. 97.   Distribution of generator losses.

Figure 97 illustrates the process by which the mechanical power delivered to a self-excited shunt generator is transformed into electrical form and shows the stages at which the various losses occur.

150. Efficiency in Terms of Output.   It is often desirable to use the method of losses to determine the efficiency of a motor at a stated power output when the current corresponding to this output is unknown.   Let the following symbols be used:

V = applied voltage. R_f = shunt field resistance.
R_a = armature resistance. I_f = shunt field current.
I_a = armature current. W = motor output, watts.
S = rotational losses (watts) measured at no load and assumed constant.

From equation 57,

$$\text{Output} = \text{Input} - \Sigma \text{ losses.}$$

$$W = V(I_a + I_f) - R_f I_f^2 - R_a I_a^2 - 2I_a - S,$$

since $$VI_f = R_f I_f^2,$$

$$W = (V - 2)I_a - R_a I_a^2 - S. \qquad (59)$$

This is a quadratic equation in I_a which may be solved by the use of the quadratic formula, as follows:

$$I_a = \frac{(V-2) \pm \sqrt{(V-2)^2 - 4R_a(S+W)}}{2R_a}. \tag{60}$$

The above equation must be solved with some care, as the quantities separated by $\pm$ do not differ much in magnitude and the denominator is a very small quantity. Small errors in simplifying the numerator will have large effects on the final result.

Typical input, output and loss curves of a shunt motor are shown in Fig. 98. The physical significance of two armature current values for a stated output can be understood by noting the shape of the output curve. In solving equation 60 the smaller value of I_a is always selected, as the larger value lies beyond the normal operating range of the motor.

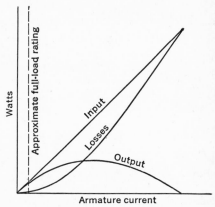

FIG. 98. Variation of losses with current.

151. Maximum Output and Efficiency. An inspection of the curves of Fig. 98 suggests a method for finding the armature current at which the output is a maximum. Obviously the slope of the output curve will be zero at this point, and the method of the calculus may be used. Using equation 59 and taking the first derivative:

$$\frac{dW}{dI_a} = (V-2) - 2R_aI_a - 0.$$

Putting $dW/dI_a = 0$, the condition for maximum output is obtained.

$$(V-2) - 2R_aI_a - 0 = 0,$$

$$V - 2 = 2R_aI_a,$$

$$R_aI_a = \frac{V-2}{2}. \tag{61}$$

Hence the armature current accompanying maximum output is such that approximately half of the supply voltage is consumed in RI drop.

Maximum output is of theoretical interest only, as it is much greater than the machine can carry without reaching a dangerous temperature and sparking badly at the commutator.

The determination of the conditions for maximum efficiency is approached in a similar manner. Since the efficiency of a motor may be expressed:

$$\text{Efficiency} = \frac{\text{Input} - \sum \text{losses}}{\text{Input}}, \qquad (57)$$

and since the numerator of the right-hand term may be written in the form of equation 59, the efficiency expression becomes:

$$\text{Efficiency} = \frac{(V - 2)I_a - R_aI_a^2 - S}{V(I_a + I_f)}.$$

To simplify the expression, I_f may be omitted from the denominator without introducing a serious error, since maximum efficiency usually occurs at or near rated load when I_f is very small compared to I_a. The first derivative with respect to I_a may then be found and equated to zero.

$$\frac{d \text{ Efficiency}}{dI_a} \approx \frac{VI_a[(V - 2) - 2R_aI_a] - V[(V - 2)I_a - R_aI_a^2 - S]}{V^2I_a^2},$$

$$\approx \frac{(V - 2)I_a - 2R_aI_a^2 - (V - 2)I_a + R_aI_a^2 + S}{VI_a^2},$$

$$\approx \frac{-R_aI_a^2 + S}{VI_a^2}.$$

Equating this expression to zero, the condition for maximum efficiency is found to be

$$S = R_aI_a^2. \qquad (62)$$

Because of the variation of S with load in a series motor, application of the above expression should be restricted to shunt and compound motors.

The relative magnitudes of the so-called constant losses (shunt field and rotational) and the variable losses (armature copper and brush contact) have a direct bearing on the shape of the efficiency curve and on the location of its maximum point with reference to the rated load of the machine. By careful proportioning of dimensions and materials the manufacturer may cause maximum efficiency to occur at any desired fraction of full load. It might seem logical to locate the point of maximum efficiency at full load in every case, but in many industrial applications the machine is operated for considerable periods at loads below its rating and there would be some economic advantage to the user to have its maximum efficiency occur at approximately 3/4 load. For further discussion of the factors to be considered in the selection of motors and generators see Chapter 15.

BIBLIOGRAPHY

1. Experimental Electrical Engineering, KARAPETOFF-DENNISON, 4th edition John Wiley & Sons, 1933.
2. Electrical Engineering Laboratory Experiments, RICKER-TUCKER, 3rd edition, McGraw-Hill Book Co.

PROBLEMS

1. The following data were obtained by test on a series motor. Calculate its output values and plot efficiency vs. motor current.

LINE VOLTS	ARMATURE CURRENT	RPM.	DELIVERED TORQUE, lb-ft.
600	130	190	2420
600	100	205	1755
600	70	232	1115
600	40	288	498
600	20	423	141

2. A 50-hp., 230-volt series motor is drawing an armature current of 94 amperes for a given load. The RI^2 losses in armature, series field and interpoles amount to 985 watts. The brush contact loss is 188 watts, and the efficiency at this load is 86.7%. Calculate the rotational loss, and determine at what fraction of rated load it is operating.

3. What is the efficiency of a 230-volt shunt motor when its armature current is 108 amperes? $R_a = 0.095$ ohm; $R_f = 92$ ohms. The no-load line current is 5.7 amperes.

4. A certain generator is rated at 100 kw., 250 volts, 1200 rpm. It is a compound machine, adjusted for flat-compounding, and is connected long shunt. The following resistances were measured: armature, 0.02 ohm; series field, 0.0075 ohm; shunt field, 25 ohms. In a test with no load on the generator except its own field excitation the input from the driving engine was 6.0 hp. What is the full-load efficiency of this generator?

5. Determine the efficiency of a compound generator when the output is 600 kw. at 600 volts. The resistance of the armature and series field circuit is 0.006 ohm. The shunt field resistance is 20 ohms, and the long shunt connection is used. The rotational loss is 30,000 watts.

6. A shunt machine is connected to 100-volt supply mains. $R_f = 50$ ohms; $R_a = 0.1$ ohm. When the machine is drawing 52 amperes from the line the speed is 950 rpm., and the output is 4550 watts. Determine the rotational losses.

If the rotational losses remain constant, how much mechanical power must be delivered to the machine and at what speed in order that 38 amperes may be returned to the supply lines?

7. A 200-volt shunt motor takes a field current of 1 ampere. When the armature current is 49 amperes the efficiency is 90%, and when the armature current is 24 amperes the efficiency is 84.5%. Assume the rotational loss to remain constant. Find: (a) the resistance of the armature; (b) the line current when the output is zero; (c) for what armature current the armature efficiency will be a maximum.

8. A 230-volt shunt motor rated at 250 hp. has resistances as follows: $R_a = 0.0075$ ohm; $R_f = 51$ ohms; $R_{\text{interpole}} = 0.0016$ ohm. The estimated brush contact loss is 1700 watts. When this motor is turned at rated speed and with rated field excitation by means of a calibrated driving motor, the driving motor draws a line current of 38.5 amperes from 230-volt mains. The efficiency of the driving motor at this line current is 86%.

Compute the efficiency of the 250-hp. motor when it is drawing a line current of 890 amperes from 230-volt mains.

9. A certain self-excited shunt generator was rated at 250 volts, 40 amperes, 1200 rpm. $R_f = 312$ ohms; $R_a = 0.30$ ohm. For test purposes it was driven at 1200 rpm. with its field self-excited, but without load. The small motor used for this purpose required 3.4 amperes at 220 volts, and its efficiency at this input was 80%. Find the efficiency of the generator when operated at its rating.

10. A 230-volt shunt motor when delivering 40 hp. runs at 1200 rpm. Under these conditions the motor efficiency is 89%; the field circuit resistance is 57.6 ohms; the armature circuit resistance is 0.1 ohm. Find: (a) the armature copper loss; (b) the rotational loss; (c) the net torque delivered at the pulley; (d) the gross torque developed by the armature conductors.

11. A 115-volt motor has a shunt field resistance of 67.6 ohms and an armature resistance of 0.055 ohm. When running idle this motor draws a line current of 5.2 amperes. What will be the efficiency and armature current when the output is exactly 12 hp.?

12. A 10-hp., 230-volt compound motor has a total no-load input of 450 watts. R_a (including series field) is 0.2 ohm. Rotational loss and shunt field loss are equal. What is the full-load armature current?

13. A certain shunt motor when running without load draws a current of 10 amperes from the supply line, and runs at 1100 rpm. The supply voltage is 220. When running with full load 60 hp. is delivered by the driving pulley. $R_f = 110$ ohms; $R_a = 0.05$ ohm. Determine the speed and the efficiency at full load.

14. A shunt motor operated at constant voltage has an efficiency of 90% at rated load, and 85% when its armature current is half the rated value.

(a) What will be the efficiency at 1/4 and at 1 1/4 of the rated armature current?

(b) What will be the maximum efficiency of this motor, and at what percentage of rated amperes input will it occur? Assume rotational loss constant.

15. Two motors have the same full-load rating, and each has a full-load efficiency of 88%; but motor 1 has constant losses (shunt field and rotational) amounting to 5% of the full-load input, while in motor 2 these losses amount to 7% of the full-load input. What is the approximate efficiency of each motor at 1/2 rated load?

16. Generators A and B have the same full-load efficiency and each has a nameplate rating of 100 kw. at 230 volts. Their losses are distributed as follows:

	$R_a I_a^2$	ROTATIONAL	SHUNT FIELD	BRUSH CONTACT
Gen. A	3200	4500	500	800
Gen. B	4175	3525	475	825

Which generator will have the better efficiency at 3/4 load, and why?

17. Generators *A*, *B* and *C* are each rated at 100 kw. and 230 volts. Their full-load efficiencies and the distribution of their full-load losses are as follows:

	EFFIC.	$R_a I_a^2$	ROTATIONAL	SHUNT FIELD	BRUSH CONTACT
Gen. *A*	92%	3000	4500	450	750
Gen. *B*	92%	4000	3500	400	800
Gen. *C*......	90%	5000	4600	600	900

Which generator will have the best efficiency at 3/4 load, and why?

18. A 10-hp., 115-volt shunt motor is used to drive a ventilating fan. $R_a = 0.08$ ohm; $I_f = 3.5$ amperes. Assume that the rotational losses vary with the speed and may be expressed by the equation:

$$S = 100 + 0.15N,$$

where *S* is the rotational loss in watts and *N* is the speed in rpm.

When the speed of the motor is 1800 rpm. the line current is 62 amperes. If the power required to drive the fan varies as N^2, how much resistance must be added in the armature circuit to reduce the motor speed to 1200 rpm.? What will be the power loss in this resistance? What is the overall efficiency of motor and controller?

19. Suppose that the generator of Problem 4 operates daily at full load for 3 hours, 3/4 load for 10 hours, 1/2 load for 6 hours and 1/4 load for 5 hours. Determine the ratio of the total kilowatt-hours output to the kilowatt-hours input for the 24-hour period. (This ratio is sometimes called the all-day efficiency.)

CHAPTER 11

ARMATURE REACTION

152. Conductor Field Patterns. A portion of the magnetic field around a long, isolated conductor is shown in Fig. 99a. The lines of flux in this familiar field are concentric circles, and a few of the radial

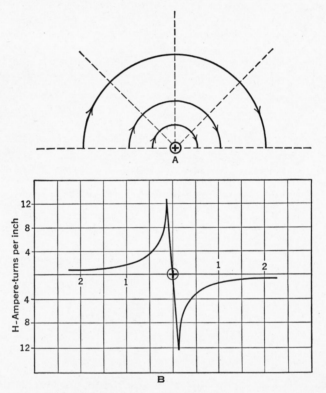

Fɪɢ. 99.   Conductor field pattern.

equipotential lines are shown.   If the field intensities, H, at various distances from the wire center are calculated for a current of 10 amperes, using the equation

$$H = \frac{I}{5r} \frac{\text{dynes}}{\text{unit pole}}, \qquad (29)$$

172

where I = current in amperes, and

   r = distance from the wire center in centimeters,

the curve of Fig. 99b will be obtained.   For convenience H is evaluated in ampere-turns per inch, using the relationship

$$H \frac{\text{dynes}}{\text{unit pole}} \times 2.02 = H \frac{\text{ampere-turns}}{\text{inch}}. \tag{63}$$

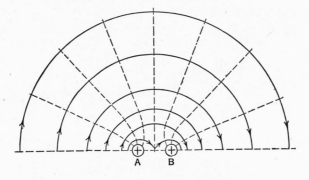

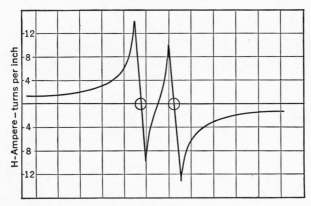

Fig. 100.   Field of two conductors.

   In Fig. 100a a portion of the field in the vicinity of two parallel conductors carrying equal currents in the same direction is sketched.   As in Fig. 99a the dashed lines are equipotentials.   Figure 100b shows the calculated values of H for various points along the line through the wire centers with 10 amperes in each conductor.   Notice that H is considerably increased to the right of B and to the left of A, but in the space between the conductors the two fields are in opposition, producing an average H of zero and maximum values noticeably less than the maxima occurring at the outer surfaces.

The field in the vicinity of six parallel conductors carrying equal currents in the same direction is shown in Fig. 101a, and the values of H for points along the line through the wire centers have been plotted in Fig. 101b. A current of 10 amperes is assumed in each conductor. If

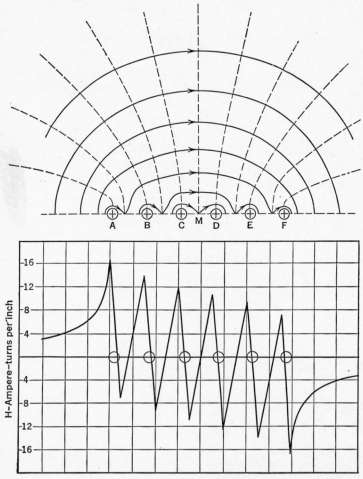

FIG. 101. Field of six conductors.

this field is compared with the two-conductor case the following facts will be evident:

1. The field is symmetrical about a perpendicular through M.
2. H has larger upward values to the left of A.
3. H is predominantly upward in the space between A and B, but is somewhat weaker than in the region to the left of A.

4. H is predominantly upward in the space between B and C, but is still further reduced in strength.

5. H has an average value of zero in the space between C and D.

In Chapter 7 it was pointed out that the mmf. drop around a closed path of flux linking with a current must necessarily equal the mmf. generated by the current. It will be helpful to reexamine Figs. 99a, 100a and 101a with this in mind. The mmf. drop in a flux path encircling a single conductor carrying 10 amperes will be 10 ampere-turns. Since the conductor shown in Fig. 99a is isolated its flux paths are circles. If a particular circle is selected the mmf. distribution along its circumference will be uniform and constant for each inch of path.

One of the somewhat elliptical paths enclosing the two conductors of Fig. 100a will have a total mmf. drop of 20 ampere-turns. Evidently the mmf. distribution along such a path will be non-uniform, as indicated

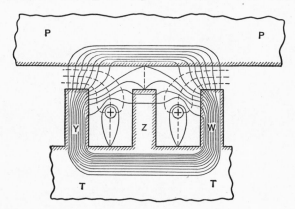

Fig. 102. Two conductors in slots.

by the varied spacing of the equipotential lines. In a similar manner we find that a flux path enclosing the six conductors of Fig. 101a will have a total mmf. drop of 60 ampere-turns, and that its distribution will be decidedly non-uniform.

Figure 102 is a rough sketch of the field in the vicinity of two conductors that are partially surrounded by iron of very high permeability. No attempt has been made to approximate even a correct representation of the flux paths in the iron parts of the magnetic circuit. It is certain, however, that a little flux cuts across tooth Z and that a great deal more travels upward through tooth Y into P, downward through W and returns through T. If each conductor carries 10 amperes the total mmf. drop around a flux path including tooth Y, P and tooth W will be 20 ampere-turns, but the mmf. distribution will be very different from the

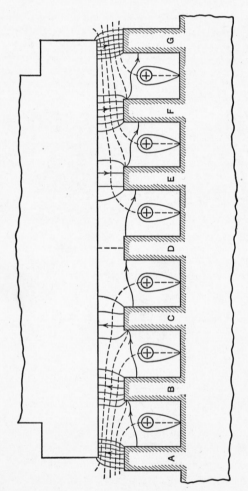

Fig. 103.　Six conductors in slots.

two-conductor case of Fig. 100a. The drop in the iron part of the circuit will be practically zero, so that half of the total drop is concentrated in the air gap over each tooth.

153. Armature Reaction. An interesting field pattern is formed when current is supplied to a band of armature conductors lying in slots under a main pole. In the developed diagram of Fig. 103 a band of six armature conductors, each carrying 10 amperes, is shown, and portions of the air-gap flux distribution have been sketched roughly. Following the method already established, one of the outermost flux paths may be

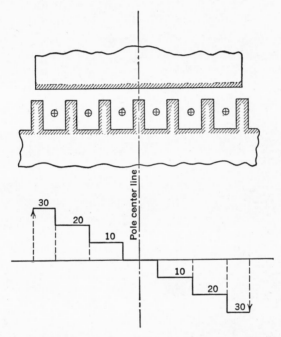

Fig. 104. Airgap mmf. due to armature current.

assumed to have a total mmf. drop of 60 ampere-turns since it encloses all six conductors. As practically all this drop occurs in the air gap the region above tooth A will account for 30 ampere-turns and that above tooth G will have the remaining 30. Teeth B and F are parts of a shorter flux path linking with four conductors; accordingly the mmf. drop in the air gap over these teeth will be 20 ampere-turns each. Similarly a drop of 10 ampere-turns may be expected above tooth C and tooth E.

The approximate relationship between air-gap mmf. drop and perpendicular distance from the pole center line is indicated in Fig. 104. It is evident that the flow of current in the armature conductors under a main pole produces a concentration of mmf. in the air gap tending to cause flux to enter one pole tip, flow across the pole and leave at the other tip, and that this effect will vary with the amount of armature current and hence with the load for both motor and generator operation.

For example, the field coils of a shunt motor operating without load may be expected to produce a strong air-gap flux that is quite uniformly distributed under the pole and is symmetrical about the pole center line. If a heavy load torque is added a large armature current will be required and the ampere-turns of the conductor band under the pole will become strong enough to have a very noticeable effect on the amount and the distribution of the air-gap flux. This phenomenon is usually termed armature reaction.

154. Reaction Ampere-turns. The brushes of most modern machines are placed permanently on the geometric neutral axis, where the winding elements in immediate contact with them are halfway between the main poles. For reasons which will appear later the conductors (of such machines) lying in the space between the poles have practically no armature reaction effects. The reaction ampere-turns of the remaining conductors may be evaluated as follows:

Let S_p = number of slot pitches under one pole.

z = number of conductors per slot.

I = amperes per conductor.

Then

$$S_p z I = \text{reaction ampere-turns per pole.} \tag{64}$$

The reaction ampere-turns at each pole tip will then be

$$\tfrac{1}{2} S_p z I. \tag{65}$$

If S_p must be determined from design data it may be necessary to determine the pole pitch by dividing the total number of slots by the number of poles, and then obtain S_p by multiplying the pole pitch by the ratio pole face arc/pole pitch. S_p is not necessarily an integer.

I, of course, is equal to I_a/m, where I_a is the armature current and m is the number of armature winding paths between brushes.

155. Air-gap Ampere-turns of Main Field. The flux pattern in the air gap of an unloaded shunt motor or generator will be governed almost entirely by the number of ampere-turns of the main field and by the air-gap and tooth reluctances. With a small number of field ampere-turns the mmf. drop in the iron portion of the magnetic circuit will be negligible and practically all the drop occurs in the gap. Most of the air-gap flux will enter the armature through the tooth tops. With increased field excitation the air gap and teeth will receive more flux and the reluctance of the teeth will be increased, so that the mmf. drop in the teeth will become too important to be neglected.

156. Reaction Ampere-turns Combined with Main Field. When load is placed on a shunt motor or generator the flux-producing effect of the armature current can no longer be neglected. The reaction ampere-turns of the armature conductors under each pole combine with the main field ampere-turns to create a resultant mmf.

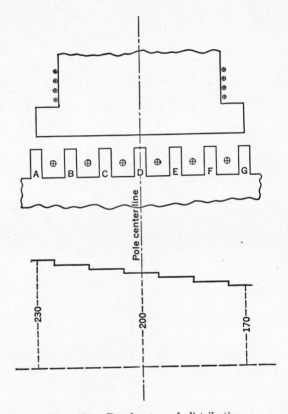

FIG. 105. Resultant mmf. distribution.

As an illustration of this effect the machine pictured in Figs. 103 and 104 is chosen. A main field excitation of 200 ampere-turns is assumed. Figure 105 shows the general shape of the resultant mmf. curve. Since the mmf. and flux values in this example are so small as to permit the mmf. drop in the iron to be neglected a linear relationship exists between the air-gap flux density and the resultant mmf. Thus the density in the region over tooth *A* will be 230/200 of the density at *D*, and over tooth G it will be 170/200 of that at D. Furthermore, it will be evident that the average density in the air gap is the same as would be produced by the 200 ampere-turns of the main field acting alone. The reaction ampere-turns in this case tend merely to distort the polar flux and to strengthen the density near one tip at the expense of the density near the other.

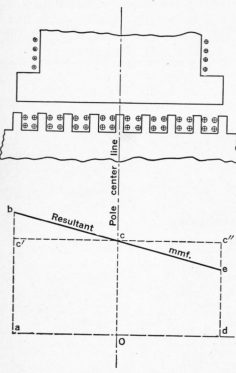

FIG. 106.   Resultant mmf. — many conductors in polar region.

Actually a loaded machine will be operating under conditions that are quite different from those just discussed. The main field mmf. will be strong, producing a high flux density in the air gap, appreciable mmf. drops in yoke, core and teeth, and a considerable amount of saturation in the teeth. The reaction ampere-turns will also be strong because there will be more slots under the pole and more conductors in each slot. There will be so many steps to the reaction mmf. curve if drawn as in Fig. 104 that it may be represented with sufficient accuracy by a straight line drawn between the outermost steps, as in Fig. 106.

The trend of the resultant mmf. is quite similar to that of the unsaturated case illustrated in Fig. 105. The distance of the horizontal dashed line $c'-c''$ from the reference base in Fig. 106 is proportional to that part of the main field ampere-turns which take care of the gap-and-tooth mmf. drop at no load. It is reasonable to assume that this component mmf. remains unchanged as load is added to the machine, so that the curve of resultant mmf. may be obtained by the addition of the reaction ampere-turns corresponding to the amount of load.

In Art. 88, Chapter 7, the procedure was outlined for obtaining the relationship between Φ_g, the useful air-gap flux per pole, and NI, the ampere-turns required in the field coil on each pole. The graphical representation of that relationship was called the saturation curve. A slight modification of that procedure is now recommended. Assuming that the design data and B–H curves for the machine of Fig. 106 are available, let various values of Φ_g be assumed. For each value let the values of B, H and NI be calculated for the air gap under one pole and for one set of teeth. The total gap-and-tooth mmf. drop can then be determined, and a curve of gap flux density, B, vs. gap-and-tooth mmf. drop, can be plotted. Figure 107 shows such a curve, plotted in the second quadrant so that it can be applied more conveniently to the example shown in Fig. 106.

Let the mmf. drop at the pole center line (Oc, Fig. 106) be laid off along the horizontal axis, Fig. 107. The ordinate cx will be the gap flux density at the center of the pole. At the left pole tip the mmf. is $ab = Oc + c'b$ (Fig. 106), and the density at this location may be found by stepping off the distance $c'b$ to the left of c, Fig. 107, and erecting an ordinate to the curve at y. At the right tip the mmf. is $de = Oc - c''e$ (Fig. 106), and the corresponding density is indicated at z, Fig. 107.

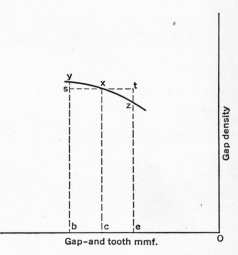

FIG. 107. Density — mmf. curve.

Since the mmf. is a linear function of the horizontal distance from the pole center line, xs (Fig. 107) may be considered proportional to the gap area under the left half of the pole, and the area bounded by xsy is a measure of the increase in flux through the left half due to armature reaction. Similarly the area xtz measures the decrease in flux through the right half due to the reaction ampere-turns. It is evident by inspection that the area $xtz > xsy$, leading to the conclusion that when saturation is appreciable armature reaction produces a reduction as well as a distortion of the gap flux. This is confirmed by experimental evidence obtained under actual operating conditions, as was noted in Art. 51, Chapter 4.

157. Effect of Brush Shift. Although modern machines are designed to be operated with their brushes at the geometric neutral where they will be in contact with armature conductors lying halfway between the poles it is desirable to give some consideration to the effect of operating with the brushes shifted to a different position.

For simplicity a somewhat idealized form of two-pole generator is pictured in Fig. 108. The horizontal dashed line marks the normal brush position, and the brushes are shown shifted approximately three conductor pitches ahead of their normal position. Particular attention is directed to the twelve conductors of Fig. 108 whose cross-sections have been enlarged for clarity. The following facts will be quite evident:

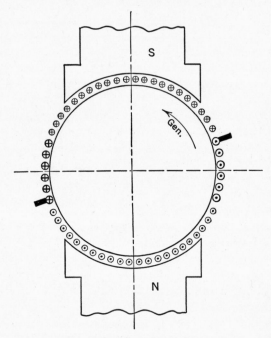

Fig. 108.   Effect of brush shift.

1. The width of this conductor band is twice the brush displacement.

2. The ampere-turns of the band are directed along the pole center line.

3. The current direction in the band is in this case such as to create a downward mmf. through the poles and armature in opposition to that of the main field.

4. The number of ampere-turns per pole produced by this band is equal to the product of the band width (in conductors) and the current per conductor.

If the brushes of the machine of Fig. 106 were shifted in this manner it would therefore be necessary to lower the resultant mmf. line by an amount equal to the band mmf. and the flux would evidently undergo an additional reduction. A backward shift of the brushes to a similar position on the other side of the neutral line would cause the mmf. of this band to assist the main field and the polar flux would be increased. In either case the permissible angle of shift is quite small, if commutation difficulties are to be avoided.

The above discussion presupposes the use of full-pitch winding elements. The demagnetizing (or magnetizing) action of the conductor bands between the poles is somewhat reduced if fractional-pitch winding elements are used, owing to the presence of opposition current in one or more of the conductors in each band. Since machines equipped for brush shift have been rendered somewhat obsolete by the general adoption of commutating poles (to be discussed in the next chapter) it seems permissible to omit certain theoretical aspects of brush shifting for the sake of brevity.

158. Pole-face Windings. The most satisfactory method for combating armature reaction has required the installation of special windings in the pole face known as pole-face or compensating windings. Although they are very effective, the accompanying increase in manufacturing cost has limited their use to machines designed for very severe operating conditions. An inspection of Fig. 109 will help in acquiring an understanding of their operation. Four conductors are shown in slots cut in the pole face. An eight-conductor band is shown in the armature, and if each conductor is carrying 10 amperes the total reaction ampere-turns will be 80, acting in a clockwise direction. If 20 am-

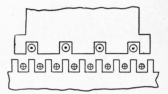

FIG. 109. Pole-face winding.

peres can be sent through each of the four pole-face conductors in the indicated direction their total mmf. will also be 80 acting in a counter-clockwise direction. Since the two conductor bands are in parallel planes very close together and are producing equal and opposite mmfs., approximate neutralization occurs and the tendency of the armature current to produce a distortion of the main field is largely eliminated.

To obtain proper neutralization at all loads any change in armature conductor current must be accomplished by a simultaneous and proportional change in pole-face conductor current. This can be accomplished most easily by designing the pole-face winding to be connected in series with the armature.

The current in each pole-face conductor will in general be mI, where m is the number of parallel paths in the armature winding and I is the current per armature conductor. The necessary number of pole-face conductors may therefore be written:

$$z_p = \frac{S_p zI}{mI} = \frac{S_p z}{m}, \tag{66}$$

in which z_p is the number of conductors in one pole face, and the other symbols are familiar (see equation 64).

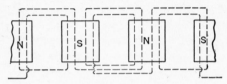

FIG. 110. Pole-face winding connections.

It will be evident that the number and spacing of the pole-face slots need not be the same as the armature. The only requirement is equality of the mmfs.

Figure 110 shows a convenient method of connecting pole-face conductors. A four-pole machine has been assumed, with four slots and four conductors in each pole, and enough connections have been indicated to establish the winding pattern.

159. Experimental Flux Distribution Curves. The accepted methods for obtaining experimental data on air-gap flux distribution in motors and generators have in general been based on the familiar $e = Blv \sin \theta$ relationship. One method requires the installation of a full-pitch " search coil " in the armature slots with the connections brought out as indicated in the sketch of Fig. 111. One end of the search coil is grounded to the shaft, S. The other end

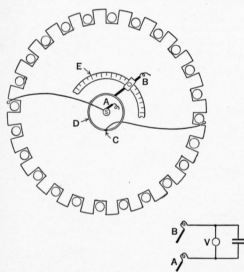

FIG. 111. Distribution determination with a search coil.

is connected to a thin brass strip, C, which is inserted flush with the outer circumference of a fiber or Bakelite ring, D, secured to the shaft.

A voltmeter with a suitable condenser across its terminals is connected to brushes A and B.   Brush A is in contact with the shaft; brush B is in contact with the fiber ring.   The voltage generated by the search coil as the armature rotates is applied to the voltmeter and condenser for an instant each revolution when C and B come in contact.   A charging current rushes into the condenser at this instant, and during the remainder of each revolution the condenser discharges through the voltmeter. At ordinary speeds contact reoccurs so frequently that the average condenser current is not much below its peak value and the voltmeter takes on a steady deflection which is proportional to the instantaneous value of the voltage applied.   This in turn is proportional to the flux density in the region occupied by the search coil at the instant of contact.

Brush B may be moved along its supporting sector E througn an angle of at least one pole pitch, and by plotting the corresponding voltages against the angular position of the search coil a curve whose ordinates are proportional to the flux density will be obtained.

Another method utilizes the voltages generated in the regular armature elements.   A fiber sector mounted over the commutator with its plane perpendicular to the axis of rotation serves as a support for a small carbon pencil or pilot brush.   By means of etched marks or by notches cut in the edge of the sector at spacings equal to the center-to-center dis-

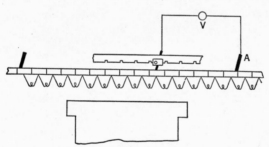

FIG. 112.   Distribution determination with a pilot brush.

tance between commutator bars it is possible to place the pilot brush a known number of commutator bars from a main brush while the armature is rotating.   A voltmeter is connected between the pilot brush and the main brush as indicated in the schematic diagram of Fig. 112.

Voltmeter readings obtained as the pilot brush is advanced to the left are totals for all the armature elements between the pilot brush and brush A.   If these voltages are plotted against commutator bar numbers and graphical differentiation methods are applied to the resulting curve a new curve showing the bar-to-bar voltages may be derived, and its ordinates when corrected for armature RI drop and brush contact resistance drop will be proportional to the flux densities throughout the region studied. In other words, the difference between the total voltage measured between the nth bar and brush A and the voltage between the $(n + 1)$th bar and A may be thought of as the bar-to-bar voltage of the nth armature element.

A third method based on a peculiar property of bismuth deserves mention because of its radically different approach. It has been observed that this metal exhibits a relationship between its resistance and the strength of magnetic field in which it is placed. A very satisfactory scheme utilizing this phenomenon has been devised recently by G. S. Smith (see reference list). A small probe is formed containing two non-inductively wound bismuth spirals which are made to serve as diagonally opposite arms of a special Wheatstone bridge. After the bridge is properly calibrated the probe may be moved from point to point throughout the air gap to be investigated, and the bridge meter will indicate the corresponding flux densities. Variations in probe temperature and in bridge temperature produce very noticeable changes in meter readings, so that calibration curves for various operating temperatures are necessary.

SUGGESTED BIBLIOGRAPHY

Principles of Direct Current Machines, A. S. LANGSDORF, 4th edition, McGraw-Hill Book Co.
Experimental Electrical Engineering, KARAPETOFF-DENNISON, 4th edition, John Wiley & Sons, 1933.
A new magnetic flux meter, G. S. SMITH, *Electrical Engineering*, Vol. 56, p. 441, 1937.

PROBLEMS

1. Assume that the conductors of Fig. 100*a* are 0.25 in. in diameter, separated 1 in., center to center. Let the current in each be 15 amperes, directed as in the figure. Calculate the magnetic field intensity at a point on the center line 1 in. to the left of A. Express it in gilberts per centimeter (oersteds) and in ampere-turns per inch, and indicate its direction.

2. Assume that the conductors of Fig. 101*a* are 0.25 in. in diameter, separated 1 in., center to center. Let the current in each be 15 amperes, directed as in the figure. Calculate the magnetic field intensity at a point on the center line 0.5 in. to the right of E. Express it in oersteds and in ampere-turns per inch, and indicate its direction.

3. A 4-pole shunt generator has a simple lap winding. Each pole covers 7 1/2 slots and each slot has 4 conductors. What will be the value of the reaction ampere-turns per pole when the armature current output is 60 amperes?

4. A certain 4-pole generator has a simple lap winding (2-layer) with 120 one-turn winding elements and a ratio of pole arc to pole pitch of 65%. What reaction ampere-turns per pole will be produced by an armature current of 100 amperes?

5. A 6-pole motor has a 49-slot armature with a simple wave winding. There are 49 two-turn winding elements. The pole arc is 70% of the pole pitch. What will be the reaction ampere-turns at each pole tip when the armature current is 50 amperes?

6. If the mechanical load of a shunt motor equipped with pole-face windings is suddenly removed and replaced by a driving torque which keeps the motor running in the same direction but raises the speed sufficiently to convert the machine into a generator, will the pole-face windings continue to function properly without the necessity of altering their connections? Why?

7. The machine of Problem 19, Chapter 7, is to be operated as a separately excited shunt generator. The field current is adjusted to give an effective flux per pole of 2,750,000 lines and is then held constant. Determine the approximate amount of flux reduction due to armature reaction if the armature current output becomes 100 amperes and the speed is held constant.

8. The machine of Problem 28, Chapter 7, is operating as a shunt motor from 230-volt mains. The shunt field current is adjusted to produce 5600 ampere-turns per pole and is then held constant. What will be the approximate speed at no load? Assuming all the excitation ampere-turns to be absorbed by gap-and-tooth NI drop, determine the approximate operating speed when the armature current is 660 amperes, taking into account the effects of armature reaction. ($R_a = 0.0075$ ohm; pole arc/pole pitch $= 0.65$.)

9. The characteristic magnetization curve applies to a 75-kw. shunt generator if one abscissa unit $= 4200$ ampere-turns per pole and one ordinate unit $= 2.7 \times 10^6$ maxwells per pole. It generates a no-load voltage of 220 when driven at 600 rpm. and supplied with a shunt field excitation of 5500 ampere-turns per pole. The speed and shunt field excitation remaining constant, what will be the approximate value of its terminal voltage when delivering a current of 320 amperes? (The armature winding is simple lap, with 57 slots and 6 conductors per slot. $R_a = 0.014$ ohm; $p = 4$; pole arc/pole pitch $= 0.72$.)

10. A 4-pole, 64-slot armature is wound with a full-pitch simple lap winding (64 two-turn winding elements). The machine is operating as a motor with an armature current of 28 amperes, and the brushes are shifted two slots backward (against the direction of rotation) from their neutral position. Will the conductor bands lying between the poles exert a magnetizing or a demagnetizing effect on the main polar flux? What will be the amount of this effect, in ampere-turns per pole?

CHAPTER 12

COMMUTATION

160. Commutation Time Interval. In Chapter 3 and again in Chapter 8 the function of the commutator was discussed briefly. It is the purpose of the present chapter to give more detailed consideration to this function and to the problems associated with it.

Two closely related phenomena occur at the area of contact between a brush and the moving commutator.

1. A unidirectional current is drawn from the armature winding and sent out to the external circuit.

2. The current in each winding element is reversed in direction as the commutator bars to which it is attached pass under the brush.

If these are accomplished without excessive heating of the brush and commutator, and without noticeable sparking at the brush, commutation is considered satisfactory.

The time required to complete the reversal of current in a winding element, usually termed the commutation time interval, depends upon the brush thickness and the peripheral velocity of the commutator if the winding is simple and the thickness of the mica between bars is neglected. This will be evident from an inspection of the accompanying schematic diagram (Fig. 113), which shows three stages of the commutation process. An element, C, of a simple lap winding is connected to the adjacent commutator bars X, Y. In part (a) this element is approaching the brush, and is carrying a steady current equal to half the brush current. Part (b) shows the same element an instant later with the brush overlapping X and Y; commutation is now in progress. In part (c) the element has just left the brush and is carrying half the brush current again, but in the reverse direction.

Evidently commutation of the current in this element cannot begin until the brush overlaps X and Y and must end when the overlap is terminated. If the mica between bars X and Y is considered as a boundary of zero thickness the commutation of element C begins when the boundary reaches the leading tip of the brush and ends as it passes the trailing tip. The commutation time interval may therefore be stated:

$$T \approx \frac{S_b}{V_c},$$ (67)

where T = commutation time interval, in seconds.
  S_b = brush thickness, in inches.
  V_c = peripheral velocity of the commutator, in inches per second.

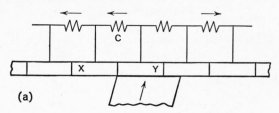

(a)

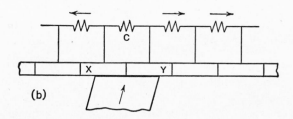

(b)

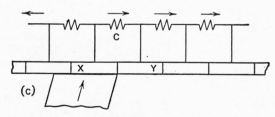

(c)

Fig. 113. Commutation time interval.

Let m, Fig. 114a, be the actual thickness of the mica in inches. The commutation time interval for element C becomes

$$T = \frac{S_b - m}{V_c}.$$ (68)

Since $p/2$ winding elements are connected in series between adjacent commutator bars in a simple wave winding it is apparent that the commutation time interval for this unit of $p/2$ elements is governed by the same conditions that have just been established for a single element of a simple lap winding; accordingly equation 68 applies to both classes of windings.

The problem of determining the commutation time interval for a duplex winding yields to the same method of attack. Since the bars serving as terminals for a typical winding element have another bar and two mica separators interposed, the amount of commutator travel occurring between the beginning and end of the commutation period for one element is reduced and the commutation time interval will suffer a

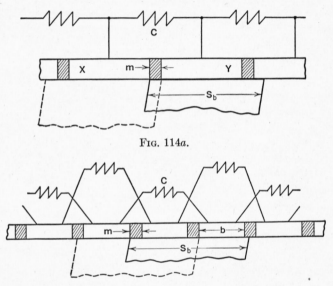

FIG. 114a.

FIG. 114b.   Commutation time interval — additional factors.

serious reduction unless thicker brushes are used. Figure 114b represents a portion of a duplex lap winding, with the direction of commutator travel assumed from left to right. The brush position indicated by the solid line marks the beginning of commutation for coil C, and the dashed outline indicates the brush position at the end of the commutation period. Evidently the commutation time interval will be the time required for any reference line on the commutator to move a distance equal to $S_b - (b + 2m)$ inches, or

$$T = \frac{S_b - (b + 2m)}{V_c},$$
(69)

where b = width of one commutator bar, in inches, and the other symbols have already been defined (see equation 68). Equation 69 applies to duplex wave windings as well.

161. Current Rate of Change. It has been shown that the value of the steady current carried by element C, Fig. 113, at the beginning of its commutation period is $1/2\,I_b$, where I_b is the brush current, and at the end of commutation the current is again $1/2\,I_b$ but in the opposite direction. Hence the total change in current in the commutation time interval, T, is simply I_b, and the average rate of change of current is I_b/T. In Fig. 115, Ot is the commutation time interval, T; OA represents the steady current value just as commutation begins; and tB is the current at the end of the commutation period. The straight line AB represents the behavior of the current under ideal conditions, and its slope $= AO/OM = \frac{1}{2}\,I_b/\frac{1}{2}\,T = I_b/T$, the average rate of change.

Even under ideal conditions it is an exacting task to bring about a current reversal in each winding element, as its terminal bars pass under a brush, without serious sparking. The average rate of change of current that must be attained is very high under normal operating conditions. As a typical example consider a machine operating at 1200 rpm. with a brush current of 50 amperes, a brush thickness of 0.5 in. and a commutator diameter of 6 in. The commutator velocity is 377 in.

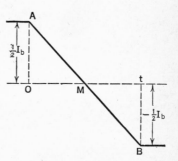

Fig. 115. Ideal commutation current-time curve.

per second, which makes the commutation time interval about 0.00133 second and the average rate of change becomes 37,700 amperes per second.

Since high velocities and heavy currents seem unavoidable the next most obvious means of reducing current rate of change would be the use of thicker brushes, thus increasing the commutation time interval. But if very thick brushes are used a new difficulty will be created. Commutation will begin before the winding element has moved far enough into the interpolar region to escape the voltage-producing action of the main polar flux and will end with the element too close to the next pair of poles. As a practical compromise the brush thickness is usually made sufficient to cover two to four commutator bars, a high current rate of change is accepted as a necessary evil and the ingenuity of the designer is challenged to produce good commutating characteristics in spite of this handicap.

162. Properties of Carbon Brushes. Since practically all direct-current machines utilize carbon in one form or another as a brush material it is desirable to discuss some of its properties briefly.

At first thought, carbon brushes would seem to possess many undesirable characteristics when compared to copper or aluminum. The resistivity of carbon is about 2000 times that of copper, and the contact resistance between brush and commutator seems extremely high. Both these properties would appear to cause unnecessarily large RI^2 losses. In addition its thermal conductivity is rather poor so that the heat produced by the flow of current is slow to reach the brush surface where it can be transferred to the surrounding medium. But more careful analysis reveals that high resistivity and high contact resistance are of considerable assistance in the process of reversing the current in the elements undergoing commutation.

Carbon has a negative temperature coefficient of resistance, which means that its resistivity decreases as its operating temperature increases. This is an advantage in reducing the brush RI^2 loss at heavy loads. On the other hand, in large machines having a number of brushes side by side on the same supporting arm any unbalance in the current distribution between the brushes in a brush set may increase the temperature of the overloaded brushes, and this in turn will reduce their resistance and cause still further current unbalance. There is good reason to believe that, if a non-uniform current distribution should exist within a single brush, differences in temperature will be created between adjacent layers which will alter their respective resistances and cause still further variation in current density.

For the purpose of still further discussion carbon brushes may be classified in four groups.

1. Carbon graphite: One of the older forms, not suitable for high speeds and heavy currents. Contains enough graphite in its composition to provide some lubrication, but has considerable cleaning and abrasive action on the commutator. May be used with current densities up to about 40 amperes per square inch. Its coefficient of friction ranges from 0.25 to 0.35.

2. Electrographite: Formed by additional heat treatment of carbon graphite. Has largely supplanted carbon graphite as a brush material. May be used with current densities up to about 70 amperes per square inch. The coefficient of friction and abrasive action are reduced.

3. Resin bonded: A laminated brush material in which the resistance across the laminations is 5 to 8 times the resistance parallel to the laminations. Brushes of this material are particularly suited to machines with relatively large commutating voltages, as with certain interpole machines.

4. Metal graphite: Formed by molding and baking a mixture composed of graphite and a good metallic conductor such as copper or tin. Their use is restricted to machines requiring very low brush contact drop and high current capacity, such as electroplating generators. The current density may be as high as 150 amperes per square inch, with permissible short-time values of two or three times this amount.

163. Effect of Brush Contact Resistance on Commutation. Consider the example illustrated in Fig. 116. The following conditions are assumed:

1. Brush current = 40 amperes.

2. Contact resistance between segment Y and brush = 0.1 ohm.

3. Contact resistance of each segment varies inversely as its area of contact with brush.

4. Resistance of the commutated element is negligible.

5. No flux lines are linked with the element during commutation.

Diagram (a) shows element C about to begin commutation. All the brush current is entering through segment Y, and C is carrying 20 amperes to the left, as shown in circuit diagram (b).

In diagram (c) commutation is one-fourth completed. The brush is now in contact with 3/4 Y and 1/4 X, and the contact resistances at these segments are such as to cause a division of the brush current between them in the ratio of 3 to 1. Circuit diagram (d) shows this condition, and it is evident that the current in C is forced down to 10 amperes.

Commutation is half completed in diagrams (e) and (f). The brush now overlaps Y and X equally and delivers equal currents to them. The current in C must drop to zero.

The next stage is shown in diagrams (g) and (h), with 1/4 Y and 3/4 X in contact with the brush. The current ratio now becomes 1 to 3, and a current of 10 amperes flows to the right through element C.

Diagrams (i) and (j) show C at the end of its commutation period with a current of 20 amperes flowing to the right.

It is evident that under these ideal conditions the current rate of change in element C will be uniform, as represented in Fig. 115.

A brush thickness of 2.75 times the commutator bar thickness is assumed in the next example, and the mica between bars is given a convenient value of 25% of the bar thickness. (In commercial designs the mica is seldom more than 15% of the bar thickness.) The previous assumptions as to brush current, contact resistance, element resistance and flux are carried over to the present problem. The brush position outlined by solid lines in the diagram at the top of Fig. 117 marks the

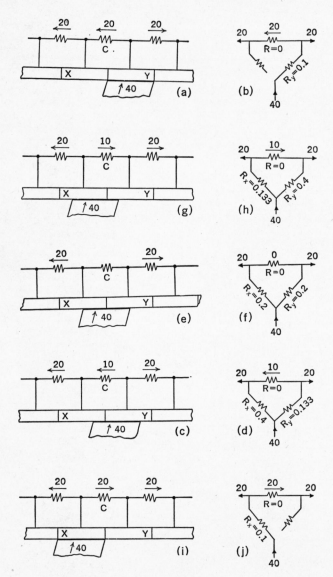

Fɪɢ. 116. Effect of contact resistance on commutation.

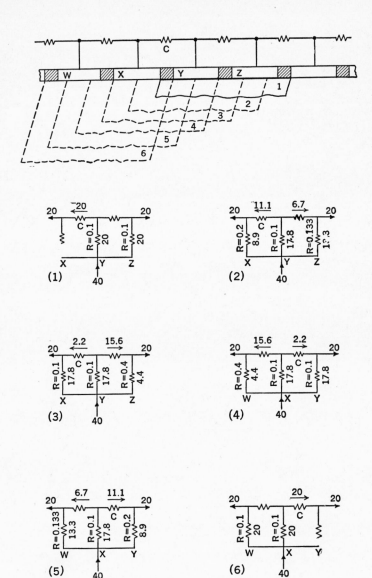

Fig. 117. Commutation with thick brush.

beginning of commutation for element C. Five succeeding positions are shown by the dashed lines, and in the circuit diagrams below this figure will be found the calculated current distribution in the commutator bars and winding elements.

In Fig. 118 the current in the element undergoing commutation has been plotted vertically and commutator position horizontally. The peculiar change in the slope of the curve is evidence that in machines

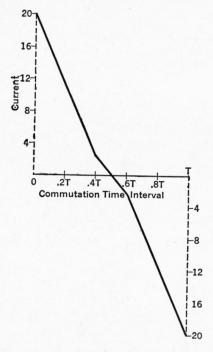

Fig. 118.   Current-time curve for conditions of Fig. 117.

with thick brushes and relatively thick mica the rate of change of contact area at the bar under the leading tip of the brush is not at all times properly balanced by the rate of change at the bar touching the trailing tip. In commercial designs, however, the mica is so thin that its influence on the form of the current curve is negligible.

The resistance of the element undergoing commutation has a slight tendency to speed up the current reversal during the first part of the commutation period, and to retard it during the remaining interval. For illustrative purposes the simple arrangement shown at the top of Fig. 119 has been chosen. A resistance of 0.04 ohm has been assumed for the commutated element, and the contact resistance of a whole bar

is taken to be 0.1 ohm as before.   The initial position of the brush is in
solid outline, and four succeeding positions are shown in dashed lines.
For each position the currents entering each bar and the current in the
element have been computed and marked on the circuit diagram.
Although these computations serve to determine just half of the curve of

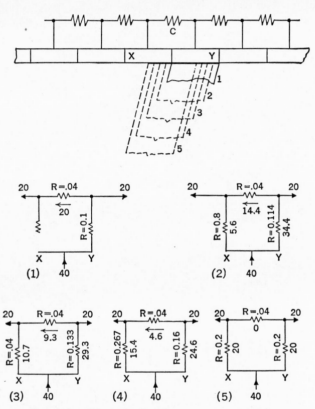

FIG. 119.   Effect of coil resistance on commutation.

element current vs. brush position the remaining half may be obtained
by symmetry and the complete curve is plotted in Fig. 120.   A very
slight deviation from the ideal linear relationship will be noted.

A similar analysis has been made of a more general case.   With the
bar thickness taken as unity the brush thickness is 2.6 and the mica is
0.1, as illustrated at the top of Fig. 121.   Below it is shown the current
curve for the commutated element.   Again it is evident that the
assumed conditions cause very little departure from a linear relationship
between current and brush position.

Early types of motors and generators used copper brushes, and com-

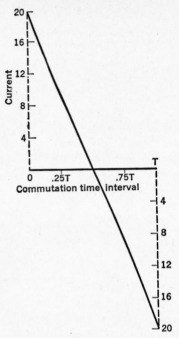

Fig. 120.   Current-time curve for conditions of Fig. 119.

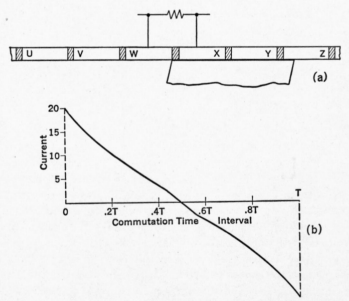

Fig. 121.   Commutation — thick brush and appreciable coil resistance.

mutation was usually accompanied by severe sparking at the brushes. When carbon came into use as a brush material sparking was almost completely eliminated.   The examples which have been given should make it clear that this improvement was largely due to the coercive action of the relatively high contact resistance on the reversal of current in the commutated elements.   High contact resistance not only carries this current down to zero and forces it to rise in the reverse direction, but in the absence of disturbing factors it accomplishes the reversal at a fairly uniform rate.

164. Effect of Reaction Ampere-turns on Commutation.   In the discussion of armature reaction, Chapter 11, the disturbing effects of the armature current on the magnitude and distribution of the flux under

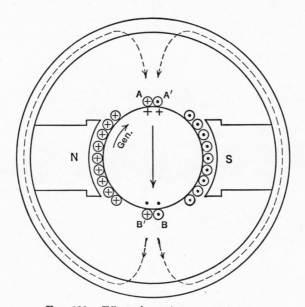

Fig. 122.   Effect of reaction ampere-turns.

the main poles were emphasized.   The effect of the flux produced by the armature current in the commutation zone will now be considered.

The armature of the machine shown in schematic form in Fig. 122 is assumed to be rotating clockwise as a generator.   With the polarity of the main poles as indicated, the generated voltages in the band of active conductors near the poles will be in the direction shown by the crosses and dots within the conductor sections.   This will also be the direction of the current which will flow in the conductors if a load circuit is connected to the generator terminals.   It is now evident that the ampere-turns of the active conductors will tend to send a flux downward through the armature in the general direction of the long, vertical arrow. Most of the resulting flux traverses the pole faces and combines there with the main field (see Arts. 153–156 and Figs. 103–105). A small but important part of the flux takes a longer path through the yoke, entering and leaving the armature in the commutation zones as indicated roughly by the dotted, arrowheaded lines. A winding element AB, about to begin commutation, will cut this flux as it moves to position $A'B'$ and thus generate a voltage which will either help or hinder the reversal of its current.

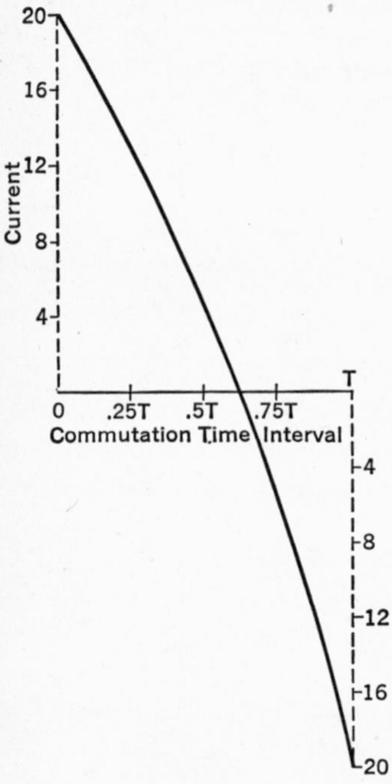

By application of the familiar rule for the prediction of voltage direction it may be shown that conductors A and B will have induced voltages in the direction indicated by the crosses below A and the dots above B. Notice that the direction is such as to hinder the entire process of current reversal in the commutated coil, for during the first part when the current is being reduced to zero the direction of the induced voltage is such as to tend to maintain the current at its original value, and during the latter part when the current is building up in the reversed direction the induced voltage opposes its increase. It should also be evident that the voltage induced in A and B by their motion through the so-called reaction flux will be practically constant because this flux is quite uniform throughout the commutation zone.

FIG. 123. Effect of retarding voltage.

The presence of a retarding voltage in the winding elements undergoing commutation may cause sufficient departure from the ideal current rate of change to produce marked variation in contact resistance drop and serious sparking at the brush tips. In such a case the rate with which the current drops to zero is so retarded that considerably less than half of the commutation time interval remains during which the current must build up in the reverse direction. Consequently the rate of change during this latter portion of the commutation time interval may reach very high values. As an example a constant retarding voltage of 2 volts has been added to the conditions governing the curve of Fig. 119, resulting in the noticeably different curve of Fig. 123.   The steepness of the right-hand portion of the curve is evidence of increased rate of change in that region.

165. Effect of Self- and Mutual Induction. A discussion of the phenomenon known as self-induction was given in Art. 90, Chapter 7. Restated very briefly, if the current in a coil changes in value the magnetic flux produced by the current changes with it and a voltage appears in the coil which tends to prevent the change in current.   This retarding voltage is often called the voltage of self-induction.

Quantitatively it may be expressed in terms of the self-inductance of the coil and the rate of change of current,

$$E = -L\frac{dI}{dt} \, ;$$

or in terms of the number of turns in the coil and the rate of change of flux,

$$E = -N\frac{d\Phi}{dt} \times 10^{-8} \, .$$

Since the current in an armature winding element changes rapidly during commutation it is apparent that a voltage of self-induction will be generated in each commutated element.   We may, furthermore, expect its value to be quite appreciable because of the extremely rapid rate of change of current and because the values of winding-element size and number of turns and the permeability of the armature iron are likely to be such as to make L quite large.

In the preceding article, evidence of the harmful effects of a retarding voltage in the commutated coils was presented.   Self-induction is likely to be a more effective source of retarding voltages than the reaction ampere-turns.   Consequently it becomes extremely important to find ways to neutralize retarding voltages in the commutation zone, or sparking and excessive brush heating may become serious handicaps to operation.   Two methods of accomplishing this neutralization will be considered later in this chapter.   (See Arts. 170 and 171.)

Mutual induction may be defined as the production of voltage in one conductor by means of flux set up by current in a neighboring conductor. Since commutation usually occurs in several winding elements simultaneously the changing current in one element may, under favorable conditions, create appreciable voltages in others by mutual induction.

The following example is typical of the conditions under which the effect of mutual induction on commutation is of the same order of magnitude as the effect of self-induction.

EXAMPLE: Consider a multipolar machine provided with a two-layer lap winding using full-pitch winding elements. The number of slots is a multiple of the number of poles. Figure 124a shows two of the winding elements just beginning commutation. Conductor B of the left-hand element and conductor A of the right-hand element lie in the same slot and are carrying equal currents in the same direction, as shown in Fig. 124b. Conductors A and B lie so close together that most of the flux set up by the current in B will cross from one tooth to the other *above* conductor A. The linkage thus established with A will generate a voltage in it as the current in B

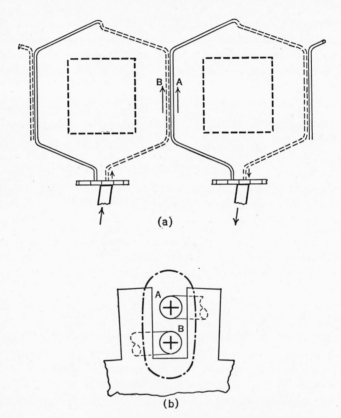

(a)

(b)

FIG. 124.   Effect of mutual induction.

changes. To discover whether the voltage generated in A by mutual induction is a helping or a retarding voltage note that under the assumed conditions the currents in A and B have the same direction at the beginning of commutation, fade to zero at the same rate and build up together in the reverse direction. During this whole period then that portion of the flux produced by the current in B which links with A circulates around A in the same direction as the flux produced by A's current. Now it has been shown that the voltage of self-induction, generated in A by its own changing current, is a true retarding voltage. Hence the voltage produced in A by mutual induction from B is a retarding voltage also.   The current in B may be thought of as augmenting the flux produced by the current in A, and thus contributing to its back voltage.

If the armature winding elements have a span somewhat less than a full pitch, or if the number of slots is not a multiple of the number of poles, conductors A and B will no longer be commutated at the same instant.   The increase in A's flux linkage due to current in B will then be very small and commutation will be benefited to some extent by such changes in the winding.

166. Reactance Voltage.   It is often desirable to have a term which denotes the combined effect of the various retarding voltages generated in a commutated element by self- and mutual induction and by armature reaction flux.   The name reactance voltage has been used quite generally for this purpose.

There are at least two accepted methods of calculating its value.

(a) Determine the effective inductance of the commutated element, including its combined self- and mutual inductance, and multiply by its average di/dt.

(b) Determine the total change in the amount of flux linking a winding element during its commutation time interval, thus getting the average rate of change of flux, and multiply by the number of turns in the element.

The task of making a rigorous determination of these quantities has proved insuperable and will probably remain so.   However, by means of various approximations it is possible to arrive at values that come reasonably close to the results of experimental determinations.   For various reasons a modification of the second method seems best suited to the scope of this book.

167. Calculation of Retarding Voltage Due to Reaction Flux.   A sufficiently accurate value of the retarding voltage in a commutated coil due to armature reaction flux can be determined easily.   As a convenient example, part of the magnetic circuit of a four-pole machine has been drawn approximately to scale in Fig. 125.   The computation can be divided into a number of steps.

1.   Calculate the effective ampere-turns of the band of armature conductors under pole N.   This may be written:

$$\text{Effective } NI \text{ per pole} = I \times Z_e,$$

where I = current per conductor.

Z_e = number of conductors actually effective in the production of the reaction flux cut by the conductors in slot R, just beginning commutation.

But $\qquad\qquad\qquad Z_e \approx z(S_{p'} - s),$

where z = number of conductors per slot.

$\quad S_{p'}$ = number of slot pitches in a pole pitch.

$\qquad s$ = amount of travel of the armature surface during a commutation period, expressed in slot pitches.

The quantity $(S_{p'} - s)$ may be considered as representing the effective number of slots in the pole pitch included between neutral lines 1 and 2, since $1/2\,s$ slots just above line 2 and $1/2\,s$ slots to the left of line 1 contain conductors that are just ending or just beginning commutation. Collecting these terms, we may write

$$\text{Effective } NI \text{ per pole} \approx Iz(S_{p'} - s). \qquad (70)$$

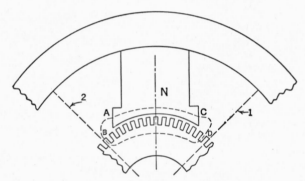

FIG. 125.   Reaction flux path.

2. Determine the mmf. drop from C to D. It is known that the summation of the mmf. drops around a reaction flux path such as shown by the dotted line $BACD$ must equal the effective armature NI per pole (equation 70). The mmf. drops in the iron parts of this path can be assumed to be negligible, so that

$$\text{mmf.}_{B\text{ to }A} + \text{mmf.}_{C\text{ to }D} \approx \text{Effective } NI \text{ per pole.}$$

Therefore

$$\text{mmf.}_{C\text{ to }D} \approx \tfrac{1}{2} Iz(S_{p'} - s). \qquad (71)$$

3. Determine the average flux density in the vicinity of point D. Some knowledge of field mapping methods will be helpful in this determination. An enlargement of the region C to D should be drawn to scale as shown in Fig. 126. With some patience and practice a flux tube can be drawn, using the line C–D as an axis, and subdivided into curvilinear squares. When correctly drawn, these squares, although differing in size, have two interesting and helpful properties in common:

(a) They all contain the same number of flux lines.

(b) They all have the same mmf. drop, so that, in a flux tube which subdivides into n squares, one-nth of the total mmf. drop along the tube will occur across each square.

Thus the tube sketched in Fig. 126 seems to divide naturally into 4 squares, so that 1/4 of the mmf. drop from C to D occurs across each square. Since the conditions near D are of particular interest the

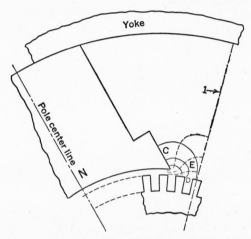

FIG. 126. Reaction field sketch.

distance from E to D is measured in inches. Let this distance be l_{ED}. The mmf. from E to D will be

$$\text{mmf.}_{ED} \approx \frac{Iz(S_{p'} - s)}{8} \text{ from equation 71.}$$

Then
$$H = \frac{NI}{l} \approx \frac{Iz(S_{p'} - s)}{8l_{ED}}, \tag{72}$$

and B, the average density in this region, can be calculated from the equation

$$B = \frac{H}{0.313}. \tag{37}$$

4. The voltage generated in one of the conductors in a slot due to the cutting of the reaction field can now be determined by means of the familiar equation $e = KBlv$. The approximate value of B was determined in the previous step. By substituting the active conductor length for l and the tangential velocity of the armature for v,

the voltage per conductor and the total voltage in the winding element can be computed.

168. Calculation of Voltage of Self-induction. In attacking the problem of evaluating that part of the reactance voltage which is due to the self-inductance of the commutated coil it is necessary to obtain a clear understanding of the location of the various fluxes set up by the current of the commutated coil and their relative importance under practical conditions. Figure 127 shows a single conductor in one of the commutating zones of a four-pole machine. The flux set up by current in this conductor divides into two paths designated by U and W in the figure. Path U may be called a localized eddy through the adjacent teeth and the air just above the conductor. Path W is observed to be

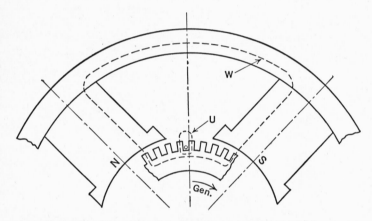

Fig. 127.   Flux paths linked with commutated conductor.

identical with one of the main flux paths through the poles, yoke and armature core.

In analyzing the conditions in path W, Fig. 127, it must be remembered that the armature core beneath the conductor is partly saturated by the useful flux created by the main field coils and that a saturation curve for this region will be required. For this problem the relationship between flux in the armature core and total NI drop around circuit W is desired, requiring a slight modification of the method explained in Art. 88, Chapter 7. Since the total NI drop around W is equal to the field coil NI per pair of poles, which will be known in this case, a definite point, p, on the curve can be located corresponding to the known operating conditions. It is now possible to select a small part of the saturation curve containing the operating point and replot it to an enlarged scale as shown in Fig. 128.

For the polarities and rotation shown in Fig. 127, the ampere-turns of the conductor about to begin commutation are opposing the main field, and the net NI tending to produce flux around circuit W = (main field NI) − (conductor NI). As the conductor current drops to zero the net NI increases from p to c, Fig. 128, where pc = conductor NI. The growth of conductor current in the new direction causes a still further increase in NI, to point c', and the armature core flux now linking with the conductor will have increased to d, a change of $c'd$ lines in the amount of flux linking the conductor. This change in linkage divided by the commutation time interval gives the value of that part of the voltage of self-induction associated with magnetic circuit W.

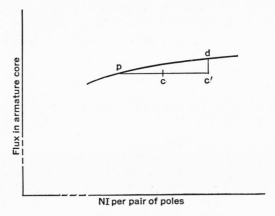

FIG. 128.   Flux — NI relations.

Most modern generators and motors differ from the machine used as the basis for this analysis in several important respects. The armatures are almost certain to have two-layer windings, with brushes covering several commutator bars so that each commutating zone contains several conductors in different stages of commutation. Consequently for every conductor just commencing commutation there will be a companion conductor just ending commutation. The NI of one conductor acting around circuit W will in general be completely neutralized by an equal and opposing NI produced by the adjacent conductor. The effect of flux in the path W on the voltage of self-induction can therefore be neglected without serious error.

The effect of the localized slot flux represented by U, Fig. 127, remains to be considered. A study should first be made of the flux set up by current in a single conductor lying in a narrow, deep slot.

If a careful field map is made for the slot shown in Fig. 129 it will be evident that:

1. The flux crossing the air space in the slot below the conductor is practically zero.

2. The flux in the slot above the conductor is nearly rectilinear and quite uniformly distributed up to about 1/4 q from the top.　Here the flux lines begin to bulge out of the slot opening and the density in this region becomes less.

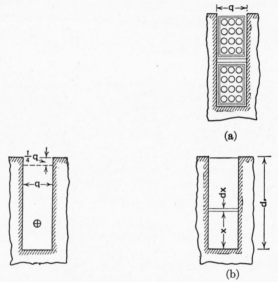

(a)

(b)

Fig. 129.　Conductor in deep slot.　　Fig. 130.　Determination of slot flux.

If the slot is in the commutation zone, a region of low flux density, the iron is unsaturated and has high permeability, and practically all the conductor mmf. is concentrated in the air space between the slot walls. The average density in the slot above the conductor may therefore be calculated from equation 37,

$$B = \frac{H}{0.313}.$$

In this case

$$H = \frac{\text{conductor } NI}{q} = \frac{I}{q}$$

for a single conductor carrying I amperes.　Therefore

$$B = \frac{1}{0.313} \times \frac{I}{q} = \frac{3.2I}{q}. \tag{73}$$

Consider the slot shown in Fig. 130a containing two bundles of conductors. If these are parts of two full-pitch winding elements undergoing commutation simultaneously, the current in the two bundles will decay and reverse in unison.

Analysis of the flux-producing action of these bundles may be simplified considerably by replacing them with a single slab of conducting material carrying the same total current uniformly distributed throughout its cross-section, as shown in Fig. 130b. The flux passing through an element of the slot having a thickness dx and a length of 1 in. (measured along the armature axis) will be

$$d\phi = B_x \, dx \text{ lines,}$$

where B_x is the average flux density for an element located at a distance x above the bottom of the slot. The total flux per axial inch ϕ, crossing from one slot wall to the other, will be

$$\phi = \int_{x=0}^{x=d} B_x \, dx. \tag{74}$$

The flux passing between slot walls at the bottom of the slot will be zero. Maximum flux density will occur at the top of the slot and may be evaluated by substituting the total current carried by the slab for I in equation 73. According to the assumption governing the method of flux production the density halfway down the slot will be half of the maximum value because the current in the lower half of the slab will be the only current contributing to it. This leads to a linear relationship for the density, and the quantity $B_m x/d$ may be substituted for B_x in equation 74, where B_m is the maximum density and d is the slot depth.

Hence

$$\phi = \int_{x=0}^{x=d} \frac{B_m x \, dx}{d} = \frac{B_m d}{2},$$

and from equation 73, the expression becomes

$$\phi = \frac{3.2 I d}{2q} = 1.6 \frac{I d}{q}, \tag{75}$$

where I is the total current in the slot.

Since an element of flux crossing the slot can induce voltage only in that part of the conductor which lies below it, not all the total flux crossing the slot is effective. A flux element halfway up the slot links with only half the conductor; a similar element one-fourth from the bottom links with one-fourth of the conductor. A new concept, effective flux density, is needed. Let the effective density one-fourth of the distance up the slot be made one-fourth of the actual density; halfway up it will be half of the active density, and so on, giving a parabolic distribution to the density in place of a linear distribution. The effective slot flux computed on this basis will become two-thirds of the amount indicated in equation 75.

$$\phi_e = 1.07 \frac{Id}{q}. \tag{76}$$

In order to include the additional flux curving over the slot from one tooth top to the next a compromise between the values stated in equations 75 and 76 is recommended.

$$\phi_e \approx 1.3 \frac{Id}{q}. \tag{77}$$

The total slot flux linking with a complete winding element just beginning commutation will be $2\phi_e L_a$, where L_a is the axial length of the armature. As commutation proceeds, the slot flux drops to zero and rises to $-2\phi_e L_a$ at the end of commutation. The average voltage induced in the winding element by this changing flux may be written

$$e_{\text{av.}} = \frac{4\phi_e L_a}{10^8 T}, \tag{78}$$

where T is the commutation time interval. Notice that the slot flux used in equation 78 represents the combined effects of self- and mutual induction, since the flux-producing action of all the conductors in a slot is included in the derivation.

169. Effect of End-connection Flux. Consider the winding element $ABDE$ short-circuited by the brush in Fig. 131. If the diameter of the armature is large enough so that the end connections shown by the heavy dashes within the parallelogram $MBDC$ can be assumed parallel to and in the same plane with BC, the total flux produced by these conductors in the zone traversed by BC during commutation can be approximated easily. The corresponding end connections parallel to CD have been omitted from the diagram for the sake of clarity.

The currents in the region MBC are flowing to the right, thus producing a downward flux at BC. Similarly the flux produced at BC by the currents in the region BCD will be downward, and a retarding voltage will be generated in BC by its motion across this flux.

For purposes of illustrating the method of computation definite constants have been assumed and an enlarged sketch of the region *BCD* is shown in Fig. 132.

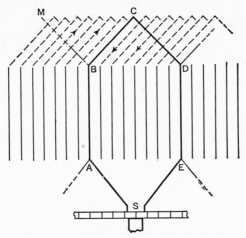

FIG. 131.   Effect of end-connection flux.

Armature winding: Two layers; full pitch; two turns per winding element.

Conductor current: 20 amperes.

Slot pitch: 2.5 cm.   Pole pitch: 9 slots, or 22.5 cm.

Armature travel during commutation: 5.0 cm.

End-connection angle, *CBD*: 45°.

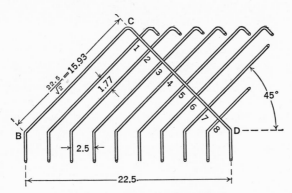

FIG. 132.   End-connection flux.

Since the end connections are not imbedded in slots we may assume that the armature iron will not affect their magnetic field pattern greatly, and equation 29 may be used to determine the value of H due to end-connection current.

$$H \text{ in oersteds} = \frac{I}{5r}. \tag{29}$$

In using this relationship to determine the value of H at BC due to current in element 1, $I = 40$ amperes (since the element has two turns), and

$$r = \frac{2.5}{\sqrt{2}} = 1.77 \text{ cm.}$$

Therefore

$$H_1 \text{ at } BC = \frac{40}{5 \times 1.77} = 4.52 \text{ oersteds.}$$

The average flux density B_1 in the region traversed by BC during commutation, due to the effects of element 1 only, will be

$$B_1 = H_1 = 4.52 \text{ gausses,}$$

and the flux,

$$\phi_1 = B_1 \times \text{(effective area of zone traversed by } BC\text{)}.$$

The width of the zone will be $5/\sqrt{2} = 3.54$ cm.

The effective length = length of element $1 = 22.5/\sqrt{2} - 1.77 = 14.13$ cm.

The effective area $= 14.13 \times 3.54 = 50.1$ sq. cm.

$$\phi_1 = 4.52 \times 50.1 = 226 \text{ lines.}$$

In like manner the flux contributed by the remaining seven conductors have been calculated and tabulated as follows:

Element	r	$\dfrac{I}{5r}$	Width	Length	Area	Flux
1	1.77	4.52	3.54	14.16	50.1	226
2	3.54	2.26	3.54	12.39	43.9	99
3	5.31	1.51	3.54	10.62	37.6	57
4	7.08	1.13	3.54	8.85	31.3	35
5	8.85	0.90	3.54	7.08	25.1	23
6	10.62	0.75	3.54	5.31	18.8	14
7	12.39	0.64	3.54	3.54	12.5	8
8	14.16	0.56	3.54	1.77	6.2	3
					Total flux	465

The conductors in the region MCB produce an equal effect so that the total flux linking with BC is 930 lines. Quite similar effects may be expected at CD, AS and SE, so that the total end-connection flux for the winding element will be about 3700 lines. If this amount be divided by the commutation time interval the average voltage produced by the end-connection flux will be obtained.

The effect of the self-inductance of the end connections can also be estimated. To evaluate the most important part of the flux set up by the changing current in BC, which pierces the narrow zone traversed by BC during commutation, merely requires the calculation of the average value of H for this zone. Using equation 29 again, with $r = 1.77$, H becomes 4.52 oersteds at the beginning of commutation, and the corresponding flux will be:

$$\phi_{\text{self-induction}} = 4.52 \times 15.93 \times 3.54 = 255 \text{ lines.}$$

At the end of commutation, $\phi = -255$ lines, so that the average voltage of self-induction generated in BC will be $510/10^8 T$, where T is the commutation time interval. The average voltage of self-induction for the complete winding element is $4 \times 510/10^8 T$.

170. Improvement of Commutation by Brush Shift. The preceding articles have discussed various effects accompanying commutation when the brushes are so placed as to cause commutation to occur in the geometric neutral zone halfway between the main poles. This region has been shown to contain a resultant flux which may without serious error be evaluated by taking the algebraic sum of the fluxes produced by armature reaction and by self- and mutual induction, since the region is unsaturated. It was also demonstrated that the fluxes so produced were such as to create retarding voltages in the short-circuited element, thus interfering with the reversal of its current and tending to produce sparking.

Since it is impracticable if not impossible to eliminate the causes of retarding voltage, various schemes for neutralizing it have been developed. If a voltage equal and opposite to the retarding voltage can be generated in the short-circuited element the conditions tending to produce sparking will in most cases be eliminated.

One method of accomplishing this result requires a shift in the brush position so that the commutation zone is brought under the influence of the fringing flux of the main poles. The proper direction of shift can be determined by reference to Fig. 122. Note that this machine is rotating clockwise as a generator and that such retarding voltages as are generated in the upper commutation zone are directed away from the observer (indicated by the crosses below the conductors). It will be necessary to shift the upper brush to the right or *with* the direction of rotation, so that the fringing flux of the S pole can induce a corrective voltage in the conductors under the brush. For the same reason a shift of the lower brush an equal distance to the left is required.

The magnitude of the retarding voltages may for all practical purposes be considered proportional to the armature current and hence proportional to the load. The amount of corrective voltage required to produce satisfactory commutation will accordingly vary with the load. At no load the best position for the brushes is at the geometric neutral; as load is applied the brush rigging must be shifted to a new position and the angle of shift may be considered as approximately proportional to the amount of load. Obviously this method of improving commutation conditions will be troublesome if the load on the machine changes frequently, for frequent changes in brush position will then be necessary.

It has been shown that the proper direction of brush shift for a generator is *forward* or *with* the direction of rotation. The reader is urged to demonstrate to his own satisfaction, by means of a sketch similar to Fig. 122, that the proper direction of brush shift to neutralize the retarding voltage of a motor is *backward* with increasing load.

171. Commutating Poles. A method for inducing the proper corrective voltage in the commutated elements which permits the brushes to be mounted permanently at the geometric neutral is particularly desirable for motors handling variable-torque loads. Narrow auxiliary poles, called commutating or interpoles, are employed for this purpose. They are mounted in the neutral zone between the main poles and are excited by coils of heavy wire connected in series with the armature. When load is added and more corrective voltage is needed in the short-circuited elements the commutating pole flux is increased automatically owing to the increased armature current flowing through the commutating pole coils.

If the space above the upper brush in Fig. 122 is assumed to contain a commutating pole, the required polarity for satisfactory commutation can be determined easily. In discussing brush shift it was shown that a forward shift was required in order to bring conductors $A-A'$ under the fringing flux of the south pole. Since the upper commutating pole is substituting for the fringing flux of a south pole it too must have south polarity. The requirements may be stated in general terms as follows: Commutating poles of generators must have the same polarity as the main pole just *ahead*; for motors the polarity of the commutating poles must agree with the main poles just behind them.

172. Effects of Commutating Poles. The addition of commutating poles to the magnetic circuit is accompanied by several complications which need special consideration by the designer. Figure 133a shows the magnetic circuit of a four-pole machine equipped with commutating poles. Part of this machine has been redrawn to a larger scale in Fig. 133b.

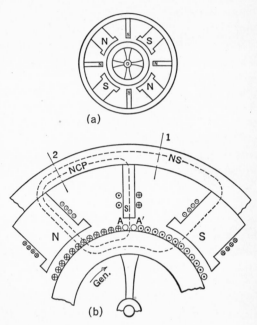

Probably the most important effect of the introduction of commutating poles is the increase produced in that part of the armature reaction flux which traverses the commutating zone A–A'. The reluctance of this region is reduced by the presence of the commutating pole core, necessitating careful analysis of the mmf. drops to insure that sufficient ampere-turns will be placed on the commutating pole to create the

Fig. 133.   Magnetic circuit of commutating pole machine.

proper corrective voltage in the commutated conductors.

Another noticeable effect is an increase in the self-inductance of the commutated conductors due to the proximity of the face of the commutating poles. A slight increase in the retarding effect of the voltage of self-induction will result.

Changes in the flux density and mmf. distribution in the yoke occur as the third effect of the addition of commutating poles. In addition to the normal path for the main pole flux, indicated by the dash line NS in Fig. 133b, there is the path NCP including the commutating pole. The flux relationships in the two parts of the yoke will be as follows:

$$\phi_2 = \phi_1 + \phi_{cp},$$

where ϕ_{cp} is the flux of the commutating pole. The cross-sectional area of the yoke and the commutating pole core are usually small enough so that changes in commutating pole flux will cause noticeable differences in their mmf. drop and thus bring about undesired changes in the magnitude and distribution of the commutating pole flux. Consequently if the ampere-turns on the commutating pole are sufficient to produce satisfactory commutation conditions at half load there will usually not be enough corrective voltage at full load.

Finally there is a slight increase in main-pole leakage flux due to the presence of the commutating pole core in the space between the main poles. There is good reason to believe that this will affect commutation only so far as the leakage flux contributes to the saturation of the commutating pole. Since most of the leakage flux travels across the commutating pole rather than parallel to its radial axis it will contribute little to saturation in the radial direction.

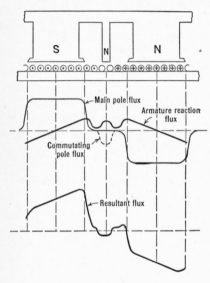

If ample ampere-turns are provided on the commutating pole and if proper sectional areas are provided to keep saturation down, the use of commutating poles will improve commutation greatly and broaden the range of loads which the machine can handle safely. Nearly all machines rated at 5 hp. or above are now built with commutating poles.

FIG. 134. Typical flux distribution curves.

In Fig. 134 some typical flux distribution curves are sketched which help to show the corrective action of the commutating pole in the commutation zone. The distortion of the resultant flux under the main poles due to armature reaction can be largely eliminated by the use of pole-face windings as described in Art. 158, Chapter 11.

173. Number and Dimensions of Commutating Poles. By the methods briefly explained in the preceding articles the designer can determine the approximate amount of corrective flux needed in each commutating zone to induce a corrective voltage equal to or slightly greater than the sum of all the retarding voltages in the commutated element. A low value of density, say 25,000 lines per square inch for full load, being chosen to keep saturation within bounds, the necessary area of the commutating pole can be determined. Since the width of the pole must be sufficient to cover the commutating zone, the axial length of the pole required to give the desired sectional area can be determined. If the length thus obtained is more than half the axial length of the armature core the full number of commutating poles will be installed. If, however, the required axial length is less than half the axial length of the armature, half the full number of commutating poles may be omitted. By doubling the axial length of the remaining poles their sectional area will be doubled and the flux output can be practically doubled by the use of the same number of ampere-turns. It is clear that the required corrective voltage in the short-circuited element can be induced just as effectively by having one side of the element cut the $2\phi_{cp}$ lines of a large commutating pole as by having the two sides of the element cut ϕ_{cp} lines each.

The evident advantages of using half the full number of commutating poles are the slight saving in the amount of wire needed on the commutating poles and the reduction in the number of parts to be stocked. The disadvantages are the increased flux distortion in the air gap, the greater saturation effects in the yoke and (in two-pole machines) the unbalanced magnetic pull between the poles and the armature.

Since it is extremely difficult to predict the proper number of commutating pole ampere-turns with great accuracy it is quite common practice to place an extra turn or two on each pole and then provide a shunt or diverter by which the commutating pole current may be adjusted to give the best operating results. Another method of adjusting the strength of a commutating pole requires the placement of shims between the pole and the yoke. By changing the number or thickness of shims the air gap may be altered.

174. Sparking at Brushes. It was pointed out at the beginning of this chapter that commutation may be considered satisfactory if the current passing between brush and commutator is handled without excessive heating and without noticeable sparking. Sparking is a cumulative evil. If it occurs for even a short period it pits and roughens the commutator surface, reduces the effective contact area and increases the brush temperature, all of which tend to increase the sparking.

Causes of sparking may be classified under two heads: mechanical and electromagnetic. The principal causes of a mechanical nature are:

(a) Rough commutator surface.
(b) High mica separators.
(c) One or more high commutator bars.
(d) Improper brush pressure.
(e) Improper brush angle.

Machines with one or more of these defects are likely to have chattering brushes with more or less severe sparking.

Some of the electromagnetic causes of sparking are easily understood. Others are so complex in nature as to require further advances in our knowledge of commutation phenomena to clarify them completely. Consider the arrangement shown in Fig. 135. The commutation of C is almost completed, and the trailing brush tip A is about to leave segment Y. The current in C is almost equal to $1/2\ I_b$, and the current from Y to the brush is diminishing rapidly. In mathematical terms, I_y is a function of two independent variables

$$I_y = f(V_y, R_y), \qquad (79)$$

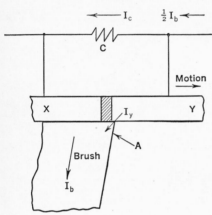

FIG. 135.   Sparking at trailing tip.

where V_y is the difference in potential between bar Y and the brush tip and R_y is the ohmic resistance of the contact area between these two surfaces. As the commutation time interval progresses it is evident that V_y may be expected to vary with time owing to resistance drop in C and to the induced voltages of one kind or another generated in C during commutation. R_y will also vary with time owing to changes in contact area and current density.   The complete expression for the variation of I_y during commutation can be stated as follows:

$$\frac{dI_y}{dt} = \frac{\delta I_y}{\delta V_y}\frac{dV_y}{dt} + \frac{\delta I_y}{\delta R_y}\frac{dR_y}{dt}. \qquad (80)$$

Consider the instant when the contact area between Y and the brush is a mere feather edge.   The current I_y at this instant $= V_y/R_y$, where V_y and R_y are the instantaneous values of contact voltage and contact resistance respectively.   What happens to the current during the next instant depends on the magnitude and algebraic sign of dV_y/dt as compared to dR_y/dt.   If, for example, both are positive and are increasing, with $dV_y/dt > dR_y/dt$, it is evident that the current will increase even though actual separation of the brush from Y occurs during this instant.

If V_y becomes zero or becomes constant at a small value as the commutation period ends, sparking at the trailing tip cannot occur.   This is the situation under the ideal conditions pertaining to Fig. 116.   With the resistance of element C zero and with its flux linkage also zero during commutation the potential of Y and the value of V_y are therefore constant. The steady increase in R_y as the contact area of Y is reduced will bring the value of I_y to zero at the proper instant, and no sparking can occur.

The effects of winding element resistance will now be considered. The machine shown in schematic form in Fig. 136a is operating as a motor from constant-voltage supply mains. Assuming that the brush voltage drop is constant, the potential of that portion of the commutator which is in contact with the minus brush will remain constant if the armature has a large number of elements equally distributed between the two paths and if all the elements in the neutral zone (including the commutated elements) are free from induced voltages. Referring to Fig. 136b, let the potentials of segment Y and the brush be P_y and P_b respectively at the beginning of commutation. At the end of commutation with the brush in position 2 the potential of Y becomes $P_y + rI_c = P_y + 1/2\,rI_b$. The difference in potential between Y and the brush is thus increased during the commutation time interval. Probably most of the change occurs in the latter half of the interval so that dV_y/dt may have a large positive value. Hence the resistance of the winding element undergoing

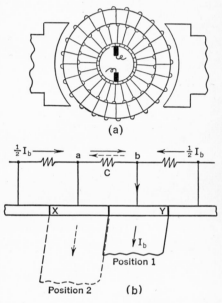

(a)

(b)

Fig. 136. Effect of coil resistance on sparking.

commutation tends to create changes in the difference of potential between the commutator and the trailing brush tip which are favorable for sparking, and it is necessary to keep the winding-element resistance small in comparison with brush-contact resistance in order to eliminate its contribution to sparking.

The experiments of Ludwig and Baker, and of V. P. Hessler (see bibliography) indicate that brush-contact resistance is itself a function of at least three independent variables: temperature, contact area and current density. Under the ideal assumptions of negligible resistance and no induced voltage in the commutated element, the current I_y, Fig. 135, may be expected to decrease in unison with the decrease in contact area and there will be no change in current density even up to the point of separation. If, however, resistance and induced voltage are not neglected the current may be expected to lag somewhat in its reversal process so that an increase in current density at the Y segment occurs near the end of commutation. Hessler's experiments confirmed the general belief that if other factors are held constant contact resistance is reduced by an increase in current density. An increase in current density at the Y segment near the end of commutation tends therefore to retard the increase in contact resistance accompanying the shrinkage in contact area. Its effects on sparking, however, will scarcely be noticed because R_y is large at this stage of commutation and is increasing at a very rapid rate. A different aspect of the effect of current density on contact resistance will be mentioned later in discussing the use of thicker brushes.

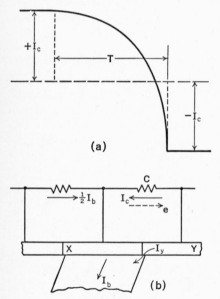

(a)

(b)

FIG. 137. Effect of reactance voltage on sparking.

Under normal operating conditions a commutated coil contains a so-called reactance voltage due to the combined effects of armature reaction, self- and mutual induction. If reactance voltage is not properly neutralized by a corrective voltage its presence in the short-circuited coil will cause sparking at the trailing tip, the severity of which increases with the load. Figure 137a shows a typical current-time curve for a winding element containing a strong reactance voltage. In Fig. 137b, commutation of element C is just ending. The dashed line e indicates the direction of the reactive voltage. If P_y is the potential of segment Y at the beginning of commutation its potential at this instant will be $P_y + e + rI_c$. Furthermore the current-time curve shows I_c to be increasing at a very rapid rate at this instant. Therefore dV_y/dt will have a very large positive value, and sparking may be expected.

To eliminate sparking at the trailing tip it is necessary to introduce a corrective voltage slightly greater than e, by means of brush shift or by the use of commutating poles. Perfect neutralization can scarcely be expected, but the current-time curve of the short-circuited element can be made approximately linear, and the value of dV_y/dt at the end of commutation will be so small as to remove the danger of sparking.

If too much corrective voltage is introduced at the beginning of commutation,
conditions will become favorable for sparking at the leading tip. Consider the situation illustrated in Fig. 138. Element C,
about to commence commutation, has just
entered a strong commutating field; the
potential of segment W is above normal
and is growing in value. The difference in
potential between W and the brush may be-

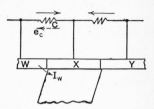

FIG. 138. Sparking at leading brush tip.

come large enough to break down the air path and establish a miniature arc before the segment actually comes in contact with the brush.

Modern machines have thick brushes covering several segments so that at any instant several winding elements are in different stages of commutation under the same brush. This condition introduces a com-plication not heretofore considered. Assuming that the current is non-linear owing to the presence of reactive voltage, the resulting current density at the brush surface will vary greatly along the brush arc. As an example let the brush arc cover 3 1/4 segments as shown in Fig. 139,

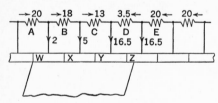

FIG. 139. Effect of thick brush on sparking.

and let the curve of Fig. 137a represent the current-time curve for complete commutation of one element. At the instant shown, element A is just commencing commutation and carries the full path current of 20 amperes. Element B has used 30.7% of its commutation time interval, and its current, scaled from Fig. 137a, is 18 amperes. Element C has used 61.4% of its time interval and has a current of 13 amperes. Element D has used 92.1% and carries a reverse current of 3.5 amperes. Element E has completed commutation and carries 20 amperes. From these values the current reaching each segment has been determined and marked. Note that W transmits 2 amperes to the brush while the equal area in contact with segment X receives 5 amperes. Calling the current density at W unity, the average density under X is 2.5; under Y, 8.25; and under Z, 33. The high temperature associated with such high density as is found at the trailing tip under the assumed conditions will certainly be an important factor contributing to sparking. In general, variations in current density and in operating temperature may be expected in the brush contact area, but unless these differences are quite large it is unlikely that they will cause commutation difficulty. Careful attention to the design of the commutating poles so that the proper corrective voltage will be introduced in the commutated coils for the proper length of time will prevent serious sparking and large variations in contact density under the brush.

175. Ring-fire and Flashovers. Under normal conditions it is inevitable that small particles of iron, copper or graphite will become wedged between the commutator bars. The bar-to-bar current carried by these particles is often sufficient to heat them to incandescence. The rapid motion of these glowing particles due to the rotation of the armature creates the semblance of an unbroken streak of light extending from brush to brush; hence the name ring-fire is applied to this phenomenon. Ring-fire, although harmless in the early stages, paves the way for more serious trouble. It is advisable to consider ring-fire as an indication that the commutator needs careful inspection and cleaning.

If for any reason the difference in potential between adjacent commutator bars should undergo a sharp increase the resistance of the air path may be broken down and the current will arc from bar to bar. An arc of this kind which spreads until it extends from brush to brush is described as a flashover. A flashover constitutes practically a short-circuit of the entire armature winding and naturally results in serious damage to the commutator, brushes and brush rigging.

The increase in bar-to-bar voltage required to initiate a flashover usually arises from a sudden large change in load. Consider a generator delivering a steady current to a receiving circuit, and assume that a short circuit suddenly occurs at the load terminals caused by the development of some fault in the receiving circuit. The armature current commences to rise at a very rapid rate, tending to reach a value many times normal. The armature reaction flux grows at the same rate, and large voltages will appear in the active conductors which link with this flux. The difference in potential between adjacent commutator bars, usually not more than 15 volts, may grow as a transient to several hundred volts, and the bar-to-bar arc follows.

In the same manner a sudden large decrease in current output of a generator, such as might result from the operation of a circuit breaker, is likely to produce a sufficiently rapid change in armature reaction flux to produce a flashover. Motors also are subject to flashovers brought on by sudden load fluctuations. The severe service conditions encountered by railway motors render them particularly liable to damage from this source.

Pole-face windings constitute about the only sure protection against flashovers. Machines so equipped have their armature reaction flux so well neutralized that sudden load changes are unable to produce much change in armature flux linkage, and high transient voltages are eliminated.

BIBLIOGRAPHY

1. Fundamentals of Electrical Design, A. D. MOORE, McGraw-Hill Book Co., 1927.
2. Influence on commutation of brush contact drop, L. R. LUDWIG and R. M. BAKER; *A.I.E.E. Trans.*, Vol. 51, 1932, pp. 959–63.
3. Commutation considered as a switching phenomenon, R. E. HELLMUND and L. R. LUDWIG, *A.I.E.E. Trans.*, Vol. 51, 1932, pp. 465–8.
4. Effect of various operating conditions upon electrical brush wear and contact drop, V. P. HESSLER, Iowa Engr. Expr. Station, Bul. 122, 1935.

PROBLEMS

1. A motor has 6 poles and a lap-wound armature with 120 commutator bars. At full load it has a speed of 1200 rpm. and an armature current of 60 amperes. If one brush spans three commutator bars and the thickness of insulation between bars is neglected, what is the average di/dt in a commutated coil at full load? If the inductance of a coil is approximately 0.002 henry, what is the average reactance voltage?

2. The following data apply to a certain motor:

Full load I_a	= 50 amperes.
Number of poles	= 4.
Armature winding	= simple wave.
Commutator diameter	= 6 in.
Commutator bars	= 70.
Brush thickness	= 0.55 in.
Rotational speed	= 1800 rpm.

Neglecting the thickness of the mica separators, compute the average di/dt in each commutated element at full load.

3. Given the following data on a shunt motor:

Armature winding	= duplex lap.
Armature rpm.	= 1200.
Commutator diameter	= 7 in.
Bar thickness	= 0.25 in.
Separator thickness	= 0.031 in.
Brush thickness	= 0.83 in.

Compute the length of the commutation time interval.

4. For the commutation conditions shown in Fig. 117, check the current values for step 2. Determine by a similar process the current values at a time instant halfway between steps 2 and 3.

5. For the commutation conditions shown in Fig. 119, check the current values for step 3. Determine by a similar process the current values for steps 2, 3 and 4, if $R_c = 0.05$ and the contact resistance of a whole bar = 0.02.

6. Calculate the current value in the commutated coil at time $0.2T$ (Fig. 121), if $R_c = 0.05$ and the contact resistance of a whole bar = 0.02.

7. By means of a sketch similar to Fig. 122, determine whether the armature reaction ampere-turns produce a helping or a harmful effect on commutation in a motor turning counter-clockwise.

8. Following the procedure suggested in Art. 167, determine an approximate value for the retarding voltage in a commutated element due to reaction ampere-turns. Use the following data:

Rpm. = 900.   Poles = 4. I_a = 208.

Armature travel during commutation interval = 0.8 in.

Armature diameter = 12.5 in.   Conductor length = 8 in.   Slot pitch = 0.8 in.

Winding data: simple wave; two-coil winding elements; 49 slots, 4 conductors per slot, 97 bars.

Assume that equation 72 applies, and that l_{ED} = 0.15 in.

9. A 6-pole, 1200-rpm. generator with a rated current of 240 amperes has a 72-slot armature with an axial length of 8 in. The winding is simple lap with 4-turn winding elements (8 conductors per slot). The slot dimensions are 0.5 in. by 1.5 in. The commutator has 72 bars and is 6 in. in diameter. The brush arc covers three bars. Determine the approximate value of the voltage of self-induction (and mutual induction) in a commutated winding element.

CHAPTER 13

PARALLEL OPERATION

176. Occasion for Parallel Operation of Generators. If a considerable quantity of power must be produced at a central point, particularly if the amount demanded varies from hour to hour, and if service must be maintained without interruption, it is unwise to depend upon a single generator for the production of this power. Instead several generators whose combined ratings are sufficient to take care of the maximum power demand should be made to share the load by means of parallel connections.

There are two obvious advantages:

1. The number of machines in service can be varied to match gradual changes in the demand for power so that the generators will always be operating at or near their maximum efficiency. If at any time the current demanded from the generators in operation is more than their combined capacity it is a very simple process to start another generator, connect it in parallel with those already operating and make it take its share of the connected load.

2. Continuity of service is made more certain, for a damaged machine can be shut down for repairs without disturbing the operation of the remaining generators.

177. Requirements for Parallel Operation. The first requirement for the successful operation of two or more generators in parallel is stability. That is, a temporary change in the distribution of the load between the various generators must automatically create restraining forces which tend to prevent the load unbalance from becoming worse. The nature of stability and the factors affecting it will be discussed more fully as the parallel operation of each type of generator is considered.

The machines intended for parallel operation must obviously have the same voltage rating. For example, a 115-volt generator cannot be expected to operate in parallel with a group of 230-volt generators.

In addition it is desirable that the motors, steam engines or other form of prime mover supplying driving torque to the generators have about the same speed regulation and that the voltage-current output curves

225

of the individual generators have about the same slope. The practical operating problem of keeping the power output properly shared by the various generators under fluctuating load conditions will be simplified considerably thereby.

Equality of current output ratings of the various generators intended for parallel operation is not necessary. However, operating difficulties arise if the current ratings differ by more than 200 or 300%, particularly under fluctuating load conditions.

178. Placing Shunt Generators in Parallel. Suppose that generator A, Fig. 140, is already in operation, delivering I_A amperes to

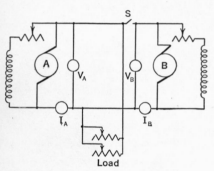

the load circuit at a terminal voltage V_A. Before switch S can be closed placing machine B in parallel with A, certain preliminary steps must be taken.

1. B's prime mover must be started and brought up to normal speed.

2. The voltmeter across B's terminals must be watched for evidence of proper voltage build-up as a self-excited generator. If the voltage does not

FIG. 140. Paralleling shunt generators.

build up promptly the remedies suggested in Art. 107, Chapter 8, must be applied.

3. The voltage generated by B must be made equal to the terminal voltage V_A already existing across the load. A rheostat is provided in B's field circuit for this purpose.

4. B's polarity must be compared with A's to make sure that the corresponding terminals about to be joined by switch S are identical in polarity. Upon the completion of these preliminaries S may be closed and the two machines will then be in parallel.

If preliminaries 3 and 4 have been observed carefully the reading of ammeter I_B will be zero after S is closed. This is necessarily so because in order for current to be indicated at I_B there would have to be a corresponding flow across switch S, but the points joined by S have previously been brought to the same potential; therefore there can be no current flow across S. In other words, the preliminary adjustments have been so made that V_A is trying to force current in one direction across S but V_B is trying to send current across S in the opposite direction and since $V_B = V_A$ no current flows.

179. Distribution of Load. Let the curve NA, Fig. 141, represent the external characteristic curve of generator A, which is delivering a current I_A to a resistance load at a voltage V_A. P, the intersection of the external characteristic and the load characteristic OL, corresponds to these operating conditions. When the adjustments preliminary to parallel operation have been completed for generator B and switch S is closed its voltage is equal to V_A and its current is zero so that its operating point lies on the vertical axis ON at V_A. In order to make genera-

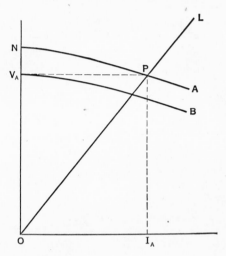

Fig. 141. Characteristics of shunt generators in parallel.

tor B deliver current to the load it is necessary to increase its $K\Phi N$, preferably by increasing its field current. By decreasing the $K\Phi N$ of generator A while increasing that of B it is possible to distribute the load in any desired ratio between the two generators without changing the voltage or current of the load. It is convenient to think that an increase in B's field excitation raises its external characteristic curve to a new position approximately parallel to the old, and that decreasing A's excitation lowers its curve in the same manner. Figure 142 shows the position of the characteristic curves corresponding to an equal division of the load between A and B with no change in load terminal voltage. CM, the current output of each generator, is equal to $1/2 \, CP$, the current drawn by the load.

If the speed and field excitation of each generator remain fixed at the values corresponding to the conditions shown in Fig. 142 and the load resistance is reduced the current output of each generator will be increased but by somewhat different amounts because of the difference in the slopes of their respective characteristic curves. Further inspection of the curves will show that variations in load resistance will cause the current output of generator B to vary over a wider range than that of generator A, since the slope of B's curve is less abrupt.

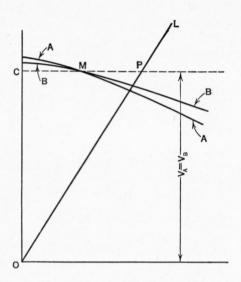

Fig. 142. Position of characteristics for equal load division.

Shunt generators in parallel are inherently stable. If, for example, the $K\Phi N$ of generator A should be increased suddenly, perhaps by a temporary sharp increase in the speed of its prime mover, the temporary unbalance thus created would be corrected as follows:

1. The terminal voltage at A would become greater for an instant than the terminal voltage at B.

2. A's current output would increase and B's would decrease.

3a. As a result of the current change the RI drop in A's armature would increase and the drop in B would decrease.

3b. As another result of the current change the counter-torque produced in the armature would increase in A and decrease in B.

4a. As a result of the change in RI drop the inequality in terminal voltage noted in step 1 would tend to disappear.

4b. As a result of the change in counter-torque the prime mover of A would have a heavier load while the load on B's prime mover would be lessened.

5. The speed of A's prime mover would tend to return to its normal value, thus forcing A's $K\Phi N$ back to normal.

Consider two shunt generators, C and D, whose characteristic curves are shown in Fig. 143. They are delivering currents of I_C and I_D respectively to a resistance load at a voltage V_1. If the resistance of the load is increased gradually the current output of each generator decreases and the terminal voltage across generators and load rises. When sufficient load change has occurred to bring the operating voltage to V_2 the output of generator D is zero and generator C handles all the load. If the load circuit is opened the terminal voltage of C tends to reach the

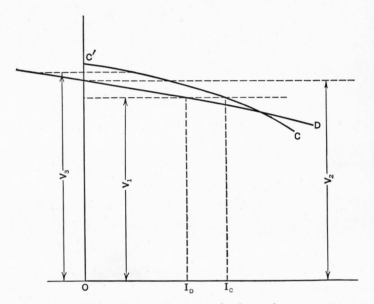

FIG. 143.   Effect of increasing generated voltage of one generator.

value OC', but its rise is arrested by the growth of a negative current in D and equilibrium is established at a terminal voltage V_3 with D motorizing on the current it receives from C.

180. Compound Generators in Parallel. If a similar attempt is made to operate two compound generators in parallel (see Fig. 144) after bringing their voltages to equality and connecting plus to plus and minus to minus, the results will be very unsatisfactory. There may be no immediate evidence of instability when the connection is completed, but usually after a very short time some slight change in the operating conditions occurs which causes a shift of load from one machine to the other. When such a shift once begins no restorative forces are available and the load unbalance grows until one machine is operating as a differential compound motor.

Suppose that the original cause of the disturbance is a momentary increase in the speed of generator A. The difference of potential at its terminals will become slightly greater than the voltage across generator B. A's current output will therefore increase, since its series field NI will increase, causing an increase in Φ and a further increase in $K\Phi N$. Meanwhile generator B is being robbed of its share of the load, its current is decreasing and its $K\Phi N$ is therefore becoming smaller. After a very short time B's generated voltage becomes less than the terminal voltage impressed on it by A, and B's current becomes negative. The direction of its shunt field current is unaltered by this change so that the negative current in its series field converts it into a differential com-

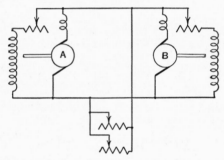

Fig. 144. Unstable connection of compound generators.

pound machine. The presence of negative current in the armature changes counter-torque to driving torque, and B therefore functions as a differential compound motor. Both machines will be damaged seriously unless the system circuit breakers open promptly.

The voltage of self-induction appearing in the series field coil while its current is increasing and the back voltage induced in the shunt coil by mutual induction tend to retard the change in load distribution and serve as elastic cushions, so to speak, which lessen the strain on the machines.

181. Method of Securing Stability. By making a slight change in the operating connections it is possible to operate compound generators in parallel without danger of instability. Figure 145 shows the required connections. It is evident that they differ from the connections shown in Fig. 144 in one important respect. The junction of the armature and series field of generator A has been tied to the corresponding junction of generator B by means of the connection marked S–S'. This tie line, called the equalizer connection, if very low in resistance, maintains S and S' at the same potential and in effect places the two series fields

in parallel.   The total load current then divides between the series fields
in a fixed ratio that is the inverse of their resistances and is entirely independent of the load distribution between the two armatures.

A momentary increase in the speed of generator A will increase its
$K\Phi N$ and its current output, but the series fields of both machines now
share this increase in a fixed ratio and the $K\Phi N$ of generator B undergoes

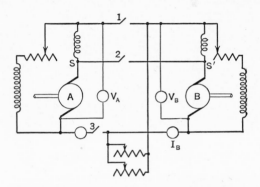

Fig. 145.   Proper connections for compound generators.

a similar increase.   Meanwhile the increased current output of generator A creates more counter-torque and tends to restore the speed to
normal.

182.   Preparations for Parallel Operation.   Suppose that B is operating as a cumulative compound generator supplying current to a resistance load at a terminal voltage V_B.   In order to place generator A in
parallel it is necessary to make the following preparations.

1.   Start A's prime mover and bring it up to normal speed.

2.   Observe A's voltmeter for evidence of proper voltage build-up.

3.   Make sure that the load current will flow through A's series field
coils in the proper direction to produce cumulative compound action.
To determine this it may be necessary to test it separately on a resistance load.

4.   Adjust A's shunt field excitation to bring $V_A = V_B$.

5.   Check polarities.   If point S is plus then S' must be plus also.

6.   Close switches 1 and 2, placing the series fields in parallel.   If
necessary, readjust shunt field excitation to restore equality between
V_A and V_B.

7.   Close switch 3.

When placing compound generators in parallel for the first time there
is, of course, an even chance that the polarity of the incoming generator

will be wrong. The correction of wrong polarity is not as simple a task as for shunt generators. Merely interchanging the output leads disturbs the symmetry of the circuit, and inspection of Fig. 145 indicates that such an interchange places the series field of one machine in parallel with the armature of the other. It is therefore necessary to force the incoming machine to build up its voltage in the reverse direction without disturbing its field connections. This can be done by the following procedure, assuming that generator A in Fig. 145 is the incoming machine whose polarity is to be reversed.

1. Open A's shunt field circuit, thus reducing A's voltage to the residual value.

2. Close switches 1 and 2, thus placing the series fields in parallel. Some current from generator B will now flow over the equalizer and pass through the series field of generator A in the proper direction. The excitation produced by this series field current will under normal conditions be sufficiently strong to kill the original residual flux in A's magnetic circuit and reestablish it in the opposite direction.

3. Close A's shunt field circuit. It will now build up its voltage with the correct polarity.

4. Adjust A's shunt field rheostat to bring $V_A = V_B$, and then close switch 3.

183. Distribution of Load Between Compound Generators. After the parallel connection has been completed any desired fraction of the system load may be placed on the incoming machine, without disturbing the system voltage, by increasing its shunt field excitation, while decreasing that of the machines already in service.

It is usual to distribute the system load among the various machines in proportion to their ratings. If the load changes after such a distribution has been arranged the percentages of the total load handled by the individual generators will usually change more or less because of differences in their external characteristics. The tendency of a generator to take more than its proper share of the load as the total load increases may be corrected by decreasing the compounding effect of its series field. In Art. 112, Chapter 8, it was shown that the compounding of an isolated generator could be reduced by connecting a diverter in parallel with the series field. This method cannot be employed here because the effect of the diverter would not be confined to one series field but would reduce the compounding of all the generators in about the same ratio, since all the series fields are now in parallel. However, by placing a suitable resistance in series with the series field of the machine requiring a reduction in compounding, a smaller fraction of the total current will flow through this field and its compounding effect will be reduced.

184. Parallel Operation of Motors. When two or more motors are coupled to the same mechanical load so that they are compelled to run at the same speed the motors are said to be operating in parallel.

There are numerous occasions for such a connection. For example, space limitations in certain factory installations prohibit the installation of a large motor so that the required horsepower must be furnished by two or more smaller ones. There may be several drive shafts at widely separated points where power must be supplied at the same shaft speed or at related speeds, as in the rolling of steel or the manufacture of paper. The production of draw-bar pull in an electric locomotive results from the united power output of several motors transmitted through appropriate gearing to the drive wheels.

Assume that two 230-volt shunt motors having the same power rating are coupled so that they must turn at the same speed. The motors may be started and operated with both armatures in parallel across 230 volts, starting protection being given by a single resistor carrying their combined current. Motors of the same type and rating usually differ appreciably in their operating characteristics so that when a parallel combination of motors is used to drive a constant-torque load they will divide the load unequally. Equality may, however, be secured in most cases by decreasing slightly the shunt field excitation of one machine while increasing that of the other. If motor 1 is delivering less than its share of the torque a slight decrease in its shunt field current will cause its $K\Phi N$ to decrease and its armature current will be considerably increased, thus building up its torque to a higher level. A corresponding increase in the field of motor 2 will lower its torque output by a similar process.

If the load torque varies over a considerable range, frequent readjustments of the field excitations will be necessary to restore torque balance unless the operating characteristics of the motors can be adjusted sufficiently to make their speed-torque curves coincide. This may necessitate a change in the armature resistance of one machine, or perhaps a slight shift in its brush position.

Slight changes in the speed of shunt motors are accompanied by large changes in armature current and torque. Hence this particular type of motor is inherently unsatisfactory for parallel operation under varying torque conditions. Compound motors have steeper speed-torque curves, making their operation in parallel more satisfactory. Slight changes in speed are not accompanied by such large changes in armature current, so that it is easier to keep the load torque properly distributed between compound motors.   Series motors, however, are the best of all the direct-current motors for parallel operation, judged by the ease of maintaining proper torque balance between individual motors.

185. Series-parallel Control. A brief explanation of the series-parallel scheme for accelerating series railway motors was given in Art. 68, Chapter 6.   In line with the present discussion it may be added that series-parallel control has two advantages that justify its occasional use in two-motor installations of the shunt or compound type.   These advantages are:

1. A marked reduction in rheostatic loss during the first part of the acceleration period when the motor armatures are in series and their counter-emf.'s absorb a large share of the line voltage.

2. The motors may be operated for long periods at half speed with no rheostatic loss.

With the armatures of two motors connected in series, occasional difficulty may be caused by a temporary loss of load on one motor, if the motors are not rigidly coupled to the load.   In accelerating a streetcar equipped with one motor-driven axle on each truck and with the two motors connected in series, adhesion may be insufficient and the drive wheels of the forward truck may lose their grip and begin to spin rapidly. The $K\Phi N$ of the forward motor rises, and the sum of the counter-emf.'s of the two motors becomes more nearly equal to the supply voltage. The motor current is forced down to lower values, reducing the flux of the rear motor and cutting its torque (which is already insufficient for the load) to still lower values.   The car slows down and will stop completely unless the power is shut off promptly and a new start made.

BIBLIOGRAPHY

1. KARAPETOFF, Experimental Electrical Engineering, Vol. 1, 3rd edition, John Wiley & Sons, 1922, pp. 322–330.
2. WHIPPLE, R. A., Overcompounded d-c generators in parallel without an equalizer, *Trans. A.I.E.E.*, Vol. 54, November, 1935, pp. 1276–1277.
3. HARWOOD, P. B., Control of Electric Motors, John Wiley & Sons, 1936, Chapter 7.

PROBLEMS

1. There are two shunt generators in a power house.   Each is rated at 100 kw., 250 volts, and has an armature resistance of 0.025 ohm.   At a time when the load on the power house is 100 kw. the first machine is carrying the load with a terminal voltage of 250.   The second machine is started and its terminal voltage brought to 250 when it is thrown in parallel.   What load does it assume?   How much must the speed of each machine be changed in order that they may divide the load equally and maintain the station voltage at 250?

2. A 75-kw. generator is operating in parallel with a 100-kw. generator at a voltage of 230, and they are sharing a load of 140 kw. in proportion to their ratings. Each generator has a separately excited shunt field and a no-load voltage of 240. The flux of the 100-kw. generator is increased 5%. What will be the approximate kilowatts delivered by each generator, the speeds and load resistance remaining constant?

3. Two shunt generators, A and B, each having a straight-line external characteristic, are operated in parallel. A has 100 amperes capacity and 3% voltage regulation; B has 250 amperes capacity and 2% regulation. If the generators have been adjusted to divide properly a total load of 350 amperes at rated volts, what current will each be delivering when the total load is 250 amperes? What percentage of rated value will the terminal voltage be? What will be the conditions when the amperes output from the bus bars is zero?

4. Two separately excited generators are operating in parallel and supply equal currents at a terminal voltage of 110 volts to a load rheostat whose resistance is 0.25 ohm. Generator A has an armature resistance of 0.03 ohm, and generator B has an armature resistance of 0.04 ohm. The generators are being driven by separate prime movers at a constant speed of 500 rpm. The field excitation remains constant.

(a) What will be the terminal voltage and the current delivered by each generator if the load resistance is changed to 0.5 ohm?

(b) What will happen if the load is taken off the system?

(c) What will be the terminal voltage and the current delivered by each generator if the speed of generator B drops to 475 rpm.?

(d) What will be the terminal voltage and the current delivered by each generator if the flux of generator A is increased 10%?

Note: Each part of the problem should be considered separately. Each part is based on the original data.

5. Two 250-kw. compound generators are to be operated in parallel. Each will be driven at a constant speed of 1200 rpm. and will be supplied with a constant shunt field current of 26 amperes from a separate source. Generator A has the following data: $R_a = 0.007$ ohm; series field resistance $= 0.003$; series turns per pole $= 5$; shunt turns per pole $= 500$. Generator B is identical with A except that its series field resistance is 0.0025. The characteristic magnetization curve applies to each machine at 1200 rpm. if

One abscissa unit $= 20$ amperes in the shunt field,
One ordinate unit $= 100$ volts generated.

The generators are placed in parallel at no load with a terminal voltage of 240. An equalizer is used for stability. How will the two generators share a total load current of 1500 amperes, and what will be the voltage at the armature terminals?

6. (a) Generator A of Problem 5, operating alone, is supplying a load current of 1000 amperes. It is supplied with a shunt field current of 26 amperes from a separate source, and its speed is 1200 rpm. What will be its terminal voltage?

(b) How many amperes will the shunt field of generator B require to bring its no-load voltage up to equal A's terminal voltage, in preparation for paralleling?

(c) The two generators are now connected in parallel and the shunt field currents are altered so that the two armatures deliver 500 amperes each at the same terminal voltage as in part (a). What shunt field current will each require?

7. The armatures of two identical machines are rigidly coupled. The shunt fields may be connected in series or in parallel across a 220-volt line; the armatures also may be connected in series or in parallel across the line, thus making four possible combinations. With the fields in series and armatures in parallel the no-load speed is 1667 rpm.; with the fields in parallel and the armatures in series the no-load speed is 500 rpm. Find the no-load speed for the two remaining combinations, and find the ratio of the fluxes in the two field arrangements. Neglect armature RI drop.

8. Two similar shunt motors are mechanically coupled, and their armatures are connected in series across 220-volt mains. At no load and with normal field excitations the line voltage is equally divided between them, and they run at 1200 rpm. If the field strength of one motor is increased 30%, at what speed do they run? What is the voltage across each armature? Assume armature resistances to be negligible.

9. Two shunt motors have their fields connected in parallel and their armatures in series across the supply line. The armatures are rigidly coupled to each other and to the load, which they drive at 1000 rpm. The residual flux is 10% of the normal flux, and armature resistance is negligible.

(a) At what speed will the load be driven if one of the motors has its armature short-circuited?

(b) Suppose again the normal operation; what would be the speed should the field of one of the motors be broken?

10. Two 5-hp., 220-volt motors are rigidly coupled and have their armatures connected in series to 220-volt mains. Each machine has its normal field excitation. The normal no-load speed of each motor is 1200 rpm. What will be the no-load speed of the combination? What is the approximate horsepower the combination can produce without overheating either machine?

11. A 10-hp., 110-volt, 1200-rpm. shunt motor and a 5-hp., 220-volt, 1200-rpm. shunt motor have their armatures rigidly coupled together and connected in series across a 110-volt line. The fields are in parallel on the 110-volt line. What is the maximum horsepower that can be taken out of the combination without endangering either armature, and at what speed (approximately) will the combination operate? Assume flux proportional to field current for each machine.

12. Two exactly similar shunt motors are coupled to a jackshaft by means of superimposed belts. The diameter of the pulley on each motor is 6 in., and the jackshaft pulley has a diameter of 10 in. The belts are 1/4 in. thick.

When tested separately each motor gave the following data:

$V = 200$ volts. No-load line current $= 3.61$ amperes.

No-load speed $= 1048$ rpm. Armature resistance $= 0.25$ ohm.

Field resistance $= 200$ ohms.

Find the speed of the jackshaft and the speed, the line current and the power output of each motor when no load is connected to the jackshaft. Assume 100% belt efficiency.

CHAPTER 14

GENERATORS FOR SPECIAL PURPOSES

186. Boosters. A generator whose voltage either augments or decreases the normal voltage supplied to a circuit, depending upon the amount of current in the circuit, is called a booster. Its excitation may be series, shunt or compound, as the operating conditions may require.

A simple application of a series booster is illustrated in Fig. 146. Two load circuits are connected to the station bus, which is supplied with power by the main generator, MG. It is desired to maintain the same voltage at each load regardless of independent variations in load current. Load A is located near the bus so that its requirements can be met by flat-compounding the main generator. But the distance from the bus to load B is so great that the RI drop in the connecting wires may become unduly large at times, causing large variations in the load terminal voltage. To remedy this condition a compensating voltage may be produced by means of a series generator, SB, connected as shown. The current rating of this generator must equal the maximum current drawn by the load, but its generated voltage need be only

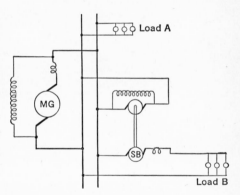

FIG. 146. Series booster application.

large enough to take care of the line RI drop, so that the power rating of the series generator is a small fraction of the power drawn by the load. The generator's magnetic circuit must be liberally proportioned so that changes in field current will produce nearly proportional changes in generated voltage. By a proper choice of driving speed the booster voltage can be made to cancel the line RI drop for practically all values of load current.

The rails of a street railway system form a rather unsatisfactory path for the return of the car current to the power station, because of the difficulty in preventing the current from leaving the rails and resuming

237

its return journey over convenient water or gas mains.   Electrolysis at
the points where the stray current leaves its temporary host and returns
to earth will carry away sufficient iron from the pipes to weaken them
and cause eventual rupture.   One very effective method of reducing
stray current requires the installation of insulated copper conductors
running from the negative station bus to rail connections made at various strategic points where conditions favor the production of large stray
currents.   Series generators frequently are installed in series with these
return conductors to make them more effective.   Generators used for
this purpose are called negative boosters, producing just enough voltage
to neutralize the RI drop of the return conductors.

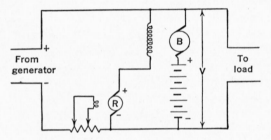

FIG. 147.   Shunt booster application.

A typical application of a shunt booster is shown in Fig. 147.   Its
purpose is to equalize the load on the main generator.   During peak
load periods it compels the storage battery to deliver a large share of the
current demanded by the load.   Then during periods of light load it
forces a charging current into the battery to condition it for the next
discharge period.

Assume that the battery contains a sufficient number of cells in series
to produce an open-circuit voltage equal to the voltage, V, maintained
by the main generator.   The armature of a small regulating generator,
R, is connected in series with the shunt field of the booster, as shown.
The field of generator R carries a definite fraction of the load current
which may be adjusted so that for average load conditions the voltage
of R is practically equal to V.   The booster field will then be zero, its
generated voltage will be practically zero and the battery will neither
charge nor discharge.   For load currents less than this amount the voltage of R will be less than V, the booster field will carry a downward
current, the booster armature voltage will be opposite to the battery
voltage and will assist the main generator in sending a charging current
through the battery.   When a large current is demanded the voltage of
generator R will become greater than V, the booster field current will be

upward and its voltage will assist the battery voltage, causing the battery to deliver current to the load circuit.

The foregoing applications of boosters have been selected as most likely to be of general interest. Descriptions of numerous other booster circuits may be found scattered through the technical literature.

187. Balancer Set. For various reasons which will be discussed in Chapter 16 the so-called three-wire system is in general use for the distribution of power. One of the three wires, say wire B, has a potential approximately halfway between the others, A and C. B is called the neutral wire, and under ideal conditions voltage AB = voltage BC = $1/2\,AC$. One of the methods which may be used to supply power to a three-wire system utilizes a balancer set.

In its simplest form a balancer set consists of two identical shunt machines, mechanically coupled and connected as shown in Fig. 148. With no load on the three-wire system both machines operate as unloaded motors, generating equal counteremfs. and drawing a small armature current to take care of their rotational losses. With a balanced load added to the system (equal currents and voltages on the two sides) all the current going out on A

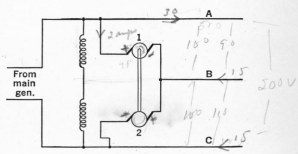

From main gen.

FIG. 148.   Shunt balancer set

returns on C, the neutral carries no current and the two machines continue to operate as unloaded motors.

An understanding of the behavior of a balancer set when the system carries an unbalanced load can best be obtained by considering a numerical example.

Let the load resistances be so adjusted that A carries an outward current of 30 amperes, while B and C have inward currents of 15 amperes each. The voltage supplied to AC by the main generator is 200, and a no-load test of the balancer set at this voltage indicates an armature current of 2 amperes. Under balanced load conditions $V_1 = V_2 = 100$ volts; but the greater load now connected to AB will pull V_1 down and raise V_2 to a higher level. For simplicity assume $V_1 = 90$, and $V_2 = 110$. Although there will be a slight reduction in speed accompanying this unbalance in load, the $K\Phi N$ of machine 1 will still be well above 90, the voltage at its terminals, so that this machine becomes a generator, driven by machine 2 as a motor. The current in B will divide between the two machines in such proportions as will satisfy the following equations:

$$I_B = I_1 + I_2,$$
$$V_2 I_2 = V_1 I_1 + W_R + R_1 I_1^2 + R_2 I_2^2,$$

where W_R is the value of the combined rotational loss of both machines. But $W_R = 200 \times 2 = 400$ watts, from the no-load test. Therefore, neglecting the RI^2 losses,

$$I_1 + I_2 = 15,$$

$$110 I_2 \approx 90 I_1 + 400,$$

from which

$$I_2 \approx 8.75,$$

and generator 1 delivers 6.25 amperes of the 30 amperes consumed by load AB.

If the heavy load is transferred from AB to BC, V_1 will rise above normal and V_2 becomes less than normal. This will cause the balancer units to interchange their operating characteristics. Machine 1 now operates as a motor supplying driving torque to machine 2, the generator.

It is evident that the power rating of a balancer set need be only a small fraction of the total power delivered to the three-wire system if reasonable care is exercised in the distribution of the load. Notice also that a balancer set prevents large voltage unbalance in the system, yet requires a considerable amount of unbalance to bring its motor-generator action into active service. This follows naturally from the operating characteristics of the shunt machines constituting the balancer. For as load is added to one side of the system and the machine connected across that side begins to function as a generator it will exhibit the drooping voltage so characteristic of shunt generators, while the added load torque it places on the companion machine causes the speed to drop and thus decreases the voltage of the generator still further.

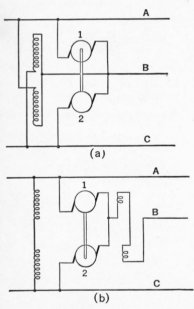

FIG. 149. (a) Shunt balancer with cross-connected fields. (b) Compound balancer set.

Figure 149a shows a slightly different circuit arrangement which tends to lessen the voltage unbalance. Suppose that the heavier load is across BC, forcing machine 2 to function as a generator. Its voltage now has less tendency to drop with increasing load because its shunt field is connected across AB and is strengthened by the gradual increase in voltage on that side. At the same time the speed-torque characteristic of machine 1 operating as a motor is improved by the gradual reduction in field strength due to the connection of its field to the decreasing voltage at BC. With the speed held more nearly constant the voltage of the generator unit is strengthened still more.

If compound machines are employed as balancer units it is possible to obtain almost perfect voltage balance in spite of considerable current unbalance. The two series fields must be connected in series and placed in the neutral line as shown in Fig. 149b. Furthermore, these connections must be so made that when side AB is carrying the heavier load, requiring generator action of machine 1, the flow of current through its series field will be in the proper direction to make machine 1 a cumulative compound generator. The series field of machine 2 is so connected that this same current makes it function as a differential compound motor. If at a later time the load across BC should become the greater, the direction of current in the neutral wire will necessarily reverse, machine 1 will become a differential compound motor and machine 2 a cumulative compound generator. Careful adjustment of series turns and restriction of current unbalance to amounts that will not produce appreciable magnetic saturation are the essential features upon which good voltage balance depends.

188. Three-wire Generator. The previous article discussed the use of a small motor-generator set as a means of establishing a mid-potential terminal for the neutral wire of a three-wire system. It is not necessary, however, to install a motor-generator set for this purpose; instead the arrangement shown in Fig. 150 may be used. The armature winding of the main generator is tapped at two points, m and n, exactly one pole pitch apart, and connections are brought out to two slip rings mounted

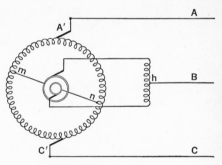

FIG. 150. Three-wire generator.

on the shaft. Electrical contact is established with these slip rings by means of two brushes which are connected to the terminals of an inductive balance coil. A tap brought out from the midpoint of the balance coil is connected to the neutral of the three-wire system.

Consider the operation of the machine when the three-wire system is unloaded, and assume that a constant voltage of 220 is being maintained between the main brushes A' and C'. Let the potential of C' be taken as zero; A' is therefore $+220$. The voltage applied to the balance coil is that which exists between points m and n. As the armature turns, this voltage undergoes a periodic variation. At the instant that m is in contact with A' its potential is $+220$, the potential of n is zero and p, the center tap on the balance coil, has a potential of $+110$. When the armature has made $1/4$ revolution, m, n and p will each be $+110$. Further rotation will bring m to C', n will be $+220$ and p again will be $+110$. The balance coil is constructed of heavy wire wound on an iron core and has a sufficient number of turns to produce a large inductance. The alternating current produced in this coil will have a very small effective value in spite of the large peak values of voltage between m and n, owing to the large counter-voltage of self-induction created in the coil. Let this current be called the magnetizing current of the balance coil.

If a load is connected between wires A and B the return current upon reaching p divides between the two halves of the balance coil and reenters the armature winding at m and n. The determination of the value of the current in either half of the balance coil at any instant is extremely difficult. It is evidently a pulsating current, made up of two components. One is the magnetizing current, whose production has already been described; the other component is a fractional part of the load current coming from the neutral wire. This load component is in itself a pulsating current because the voltage which drives it through the circuit varies from instant to instant with the change in the position of its armature tap relative to brush A'. Fortunately the average value of the load component in each half of the balance coil is simply half the neutral current, and the average ampere-turns created by it will be upward in one half of the coil and downward in the other half, resulting in no increase in magnetic saturation. The opposition to the flow of load current through the balance coil consists of a voltage of self-induction generated by the pulsating current and an RI drop, but both are small compared to the system voltage.

The extreme case just discussed in which all the system load is concentrated on one side of the system will result in a considerable shift in the potential of the neutral point p, and a low voltage on the loaded side. With reasonable care in load distribution the voltage on the two sides should never differ by more than 3%.

Instead of using an external balance coil it is possible to mount the balance coil on the armature spider so that a single slip ring will suffice to make contact with the system neutral. This arrangement is illustrated in Fig. 151a. A modification of this scheme utilizes two internal balance coils as shown in Fig. 151b. The advantages of internal balance coils are somewhat offset by the added difficulty of placing the armature in dynamic balance.

When a compound generator is to be equipped with balance coils and slip rings for three-wire service it is necessary to split the series field circuit into two parts and place one part in each of the outside wires. The

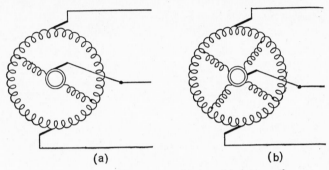

(a) (b)

FIG. 151. Two types of internal balance coils.

desired compounding can be secured in this way in spite of unbalanced loads on the system.

189. Diverter-pole Generator. Certain applications require a generator having a very constant voltage under varying load conditions. Parallel combinations of generators and storage batteries used in telephone exchanges and power stations for switch operation, emergency lighting and other auxiliary purposes are examples in point. The external characteristics of shunt generators droop too much for this work, and flat-compound generators are unsatisfactory because of the rise in their voltage characteristics between the no-load and full-load points. To meet this need a new type of generator called the diverter-pole generator has been developed. The desired flatness of its voltage characteristic curve has been obtained by the use of a magnetic circuit of unique design.

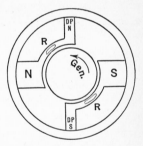

FIG. 152. Frame of diverter-pole generator.

A simplified sketch of such a machine is shown in Fig. 152. It resembles a two-pole shunt generator with the full number of interpoles, except that each interpole core is joined to a main pole by a magnetic bridge. The main poles N and S are provided with regular shunt field coils; the interpole coils consist of a few turns of heavy wire connected in series with the armature. The sectional area of the magnetic bridge is reduced at R to bring about certain saturation and leakage flux effects to be discussed later.

When the current output of the generator is zero the flux distribution is indicated roughly in Fig. 153a. Part of the main pole flux emerges from the central part of the north pole face and traverses the air gap and armature as indicated by the dotted lines 1 and 2. Also a considerable amount of useful flux emerges from a portion of the magnetic bridge and follows paths about as indicated by lines 3 and 4. Finally the leakage flux paths 5 and 6 are formed by the main pole, bridge, interpole and yoke. These paths will divert a considerable amount of flux from the armature, since their reluctance is low except where the bridge sectional area is reduced, and since the no-load current in the interpole coils is too small to create appreciable opposition. Good commutation at no load

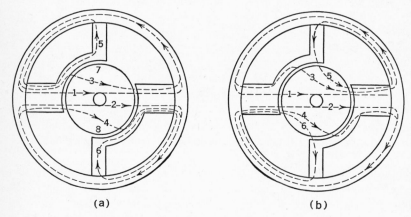

(a)   (b)

FIG. 153.   Flux distribution — diverter-pole generator.

will be assured, since the commutation zones 7 and 8 are practically empty of flux and there is no armature reaction.

The flux distribution at rated load is about as shown in Fig. 153b. The load current in flowing through the interpole coils creates flux of the proper strength and direction in the commutation zone to produce good commutation. This flux is indicated in the figure by the dashed lines 5 and 6. Most of the flux that formerly took the leakage path through the bridge is now thrown into the armature and becomes useful flux. The total effective flux per pole thus grows steadily with increasing load current, so that the effects of armature reaction and armature RI drop on the terminal voltage are neutralized.

At a critical load current (usually adjusted to a value slightly above the rated output) the ampere-turns of the interpole plus the reaction ampere-turns of the armature are sufficiently strong to reverse the direction of the flux in the magnetic bridge and thus reduce the useful flux sharply. The terminal voltage then falls to a sufficiently low value to prevent serious overload.

Figure 154 shows a typical external characteristic curve of a diverter-pole generator. It is practically horizontal over the working range and curves downward sharply just beyond full load. When this generator is in parallel with a battery and is supplying a varying load current it is possible to adjust operating conditions so that the generator carries the entire load normally, and in addition sends a small charging current into the battery. If an overload occurs the generated voltage drops sharply, allowing the battery to take most of the load. As soon as the load returns to normal the generator resumes its normal power production.

190. Dynamotor. One method of producing a supply of direct current at an unusual voltage utilizes a special machine called a dynamotor. The field frame is that of a standard shunt generator, but the armature possesses some unique features. It contains a duplex winding with a separate commutator for each part.

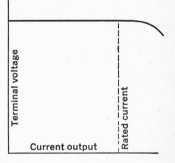

Fig. 154. Characteristic of diverter-pole generator.

Suppose that winding A has fine-wire elements of many turns such as might be needed to produce 110 volts at the brushes. Winding B in the intervening slots will contain a smaller number of heavy-wire elements, designed possibly for 6-volt operation. If the brushes on the A commutator are connected to 110-volt mains and the field is supplied with the proper current the machine will operate as a motor. The 6-volt output of winding B can then be applied to a suitable receiving circuit. Each winding will have the same nominal power rating. That is, if RI^2 and rotational losses are neglected,

$$V_A I_A = V_B I_B.$$

If desired, the low-voltage winding may be used as the motor element and the high-voltage winding as the generator element. This type of operation has been employed successfully in producing a 135-volt supply for certain automobile radios, the motor element operating from the 6-volt car battery.

A dynamotor may be expected to have somewhat higher efficiency and lower price than a standard motor-generator set of the same rating. Its fixed voltage ratio may, however, be a serious handicap for some kinds of applications.

191. Arc-welding Generators. The rapid growth in the number and variety of industrial processes in which arc welding is employed and the advantages of direct current for this class of welding have created a demand for special generators having suitable characteristics for welding.

The resistance of an arc between fixed electrodes decreases with an increase in current. This type of volt-ampere characteristic tends to produce instability when supplied with power from a standard constant-voltage source. A generator is needed that is capable of delivering a constant current to the arc at whatever voltage is required to maintain it.

In the discussion of the differential compound generator it was noted that the load resistance could be decreased step by step over a wide range of values without causing much change in the current output of the generator. Hence this type of generator evidently approaches the characteristics just stated as desirable in a welding generator. Figure 155 shows the circuit diagram of a successful welding generator of this

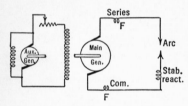

FIG. 155. Circuit of arc-welding generator.

kind. The circuit traversed by the arc current is composed of the armature, series field, commutating pole winding and stabilizing reactor. The purpose of this reactor is to generate voltages which tend to damp out rapid fluctuations in the arc current. To insure rapid voltage build-up after the short circuits that occur so frequently in arc welding it is necessary to have the shunt field separately excited. The auxiliary generator provided for this purpose is usually coupled to the shaft of the main generator.

Another generator which has proved highly satisfactory for arc welding is a modified form of the third-brush generator (see Art. 192). An understanding of its operation can be obtained with the help of Fig. 156. The armature is wound as for a standard two-pole machine. Its main brushes A and B are part of the arc circuit, which also includes the commutating poles and the two series field coils F and F'.

The shunt field coils on the four poles are connected in series to form the shunt field circuit, with the connections so made that north poles are formed at N_1 and N_2, while S_1 and S_2 are south poles. By an unequal division of the shunt ampere-turns the average flux densities in N_2 and S_2 are made very high and the densities in N_1 and S_1 very low. As a reminder of this unequal distribution the dimensions of the high-density poles are reduced in the figure. One reason for placing a two-pole armature winding in this four-pole frame will now be apparent. N_1 and N_2 are really two branches of the same pole, and S_1, S_2 are the corresponding branches of the opposite pole.

The shunt field circuit is not connected to the main brushes in the usual manner. It is connected instead between brush A and an auxiliary brush C so placed that only the small group of conductors lying under poles N_2 and S_2 contribute voltage to the field circuit.

From the indicated current directions in the armature conductors it is evident that the general direction of the armature reaction ampere-turns is downward. These ampere-turns may be resolved into two components, R_1 and R_2, parallel to each set of poles.

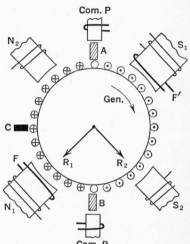

FIG. 156. Arc-welding generator of third-brush type.

The behavior of this machine under varying load conditions may now be outlined as follows:

1. A reduction in arc resistance causes a growth in arc current, and components R_1 and R_2 of the reaction ampere-turns are increased.

2. R_2 tends to strengthen N_2 and S_2, but since these poles are already highly saturated no appreciable increase occurs in their flux.

3. Since the voltage applied to the shunt field circuit originates in the conductor band under N_2 and S_2, and since the flux of these poles is practically unaffected by changes in armature current, the shunt field ampere-turns on all the poles will remain nearly constant under varying load conditions.

4. R_1 opposes the shunt ampere-turns on N_1 and S_1. Since these poles are unsaturated an increase in R_1 brought about by an increase in armature current will cause a marked reduction in their flux.

5. The armature current is sent through the series coils F and F' in such direction as to reduce the flux of N_1 and S_1 still further. Adjustable shunts are provided by which the demagnetizing action of F and F' can be regulated.

6. That fraction of the terminal voltage which is produced by the conductors under N_1 and S_1 will be reduced so that the voltage delivered to the arc circuit will be reduced.

A typical external characteristic curve for this generator is shown in Fig. 157. By proper use of the series field shunts mentioned in step 5 above, the slope of this curve can be altered somewhat to suit the requirements of a particular class of welding operations.

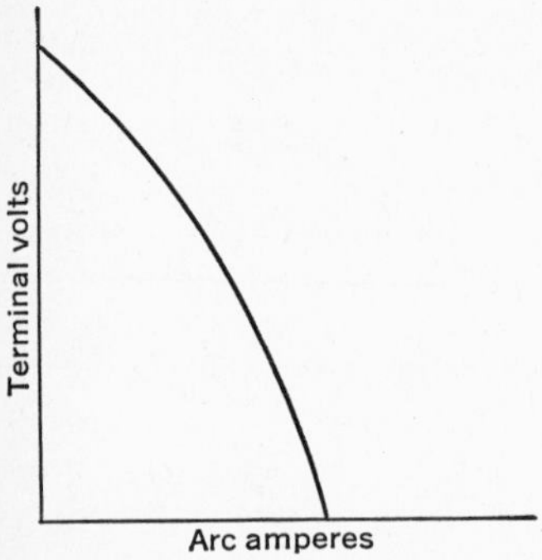

The generator field coils usually possess enough inductance to make an external stabilizing coil unnecessary in the arc circuit.

192. Third-brush Generator. The generators so far described have been intended for constant-speed operation — a condition not difficult to meet if the generator is set up in a permanent location. With the advent of the modern automobile came a need for a generator capable of delivering a fairly constant voltage at the terminals of a storage battery while being driven at various speeds within a total range of perhaps eight to one. The so-called third-brush generator has been most successful in meeting this requirement.

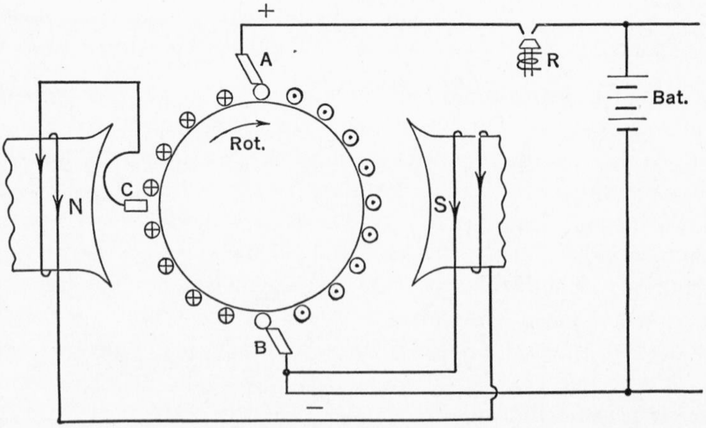

FIG. 157. Characteristic of arc-welding generator.

FIG. 158. Third-brush generator.

The principal features of the third-brush generator are shown in Fig. 158. The armature, enclosed by the two-pole frame, is designed with a liberal number of ampere-turns so that armature reaction will be powerful when the generator is delivering its normal current. The load circuit is shown connected to the main brushes A and B, which arc located at the geometrical neutral, and a magnetic switch R is designed to open the load circuit when the generator voltage becomes less than the battery voltage so that the generator cannot operate as a motor. The shunt field, instead of being connected across the main brushes in the usual manner, is connected between brush B and an auxiliary brush C placed approximately halfway between the main brushes. The shunt field must therefore be a low-resistance winding since it operates from only a fractional part of the terminal voltage.

From a study of the current directions and polarities the following facts will be evident:

1. The direction of the armature reaction ampere-turns is downward within the armature and upward in the main poles.

2. The main pole flux density will be reduced at the lower tip of the north pole and the upper tip of the south pole by armature reaction.

3. The group of conductors contributing voltage to the shunt field is cutting the flux of the pole tips that are weakened by armature reaction.

4. An increase in reaction ampere-turns tends in general to decrease the shunt field excitation.

5. The proper direction of rotation is definitely associated with the position of the third brush and the field connections. The generator will function properly for one direction of rotation only.

To obtain a clearer picture of the unique operating characteristics of this machine, suppose it to be driven at constant speed and let a rheostat be substituted for the parallel combination of battery and lamps which usually constitutes its load. If the rheostatic resistance is made fairly large the current delivered to it by the generator will be very small and its reaction ampere-turns will have a negligible effect on the air-gap flux distribution. The $K\Phi N$ appearing at the main brushes may have a very large value, the voltage applied to the shunt field circuit will be fully $1/2\ K\Phi N$ (for the assumed position of brush C) and a dangerously large field current may result. Consequently this type of generator must never be permitted to operate under conditions approaching an open circuit, and as a protection in the event that an accidental interruption of its output occurs its field circuit should contain a suitable fuse.

A reduction in the resistance of the load rheostat will be accompanied by an increase in current output and in reaction ampere-turns. Flux distortion will occur under the main poles, resulting in a reduction in the flux cut by the conductors contributing voltage to the field circuit and a consequent reduction in shunt field current. Because of this demagnetizing effect of the armature current, equilibrium is established with a much smaller increase in current than would otherwise be expected from a given reduction in load resistance. Evidently the external characteristic of this generator with constant speed and a variable resistance load will be much like that of the differential compound generator.

As a step toward normal operating conditions consider the behavior of a third-brush generator when operated at various speeds with a fixed resistance used as a load. When the speed is zero a certain residual flux, Φ_r, exists in the magnetic circuit. If slow rotation commences, the shunt field circuit will experience an impressed voltage approximately equal to $1/2\ KN\Phi_r$, due to the conductors between C and B cutting the residual flux. The field current resulting from this voltage will increase the air-gap flux, and the voltage applied to the field circuit will be increased, resulting in another increase in field current. The cumulative action thus begun will be terminated finally and equilibrium will be established owing to the partial saturation of the magnetic circuit and to the demagnetizing action of the armature current delivered to the constant-resistance load. If the generator is given another increment of speed a further increase in field current will be produced but the corresponding increment of flux will not be so large because the magnetic circuit is partly saturated. An increase in load current output will occur, but the increased armature reaction accompanying it will tend to reduce the flux and will limit the increase in load current to a small amount. Succeeding increments of speed will produce smaller and smaller increases in load current. There is, however, a definite danger that with sufficiently high speeds both the load current delivered to the fixed resistance and the field current of the generator will reach dangerous values.

Under actual operating conditions the load consists of a storage battery in parallel with lamps and other auxiliary devices, and the magnetic switch R, Fig. 158, isolates the generator until its speed is sufficient to produce a terminal voltage greater than the battery voltage. The generator is so designed that the open-circuit voltage it must build up in order to close R is accompanied by sufficient shunt field current to produce considerable saturation of the magnetic circuit.

As a specific example assume that the battery voltage is 6.5 and that at a car speed of 15 miles per hour the generator produces 6.5 volts and R is then closed. The generator current output will be zero. Now let the car speed be increased, say, to 18 miles per hour, an increase of 20%. Since the ohmic resistance of a battery is very low a small increment in generated voltage above the assumed battery voltage of 6.5 will be sufficient to send a large charging current through the battery. By the time the voltage of the generator reaches, say, 7.25 volts, it may be delivering as much as 15 amperes to the battery and the demagnetizing action of this current may be powerful enough to establish equilibrium and prevent the voltage from increasing above this point. If the speed goes up to 25 miles per hour the generated voltage attempts to rise proportionately but the first small increment of voltage produces so much increase in charging current that the increased demagnetizing action limits the new voltage to, say, 8 volts at a current of 30 amperes.

Since charging commenced, the voltage of the generator has risen only 1.5 volts or 23%, although its speed has been increased 67%. The total flux must therefore have undergone a 26% decrease, which brings it back to the straight part of the saturation curve where it will be more powerfully affected by subsequent changes in ampere-turns. Consequently the voltage increment produced by a further increase in speed causes a temporary increase in armature reaction ampere-turns which distorts the flux and reduces the field voltage by a larger percentage than the percentage increase in speed. The output voltage cannot be maintained at a higher level or even at the same level, and both it and the output current are slightly decreased. In like manner, operation at still higher speeds causes the charging current to decrease to lower and lower values. A typical curve of charging current vs. speed is shown in Fig. 159.

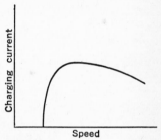

FIG. 159. Characteristic of third-brush generator.

To increase the average charging current the auxiliary brush C must be moved clockwise so that the number of conductors contributing voltage to the field circuit will be increased.

193. Rosenberg Generator. Another type of generator whose voltage-current characteristic at various speeds is suitable for battery-charging purposes is shown in Fig. 160. It is known as the Rosenberg generator and in various modified forms is widely used as an axle-driven generator for train-lighting purposes. Although making effective use of armature reaction in much the same way as the third-brush generator it possesses the additional advantage of maintaining uniform characteristics and an unchanging polarity for either direction of rotation.

As indicated in the figure the poles are provided with shunt field coils connected across the battery and hence producing a constant number of ampere-turns. With clockwise rotation, voltages will be generated in the armature as shown by the signs placed within the conductors and a large current will flow through the short-circuit path provided between brushes A and B.   Actually the armature and field ampere-turns combine to produce a resultant flux, but it is convenient to sacrifice accuracy for clarity in this case and assume that the reaction ampere-turns create a flux separate and distinct from that produced by the shunt field.   The line of action of the reaction flux will be downward through the armature, as indicated by the line ϕ_a, and this flux will follow return paths up through the heavy pole shoes especially provided for this purpose.

If it may now be assumed that the armature conductors are cutting the reaction flux alone, voltages will be generated in the conductors as indicated by the inner circle of signs.   The dividing line where these volt-

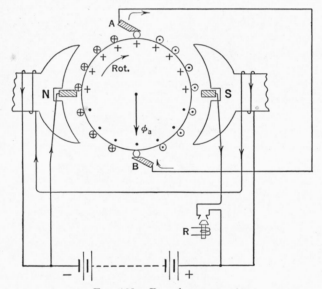

Fig. 160.   Rosenberg generator.

ages reverse in sign coincides with the polar axis, and auxiliary brushes placed on this axis are used as a source of charging current for the battery. The reaction ampere-turns of the charging current act along the polar axis, and from an inspection of the inner circle of signs it is evident that these ampere-turns are opposed to the ampere-turns of the main field and will permit just enough main field flux to maintain equilibrium.

An increased speed raises the voltage between A and B and causes more short-circuit current.   This in turn creates more reaction flux, more charging current and greater opposition to the main field.   The reaction response is so powerful that large speed changes cause comparatively small changes in charging current.

The Rosenberg generator, like the third-brush generator, must be disconnected from the storage battery when extremely low speeds cause its voltage to fall below that of the battery. A magnetic relay, R, may be used for this purpose.

If the direction of rotation is reversed, the polarity of brushes A and B and the direction of the short-circuit current flowing between them will reverse. This reverses the direction of the reaction flux, ϕ_a, but has no effect on the polarity of the auxiliary brushes since both ϕ_a and the direction of rotation are reversed. Hence the production of a voltage at the auxiliary brushes of the proper polarity for battery charging will be unaffected by reversed rotation.

The large notches observed in the poles are provided in order to weaken the field in the region occupied by the conductors that are being short-circuited by the auxiliary brushes so as to reduce the sparking at these brushes.

194. Gas-electric Drive. A recent innovation in motive-power equipment for certain types of busses and for the so-called streamlined trains is known as the gas-electric drive. The tractive effort is supplied by two or more high-speed series motors geared to the driving axles. They are supplied with current from a shunt or compound generator which is driven by a standard automobile engine or by a crude oil engine of the Diesel type.

The control mechanism is usually arranged so that the shunt field of the generator is open when the engine is idling. The voltage generated by the residual flux alone is insufficient to produce enough current in the traction motors to turn them. When the operator wishes to start he advances the engine throttle, admitting more fuel and causing a rapid rise in engine speed. A centrifugal switch closes the field circuit, and the generated voltage builds up rapidly, increasing the current to the traction motors and causing them to accelerate. From this point on, the vehicle speed is largely determined by the engine speed.

The traction motors are normally in parallel, but for long, heavy pulls they may be connected in series to give the required torque at low speed.

195. Homopolar Generator. This somewhat inappropriate name has been applied to various machines by which the generation of a unidirectional voltage may be accomplished without the assistance of a commutator.

The arrangement shown in Fig. 161 is impractical but serves nicely as an illustration of the basic principles. A disk of copper or aluminum is so mounted that it may be rotated between the poles of two magnets. Brushes A and B make contact with the edge of the disk at diametrically opposite points as shown. If the disk is rotated in the indicated direction a voltage will be generated in the disk, and if an external circuit is connected to the brushes current will leave the disk at A and return to it at B. The magnitude of the generated voltage will depend upon the diameter of the disk, its rotational speed and the strength of the magnetic field, and will necessarily be very small. If the resistance of the external circuit is made very low the current output may be quite large.

Motor operation may be secured by connecting $A-B$ to a power supply of suitable voltage. In fact, the motor element of the mercury flotation type of watt-hour meter has very similar structural features.

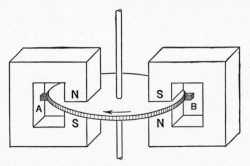

Fig. 161. One type of homopolar generator.

The difficulty of building such machines in large sizes that will compete in cost and efficiency with machines of standard design has limited this type of construction to experimental machines for laboratory use. The interested reader may find additional material on this subject by consulting one or more of the references listed below.

BIBLIOGRAPHY

1. Standard Handbook for Electrical Engineers, 6th edition, sections 8, 19, 28, McGraw-Hill Book Co.
2. Electrical Engineers' Handbook, Vol. IV (Electric Power), section 8, 1936, John Wiley & Sons.
3. Electrical Engineering Papers of B. G. Lamme, Westinghouse Electric and Manufacturing Co., 1919.

CHAPTER 15

RATING AND COST

196. Power Rating and Its Limiting Factors. Prominent among the items listed on the nameplate of a motor or a generator is its rated power output. A machine designed primarily for motor operation will have its rating expressed in horsepower; the rating of a generator is given in kilowatts. It is important to understand the significance of the power rating of a machine and to appreciate the factors limiting its value.

From the design data of the machine, supplemented whenever necessary by laboratory tests, the manufacturer is able to determine the quantity of power which can be drawn from the machine hour after hour without injuring it. This amount is the true power rating, and unless special circumstances make it desirable to give the machine a deliberate over- or under-rating this is the rating that will appear on its nameplate.

The power rating of direct-current machines is limited and restricted by the following factors:

1. Mechanical strength. Stresses in the structural parts of the machine are caused by the torsional and bending forces which originate with its use in the production of power. Such stresses must be kept well within the safe allowable values for the materials composing the various parts. The power output must never be allowed to reach so great a value that the stresses created by it will exceed the maximum allowable value in the weakest part. Fortunately the parts of most machines are so generously proportioned (in order to obtain the desired magnetic and electric properties) that other limiting factors become important long before the output can be carried to the point of probable mechanical breakdown.

2. Commutation. In both motors and generators an increase in power output is accompanied by an almost proportional increase in armature current. Since the reversal of large amounts of current without sparking at the brushes is known to be difficult, it is to be expected that commutation will in some cases prove to be a serious limitation on the quantity of power that can be obtained from the machine. Before the use of commutating poles became so prevalent, commutation was a very important factor in determining the

255

power rating of a machine. Its influence in this respect is now limited largely to high-speed machines and to machines subjected to extremely rapid load fluctuations.

3. Temperature rise. By far the most influential limitation on the true power rating of motors and generators is the rise in temperature accompanying their operation. The heat produced by friction, by the flow of useful current in the windings and by eddy currents in the iron tends to carry the temperature of the internal parts up to higher and higher values until thermal equilibrium is reached finally at a temperature sufficiently high to make the rate of heat dissipation equal to the rate of heat production. The rate of heat production is directly related to the power losses in the machine and hence varies markedly with changes in total power output. It is evident then that the amount of temperature rise is dependent upon the power output.

The many advantages possessed by certain insulating and moisture-resistant materials of organic composition, such as cotton and linen tape and the various compounds having a creosote base, make it desirable to use them extensively in the insulation of armature and field windings. Unfortunately such materials are subject to rapid disintegration if exposed to temperatures above 105°C. The continuous power output of a machine must therefore be kept below the value required to bring the temperature of the hottest spot of the machine up to 105°C.

The output which can be drawn from a machine under this limiting condition evidently depends upon the normal temperature of the air surrounding the machine when it is idle — the so-called ambient temperature. A motor driving a mechanical stoker and handicapped by the excessive ambient temperature of a boiler room cannot be expected to deliver as much power as the same motor operating in a cool, well-ventilated location. Consequently in order to secure uniformity in their power ratings most manufacturers have agreed to assume an ambient temperature not exceeding 40°C. in establishing the continuous ratings of their machines.

The test by which the manufacturer determines the correctness of the power rating of a sample machine taken from the production line is commonly called a heat run. Rated load is placed on the machine, and frequent readings of the ambient temperature and the temperature of critical parts are taken until the rate of increase of temperature becomes so small that the final temperature can be predicted accurately. Additional temperature readings at various points on the armature and commutator are taken as soon as the machine is shut down. In interpreting the results allowance must be made for the fact that temperature measurements are confined necessarily to the outer surfaces of field coils and to the top conductors in the armature slots, and that " hot-spot " temperatures within the windings will be from 10 to 15°C. higher.

On large machines the early stages of the heat run are conducted at a considerable overload in order to shorten the time required for the machines to build up their temperatures. Detailed instructions for conducting heat runs may be obtained by consulting a good laboratory manual.

197. Other Nameplate Data. Closely linked with the power rating of a machine are other data of almost as great importance in establishing correct operating conditions. A motor can scarcely be expected to deliver its rated power output safely if it is forced to operate at a terminal voltage and speed that differ greatly from its nameplate values.

The nameplate of a motor usually states the voltage of the supply mains to which it should be connected, the horsepower which it can deliver continuously without reaching a dangerous temperature, the speed at which it should operate when delivering its rated load and its full-load current.

The nameplate of a generator states the speed at which it should be driven, the kilowatts it can deliver continuously with safety, the terminal voltage at which rated load will be delivered and its full-load current. If it is a compound generator both its no-load and full-load terminal voltages are usually stated.

198. Effect of Insulation on Rating. Although there are many kinds of insulating materials they are usually grouped in three classes with respect to the influence they exert on the continuous power rating of the machine in which they are installed.

Class 0 includes cotton, silk, paper and similar organic materials that have not been impregnated.

Class A includes these same materials when impregnated (soaked in a substance having suitable insulating and moisture-resistant properties). Enamel coatings on conductors are included in this class.

Class B includes inorganic materials such as mica and asbestos in combination with suitable binding substances.

These classes differ considerably in their ability to withstand high temperatures without deterioration. Class A substances should never operate at temperatures above 105°C. The maximum temperature of Class 0 material must in general be kept 15°C. below the maximum permitted for Class A, while Class B can be subjected to temperatures 20°C. higher than Class A.

Price and convenience considerations favor the general use of Class A insulation except where it is necessary to use Class B, as in the commutator bar separators, where mica is employed.

Allowable temperatures for the various parts of machines and for the three classes of insulation are tabulated in a bulletin called Standards for Rotating Machines, published by the A.I.E.E.

199. Effect of Ventilation on Power Capacity. Proper analysis of the data secured on a heat run enables the continuous power rating to be determined, subject to the assumptions that the ambient temperature will not exceed 40°C. and that the normal provisions for ventilation will not be disturbed. Any interference with the proper circulation of air around the machine or its passage through the ventilating ducts will reduce the safe power capacity below the nameplate rating.

The frames which enclose the magnetic circuit and support the bearings may be classed as open, semi-enclosed or totally enclosed. The open type is characterized by skeleton end frames supporting the bearing housings and connecting them to the yoke. Ample ventilation for the field and armature windings is provided by the fanlike action of the armature. If it becomes necessary to put cover plates or screens over some of the end-frame openings in order to eliminate certain hazards, fan blades should be attached to the armature to increase the circulation of air. Even with the help of fan blades the power capacity of the machine is somewhat reduced. Frames of this type are said to be semi-enclosed.

If the location of the machine is such as will subject it to snow, dust, explosive vapor or other hazards it will be necessary to place tight covers over all the frame openings. This retards the heat dissipation so much that the power capacity may be reduced to 50 or 60% of its rating as an open machine. When machines are designed particularly for totally enclosed operation, arrangements can be made to provide water cooling for the frame, or special ventilating ducts are connected to a blower which will produce forced circulation of cooling air. The traction motors of many electric locomotives are cooled by forced air circulation, resulting in a large increase in their capacity. Air drawn in near the cab roof is forced by a central blower through ducts to the various traction motors and out through suitable vents in the motor frames.

200. Effect of Duty Cycle on Power Capacity. The load applied to many motors and generators is not uniform but varies from instant to instant. The variation may be haphazard, following no particular pattern, in which case it is described as varying-duty service. If the variation consists of recurring periods of constant load alternating with rest intervals the service is said to be intermittent duty. A more complex duty cycle, in which rest intervals alternate with periods of varying load, is described as periodic duty.

There is no satisfactory method of determining the temperature rise that will be produced in a machine subjected to varying duty, outside of an actual test. If possible, the actual load conditions should be duplicated on the test floor during the progress of a regular heat run. If this is not practicable a heat run conducted with a continuous load equal to the maximum to be expected under the proposed varying-duty service will at least give a rating that will have a reasonable factor of safety.

To determine whether a machine having a known continuous rating will give satisfactory service on intermittent or on periodic duty, computation methods may be employed with reasonable accuracy, although a heat run duplicating actual service conditions is recommended if practicable.

Suppose that a certain motor has a continuous rating of 5 hp., and that the armature current required with this output is 20 amperes. The armature copper loss will be

$$\overline{20}^2 R = 400R \text{ watts},$$

where R is the resistance of the armature, and this loss will be the principal cause of the rise in armature temperature. The type of load to be handled is classed as periodic duty, and it is desired to determine whether the temperature rise produced by the given periodic load will be greater or less than the rise with a constant load of rated value.

The proposed duty cycle is such that the armature current will be 40 amperes for 1 minute, 20 amperes for 3 minutes, 15 amperes for 2 minutes, 10 amperes for 2 minutes and 0 ampere for 2 minutes, after which the cycle begins again. The rate of heat production due to the copper loss at any instant is Ri^2, where i is the current at that instant, but the final temperature rise after this cycle has been continued for several hours will be dependent upon the average rate of heat production (the average copper loss) during the cycle.

Average copper loss

$$= R \frac{\overline{40}^2 \times 1 + \overline{20}^2 \times 3 + \overline{15}^2 \times 2 + \overline{10}^2 \times 2 + 0}{10},$$

$$= R \frac{1600 + 1200 + 450 + 200}{10},$$

$$= 345R.$$

The average copper loss for the proposed duty will be about 86% of the loss corresponding to the continuous rated load, so that the temperature rise will be well below the limiting value.

If the motor in question is a shunt motor operating at approximately constant speed the power delivered to the load at any instant will be approximately proportional to the armature current and energy will be transmitted to the load at the rate of 10 hp. for 1 minute, 5 hp. for 3 minutes, 3.75 hp. for 2 minutes, 2.5 hp. for 2 minutes and 0 hp. for 2 minutes, or a total energy of 37.5 hp-min. during one cycle. This is only 75% of the energy that the motor could deliver safely in the same time interval if operated steadily at its rated load.

An obvious conclusion to be drawn from this example is that machines cannot in general perform as effectively on periodic or intermittent loads as on continuous loads. In other words, if a motor could be so carefully selected for a given periodic-duty cycle that its final temperature rise in such duty would be exactly equal to its temperature rise with continuous rated load, the average power delivered to the periodic load would be less than its continuous rating.

201. Factors Affecting List Price. The principal factors affecting the list price of motors and generators may be classified as follows:

1. Cost of raw materials.
2. Labor and overhead costs of manufacturing the machine parts.
3. Labor and overhead costs of assembly, and the cost of testing and preparing the machine for shipment.
4. Competitive prices.

The first item needs little comment except to note that the manufacturer has some control of raw-material costs in so far as he is able to take advantage of the discount accompanying quantity purchases. If he has sufficient storage space he may save also by purchasing at irregular intervals whenever a low point in the normal fluctuation of prices is reached.

The manufacturer has several means at his disposal for reducing the second and third cost items to a minimum. An intelligent labor policy is needed to secure high standards of workmanship at reasonable wages and with a minimum labor turnover. Unceasing pressure must be placed on the manufacturing and engineering departments to show ingenuity in new designs for jigs, fixtures and special processes that will lessen the cost of manufacturing operations. Efforts expended in the standardization of parts to make them interchangeable and in adapting each frame size and each type of armature punching to the largest practicable number of machine ratings may also be expected to produce appreciable savings, if by so doing the number of different frame and armature sizes in stock can be reduced.

In addition to these methods of cost reduction which may be applied more or less effectively to all types of machines there is the possibility of further saving if popular demand for certain types and sizes is great enough to justify the installation of modern production line methods for quantity production.

The list price of a machine can seldom be based on cost alone but must also take into account the prices of similar machines offered by competitors. If one manufacturer has certain unique advantages in manufacturing costs which enable him to set unusually low prices on a line of machines, his competitors must adjust their prices accordingly even though it involves a loss. If their products are well diversified they will be in a position to take this loss for some little time by the profitable sale of articles or machines on which competitive prices are more favorable. Mean-while, by intensive re-search, efforts will be made to find ways to reduce costs and convert the loss to a profit.

202. List Price as Affected by Capacity. The relationships be-tween speed, voltage and power capacity of a motor and its list price are too complex to per-mit simultaneous consid-eration of all these factors. It is desirable to begin by considering how list price is affected by capacity under con-stant speed and voltage conditions. If, for ex-ample, a manufacturer offers a line of 230-volt, 850-rpm. motors at pow-er ratings from 1/2 to

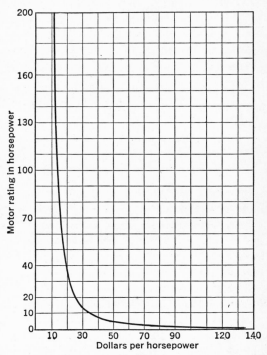

FIG. 162.   Power capacity vs. dollars per horsepower

200 hp., what relationship may be expected between the list price and the horsepower rating?

A 10-hp. motor selected from this group will be required to produce approximately twice as much torque as a 5-hp. motor, and will have twice as much armature current. The sectional area of the armature conductors will be doubled and their length will be somewhat greater so that the volume of armature copper will be more than doubled. The yoke and the armature punchings, however, will be only slightly larger, so that the total bulk of the 10-hp. machine will not be more than 45 or 50% greater than the 5-hp. unit. The labor cost of making and assembling the parts of the larger machine will show an even smaller increase so that the list price may be only 30 or 35% greater than the price of the 5-hp. machine.

The curve shown in Fig. 162 relating power capacity to dollars per horsepower is plotted from the list prices in the catalog of an important manufacturer. Note the rapid decrease in unit price as the motor size increases. A 1/2-hp. motor lists at 154 dollars per hp.; a 10-hp. motor at 35 dollars per hp. and the 200-hp. size as low as 11.5 dollars per hp.

203. List Price as Related to Speed. Since power is proportional to speed × torque, and since torque is proportional to flux × current, the expression for power becomes

$$\text{Power} = kN\Phi I.$$

Hence a motor designed to produce a certain amount of power at high speed requires relatively small values of flux and current. If the required current is small it is possible to use small armature conductors. Likewise a small value of flux permits a reduction in the size of the yoke, the size and number of poles and the diameter of the armature. Thus a very evident saving in material results from the high-speed design. The labor expended on the parts and the assembly will be about the same on a high-speed as on a low-speed machine. The total cost, therefore, of a high-speed machine is likely to be appreciably lower.

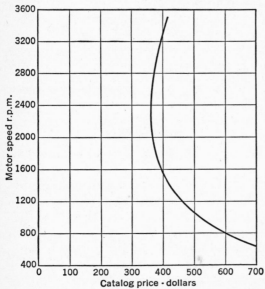

FIG. 163. Catalog price vs. speed.

There is a limited demand for motors of considerable size operating at extremely high speeds. Such a design calls for a very long armature of small diameter, special care in holding the conductors in the slots by means of stronger wedges and more band wires, more careful dynamic balancing, a stronger shaft and armature spider — all of which are reflected in a somewhat higher list price.

Figure 163 shows the variation of catalog price with speed for a group of 230-volt, 25-hp. motors.   Note the trend toward lower prices for the higher speeds, and the reversal of this trend in the jump from the 1750-rpm. to the 3500-rpm. rating.

204. Relationship of Voltage to List Price.   Motor operating voltages have gradually become standardized at the nominal values of 6, 32, 115, 230, 550 and 1500 volts.   Fractional horsepower motors are available in numerous sizes for operation on 6, 32, 115 or 230 volts. Larger motors are confined chiefly to the 115-, 230- and 550-volt ratings; 1500-volt motors of the series type give excellent service in some of the more recent railway electrification projects.

A comparison of the structural features of typical 115-, 230- and 550-volt motors having the same speed and power rating reveals some interesting characteristics:

1.   The same size of frame and yoke is used in each.

2.   The armatures have the same length and diameter.

3.   The field ampere-turns per pole are the same for each.

4.   The size of wire in the field coils, and the armature winding connections, are the chief points of difference.

Suppose that a manufacturer, having designed and built a 115-volt motor of a certain speed and power rating, wishes to design a 230-volt motor of the same rating.   In the interests of economy he will prefer to use the same frame and armature if possible.   This can be accomplished if K in the expression for generated voltage can be doubled, leaving the values of Φ and N unchanged.   By cutting the sectional area of the armature conductors in half there will be room for twice as many conductors in each slot and the number of conductors in each armature path will be doubled, which will double K.   Use of the smaller wire will cut the safe current capacity of the armature in half, but this reduced current is sufficient to give the same power output at the doubled voltage.

If the original 115-volt design utilizes a four-pole frame and a lap-wound armature it may be possible to reconnect the armature for 230-volt operation by changing the winding connections from lap to wave, thus doubling the number of conductors per path and accomplishing the desired result without changing the conductor size.

The use of the same frame for both the 115- and 230-volt designs will require some changes in the design of the field coils.   The same flux and the same ampere-turns per pole will be required, but a different combination of turns and amperes will be needed.   If the 230-volt coils are formed with twice the turns and with wire of half the sectional area these requirements will be satisfied.

If by the use of such devices the manufacturer is able to adapt the same frame and armature to the design of machines of a given power and speed for several different voltages it will be evident that the manufacturing cost will be about the same for each. Hence it is not surprising to observe numerous instances where the list prices of 115-, 230- and 550-volt motors are identical for a given speed and power rating.

205. List Price Related to Efficiency. Manufacturers of motors and generators are striving continually to build machines of high efficiency at the lowest prices consistent with the maintenance of high standards of workmanship. Unfortunately, high efficiency and low price are mutually antagonistic to some extent, and the designer of a standard line of machines must use his best judgment in effecting a compromise.

For example, the substitution of ball or roller bearings in place of the standard sleeve bearings will result in an important reduction in the bearing friction loss but the cost of the machine is increased. Some reduction in magnetic losses can be secured by the use of a better and more expensive grade of sheet steel. More copper may be used in the armature winding than is required from the standpoint of safe temperature rise at rated load, thus reducing the RI^2 loss but increasing the cost of materials.

Frequently the prospective purchaser of a machine is faced with the problem of choosing between an expensive machine of high efficiency and a cheaper one having a lower efficiency. A comprehensive discussion of all the factors that need to be considered in making this choice is out of place here, but it is desirable to note some of the fundamental principles involved.

An important part of the total cost of operating a machine is the interest on the purchase price. This is an annual charge which is unaffected by the number of hours the machine is in actual operation. The remainder of the operating cost is made up of items that depend directly on the amount of use. For example, a motor on a given duty cycle will use a certain number of kilowatt-hours of electrical energy for each hour of operation, for which payment must be made.

Obviously if a motor is to be in almost continuous service it might easily be profitable to buy a more expensive one with a high efficiency because an important saving in energy cost will result, whereas a cheaper motor will be the logical choice for service characterized by long periods of idleness.

206. Relation of Speed to Weight. It was noted in Art. 203 that high-speed motors require small values of flux and current to produce the desired power rating, and that considerable saving in material was one result of the high-speed design. It follows then that the total weight of such machines is much less than that of low-speed machines of the same rating. As a rough approximation, speed may be considered as inversely related to weight, so that a 3500-rpm., 10-hp. motor will weigh half as much as a 1750-rpm., 10-hp. motor. There is, however, an important factor tending to modify this relationship. The supporting frame

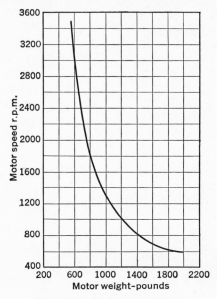

FIG. 164. Speed vs. weight.

of a light, high-speed machine accounts for a larger fraction of its total weight than the frame of a low-speed machine.

Figure 164 shows the relation of speed to weight for a group of 25-hp., 230-volt motors, as obtained from a manufacturer's catalog.

BIBLIOGRAPHY

1. Standards of the American Institute of Electrical Engineers. Section 5, or C50.
2. Principles of Engineering Economy, E. L. GRANT, Ronald Press Co., 1930.

CHAPTER 16

ELECTRIC CIRCUITS

207. Constant Current Distribution. One method of distributing electric power makes use of a series circuit linking the generators and receivers or loads. All the apparatus included in this circuit is designed to operate on a constant value of current, say 20 amperes.

The amount of voltage required of the generators depends on the number and size of the load units in the circuit. When a load unit is no longer needed it is taken out of service by short-circuiting its terminals, and the voltage which the generators must supply is reduced by the amount which was previously impressed across the terminals of the unit in question. The circuit must never be broken, as that will shut down all the loads.

This method of power distribution is used rather extensively in some parts of Europe under the name of the Thury system. Its use in this country is limited to street-lighting circuits.

208. Constant Voltage Distribution. Most of our direct-current distribution circuits operate on what is called the constant-voltage system. The generators and receivers are all in parallel and are designed for approximately the same voltage.

The amount of current required of the generators depends on the number and size of the load units connected to the circuit. When a load unit is needed no longer it is taken out of service by disconnecting it from the system, and the current which the generators must supply is reduced by the amount which was drawn previously by the load unit in question.

209. Wire Sizes. The size of a large stranded cable is designated by its sectional area in circular mils, as a 500,000-C.M. cable. Standard sizes of stranded cable begin at 250,000 C.M. and climb in steps of 50,000 to 650,000 C.M., with larger increments up to 2,000,000 C.M. See Table II.

Solid wire sizes are designated by a series of 44 numbers, constituting what is known as the American Wire Gage (A.W.G.). The largest wire, 460 mils in diameter, is called No. 0000; the smallest, with a diameter of 3.1 mils, is No. 40. The intervening sizes are so proportioned that any wire such as No. 10 has approximately half the sectional area of the third number up the table (No. 7), and is about twice the area of the third number down (No. 13). In other words, the ratio of the sectional area of any size, say No. 9, to the area of the next smaller size, No. 10, is $\sqrt[3]{2}$, or 1.26 approximately.

It so happens that No. 10 copper wire has certain constants that are easily memorized.

	Approximate Diameter	Approximate Area	Approximate Resistance per 1000 Ft.	Approximate Weight per 1000 Ft.
No. 10	0.1 in.	10,000 C.M.	1.0 ohm	$10\,\pi$ lb.

These values being known, the area, resistance and weight of any wire size in the table can be estimated quite easily, it being remembered that the area and weight are halved and the resistance doubled every three sizes down the table. Thus No. 16 has an area of about 2500 C.M., and a resistance of 4 ohms per 1000 ft., and it weighs 2 1/2 π lb. per 1000 ft., since it is six sizes down from No. 10. See Table III for A.W.G. data.

210. Wire Capacity. The selection of the proper wire size for the distribution of electric power requires consideration of three factors, any one of which may be the determining factor in a given case.

1. Limitation of the RI drop in the distribution circuit to a certain percentage of the receiver voltage.

2. Limitation of the RI^2 loss in the distribution circuit to a certain percentage of the power delivered.

3. Limitation of the conductor temperature to a safe value.

Examples illustrating the first two factors will be found in Art. 211. The third factor is of particular importance in interior wiring. Much of this wiring is concealed and in proximity to combustible materials. To minimize fire hazards it is important to install wire of sufficient size to carry the required current without incurring a dangerous rise in temperature. Numerous tests have been made under the direction of the National Board of Fire Underwriters, and detailed wiring instructions based on the results of these tests have been published under the title " National Electrical Code." A partial list of its recommendations as to the safe current capacity of copper wire with three grades of insulation is given in Table IV.

TABLE II

Bare Concentric-Lay Cables of Standard Copper

A.W.G. No.	Area, C.M.	Ohms per 1000 Ft. at 25°C.	Pounds per 1000 Ft.	Outside Diameter, Mils
4	41,700	0.259	129	232
3	52,600	0.205	163	260
2	66,400	0.162	205	292
1	83,700	0.129	258	332
0	106,000	0.102	326	373
00	133,000	0.0811	411	418
000	168,000	0.0642	518	470
0000	212,000	0.0509	653	528
	250,000	0.0431	772	575
	300,000	0.0360	926	630
	350,000	0.0308	1080	681
	400,000	0.0270	1240	728
	450,000	0.0240	1390	772
	500,000	0.0216	1540	814
	550,000	0.0196	1700	855
	600,000	0.0180	1850	893
	650,000	0.0166	2010	929
	750,000	0.0144	2320	998
	850,000	0.0127	2620	1062
	900,000	0.0120	2780	1093
	1,000,000	0.0108	3090	1152
	1,200,000	0.00899	3710	1263
	1,500,000	0.00719	4630	1412
	1,700,000	0.00634	5250	1504
	2,000,000	0.00539	6180	1631

TABLE III

STANDARD COPPER WIRE (A.W.G.)

GAGE No.	DIAMETER, MILS	SECTION, C.M.	OHMS PER 1000 FT. at 25°C.	POUNDS PER 1000 FT.
0000	460	212,000	0.0500	641
000	410	168,000	0.0630	508
00	365	133,000	0.0795	403
0	325	106,000	0.100	319
1	289	83,700	0.126	253
2	258	66,400	0.159	201
3	229	52,600	0.201	159
4	204	41,700	0.253	126
5	182	33,100	0.319	100
6	162	26,300	0.403	79.5
7	144	20,800	0.508	63.0
8	128	16,500	0.641	50.0
9	114	13,100	0.808	39.6
10	102	10,400	1.02	31.4
11	91	8,230	1.28	24.9
12	81	6,530	1.62	19.8
13	72	5,180	2.04	15.7
14	64	4,110	2.58	12.4
15	57	3,260	3.25	9.86
16	51	2,580	4.09	7.82
17	45	2,050	5.16	6.20
18	40	1,620	6.51	4.92
19	36	1,290	8.21	3.90
20	32	1,020	10.4	3.09
21	28.5	810	13.1	2.45
22	25.3	642	16.5	1.94
23	22.6	509	20.8	1.54
24	20.1	404	26.2	1.22
25	17.9	320	33.0	0.970
26	15.9	254	41.6	0.769
27	14.2	202	52.5	0.610
28	12.6	160	66.2	0.484
29	11.3	127	83.4	0.384
30	10.0	101	105	0.304
31	8.9	79.7	133	0.241
32	8.0	63.2	167	0.191
33	7.1	50.1	211	0.152
34	6.3	39.8	266	0.120
35	5.6	31.5	335	0.0954
36	5.0	25.0	423	0.0757
37	4.5	19.8	533	0.0600
38	4.0	15.7	673	0.0476
39	3.5	12.5	848	0.0377
40	3.1	9.9	1,070	0.0299

TABLE IV
ALLOWABLE CURRENT IN WIRES

(From National Electrical Code)

WIRE SIZE	A RUBBER INSULATION, AMPERES	B VARNISHED CLOTH INSULATION	C OTHER INSULATION
18	3	...	6
16	6	...	10
14	15	18	20
12	20	25	30
10	25	30	35
8	35	40	50
6	50	60	70
5	55	65	80
4	70	85	90
3	80	95	100
2	90	110	125
1	100	120	150
0	125	150	200
00	150	180	225
000	175	210	275
0000	225	270	325
200,000 C.M.	200	240	300
250,000	250	300	350
300,000	275	330	400
350,000	300	360	450
400,000	325	390	500
500,000	400	480	600
600,000	450	540	680
700,000	500	600	760
750,000	525	630	800
800,000	550	660	840
900,000	600	720	920
1,000,000	650	780	1000

211. Two-wire Circuit—Concentrated Load. In the circuit shown in Fig. 165 a generator is supplying a constant voltage, E, at one end of a two-wire distribution circuit.   At the other end of the circuit is a receiver or load represented by the variable resistance, R.   Let $1/2\,r$ represent the resistance of each of the two connecting wires, so that r may be called the resistance of the distribution line.

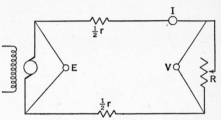

FIG. 165.   Two-wire circuit — concentrated load.

If the circuit is opened at the load, R, the current will be zero, and V, the voltage across the load, will become equal to E. With the circuit closed and R adjusted to draw a current of I amperes the expression for the voltage at the load becomes

$$V = E - rI,$$

where rI is called the voltage drop in the line, or, briefly, the line drop. Variations in R will cause I to vary, which in turn will produce changes in V.   The amount of variation in V which can be allowed often becomes the principal factor in determining the proper wire size for the line.

EXAMPLE:
  $E = 600$ volts.
The desired value of V to be not less than 550, when $I = 50$.
Distance from generator to load $= 3400$ ft.   From the voltage equation,

$$rI = E - V = 50,$$

and r must be 1.0 ohm.
  The specified distance calls for 6800 ft. of wire of sufficient sectional area to keep the resistance below 1.0 ohm.   The required resistance per 1000 ft. will be 1/6.8, or 0.147 ohm.   From Table III, No. 2 wire has a resistance of 0.159 ohm per 1000 ft., which is a little too large.   Therefore No. 1 will be required, and since its resistance is somewhat less than the specified requirement the variations in V accompanying fluctuations in I will be kept well within the desired limit.
  Occasionally it may be desirable to determine the proper wire size for a line on the basis of limiting the rI^2 loss in the line to a certain maximum value.   The following example will serve to illustrate the usual method of procedure.
  A maximum of 9200 watts is to be delivered to a resistance load which is 700 ft. away from the generator.   The voltage at the load is to be 230, and the power loss in the line must not exceed 5% of the power delivered.   Find the size of wire to be used.
  The allowable power loss is 0.05×9200 or 460 watts.   A maximum power of 9200 watts at 230 volts will require a current of 40 amperes.

$$rI^2 = r \times \overline{40}^2 = 460 \text{ watts.}$$

The line resistance, $r = 460/1600 = 0.288$ ohm.
The length of wire $= 1400$ ft.
The required resistance per 1000 ft. $= 0.288/1.4 = 0.206$.
From Table III, the best wire size is No. 3.

212. Two-wire Circuit — Distributed Load. Consider the illustrative circuit in Fig. 166a, in which loads A, B and C are shown scattered along the line at different distances from the power source, E. The following current relations will be evident:

$$I_3 = I_C$$
$$I_2 = I_B + I_C$$
$$I_1 = I_A + I_B + I_C$$

The expressions for voltage across each load will be:

$$V_A = E - r_1I_1$$
$$V_B = V_A - r_2I_2$$
$$V_C = V_B - r_3I_3$$

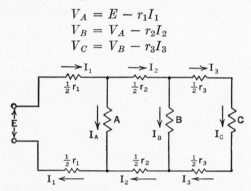

Fig. 166a.	Two-wire circuit — distributed load.

Hence if the distances from the source to the various loads are known the voltage at each load may be determined for a given wire size and supply voltage.

For example, let $E = 230$, $I_A = 10$, $I_B = 20$, $I_C = 8$.

$$\text{Distance, source to } A = 100 \text{ ft.}$$
$$A \text{ to } B = 200 \text{ ft.}$$
$$B \text{ to } C = 100 \text{ ft.}$$
$$\text{Wire size, No. 10.}$$

Required to find V_A, V_B and V_C.

Using 1.0 ohm per 1000 ft. for the resistance of No. 10 wire the voltage values at each load are as follows:

$$V_A = 230 \quad - 0.2 \times 38 = 222.4.$$
$$V_B = 222.4 - 0.4 \times 28 = 211.2.$$
$$V_C = 211.2 - 0.2 \times 8 = 209.6.$$

213. Anti-parallel System. A modification of the standard two-wire distribution system frequently employed to supply power to scattered loads is known as the anti-parallel system. Figure 166b shows the distinctive features of such a system. In the standard system the most distant load has the lowest voltage and the greatest fluctuation in voltage, as changes occur in the line current. The lowest voltage in the anti-parallel system will in general occur at the midpoint, and there will be less difference between its value at any instant and the voltages across the other loads.

As an illustration let the data of the previous example be applied to the anti-parallel circuit, and let the load voltages be computed. This type of problem is an excellent one in which to demonstrate another method of attack, known as the method of potentials. This method is based on the concept that current in a wire connecting two points cannot exist unless the two points differ in potential, and the current always moves toward the point of lower potential (like water flowing down-

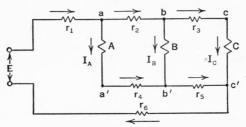

FIG. 166b. Anti-parallel circuit.

hill). Furthermore, the difference in potential between two such points always equals the rI drop in the current path between the points if the path contains no sources of voltage.

The currents and rI drops in the various sections of the line should be computed first. Thus

$$I_1 = 38, \quad I_2 = 28, \quad I_3 = 8,$$
$$I_4 = 10, \quad I_5 = 30, \quad I_6 = 38;$$

and

$$r_1I_1 = 3.8, \quad r_2I_2 = 5.6, \quad r_3I_3 = 0.8,$$
$$r_4I_4 = 2.0, \quad r_5I_5 = 3.0, \quad r_6I_6 = 15.2.$$

The potential of the upper supply terminal will be taken as 230 and the potential of the lower terminal will be zero. The potential of point a will be less than 230 because of the rI drop in the first section of the conductor.

$$\text{Pot. } a = 230 - 3.8 \quad = 226.2.$$

Similarly,

$$\text{Pot. } b = 226.2 - 5.6 \quad = 220.6,$$
$$\text{Pot. } c = 220.6 - 0.8 \quad = 219.8,$$
$$\text{Pot. } c' = 0 + 15.2 \quad = 15.2,$$
$$\text{Pot. } b' = 15.2 + 3.0 \quad = 18.2,$$
$$\text{Pot. } a' = 18.2 + 2.0 \quad = 20.2.$$

Now
$$V_A = \text{Pot. } a - \text{Pot. } a',$$
$$= 226.2 - 20.2 = 206,$$
$$V_B = 220.6 - 18.2 = 202.4,$$
$$V_C = 219.8 - 15.2 = 204.6.$$

214. Distribution at High Voltage. If operating conditions permit the distribution of power at high voltage, a small current will be sufficient and a large saving in sectional area and weight of distribution line is possible. In a previous example based on the circuit of Fig. 165 the delivery of 9200 watts at 230 volts with a 5% power loss required 1400 ft. of No. 3 wire. What wire size can be used for the same distance, power and power loss if the voltage is made 460?

The new current requirement will be 20 amperes, and, since the value of rI^2 remains at 460 watts, the new value of line resistance $= 460/400 = 1.15$ ohms, and the required resistance per 1000 ft. $= 1.15/1.4 = 0.822$, permitting the use of No. 9 wire with a sectional area only 25% of No. 3.

The use of even moderately high voltage has, however, been restricted to a few special applications such as electric traction. Incandescent lamps and many common appliances are more satisfactory when designed for 115 volts, and no device comparable in convenience and efficiency to the alternating-current transformer has yet become practicable to make it possible to generate direct current at low voltage, step it up to high voltage for the distribution circuits and lower it again at the load.

215. Economic Factors. Two kinds of costs are involved in the construction and operation of a distribution line. One includes all those items which are associated with the construction of the line and which should be charged against the line annually, regardless of how much actual transmission of power occurs over the line. The interest on the money required to build and equip the line is the principal item in this class.

The other group includes operating costs which are charged against the line only in proportion to the amount of power delivered. The principal item in this group is the cost of the power wasted in the line as rI^2.

These two groups of costs are mutually antagonistic. That is, an increase in the wire size of a proposed line for the purpose of reducing the rI^2 loss involves greater cost for copper and for installation. The selection of the best wire size for a given set of conditions requires careful study of all these factors and the exercise of good engineering judgment.

216. Maximum Power. If a concentrated load drawing a slowly increasing current is assumed at the end of a distribution line there will be some current value at which the power delivered to the load becomes a maximum. If the voltage at the source is assumed constant and if disturbing factors such as temperature coefficients be neglected it is possible to establish a simple expression for the maximum power which can be delivered by such a line.

Starting with the familiar expression relating load voltage, line drop and voltage at the source:

$$V = E - rI,$$

let each term be multiplied by I, thus converting it to a power term.

$$VI = EI - rI^2,$$

where VI = power actually reaching the load.

EI = power supplied by the source.

rI^2 = power lost in the distribution line between source and load.

Applying the usual method for obtaining the maximum,

$$\frac{d}{dI}(VI) = \frac{d}{dI}(EI - rI^2),$$

$$= E - 2rI.$$

This derivative being placed equal to zero, the condition for maximum power becomes

$$E = 2rI,$$

or

$$rI = \frac{E}{2},$$

which means that, when the current reaches such a high value as to cause half the supply voltage to be absorbed by the line rI drop, the load is receiving the maximum output of the line.

The conditions for maximum output are chiefly of theoretical interest, for it would be both unsafe and uneconomical to put such operating conditions into practice.

217. Three-wire Distribution. The three-wire system was devised by Edison in order that 115-volt lamps and appliances might be supplied with power with the added benefit of most of the distribution economy obtainable in a two-wire, 230-volt system.

Figure 167 illustrates the evolution of a three-wire system. A load composed of four 2-ohm resistors is supplied by a 115-volt distribution line as shown in part (a). By grouping them as in (b) and doubling the line voltage the current through each resistor will be unchanged, but the line current will be halved and the wire sectional area can be reduced to one-fourth of the area needed in the former system. There is the disadvantage, however, that much of the flexibility of the 115-volt system has been lost. Since two resistors are permanently in series they cannot be turned on and off separately.

Flexibility may be restored by the addition of a third wire (known as the neutral wire) connected to the load as shown in (c). A special form of power supply, such as a three-wire generator or a balancer set, will be needed in order that a mid-potential point may be made available for the neutral wire connection. If the resistances on the two sides of the three-wire system become unequal, current will flow in the neutral and a certain amount of voltage unbalance will appear, the more heavily loaded side having the lower voltage. Under ordinary conditions the voltage unbalance may be kept within reasonable limits by careful distribution of the connected load.

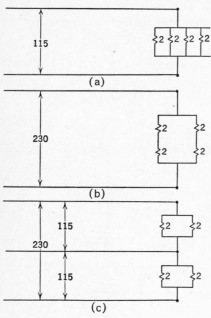

FIG. 167.   Evolution of three-wire system.

If a three-wire system is provided with overload protection by means of fuses the neutral should not be fused but should be connected solidly to the mid-potential point.   If a break in the neutral should occur while the other wires are carrying current some of the load voltages may be forced below normal and others may rise above normal.   This voltage unbalance may be so great as to cause serious damage to incandescent lamps and certain types of appliances forming part of the connected load.   It is common practice to connect the neutral of a three-wire system to ground as a safety feature.

The reader is urged to prove that the amount of copper needed in a three-wire, 230- to 115-volt system is 37 1/2% of the amount required by a two-wire, 115-volt system under the following conditions:

1. The neutral of the three-wire system is assumed to be the same size as the two outer wires.

2. The total power and the percentage rI^2 loss is to be the same for both systems.

In calculating the line rI drops and load voltages of a three-wire system the method of potentials is recommended. Consider, for example, the circuit shown in Fig. 168a. Five loads are placed on the system at the distances specified. The line wires are No. 7. It is required to compute the voltages across the loads if their currents are assumed to have the following values: $A = 4$, $B = 10$, $C = 6$, $D = 5$, $B = 7$.

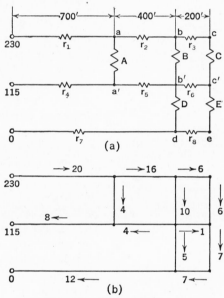

FIG. 168. Three-wire circuit.

The solution may be divided into the following steps:

1. Determination of the line current in each part of the circuit. Since there can be neither accumulation nor loss of current at a junction point, the current approaching any point such as (a) must equal the sum of the currents leaving that point. Hence the line currents can be determined by simple addition or subtraction. Their values have been indicated in Fig. 168b.

2. Determination of the resistance of each section of the line. In the example the following values will be obtained if the resistance of No. 7 wire is taken to be 0.5 ohm per 1000 ft.

$$r_1 = 0.35, \quad r_2 = 0.2, \quad r_3 = 0.1, \quad r_4 = 0.35,$$
$$r_5 = 0.2, \quad r_6 = 0.1, \quad r_7 = 0.55, \quad r_8 = 0.1.$$

3. Determination of the line rI drop in each section.

$$r_1I_1 = 7.0, \quad r_2I_2 = 3.2, \quad r_3I_3 = 0.6, \quad r_4I_4 = 2.8,$$
$$r_5I_5 = 0.8, \quad r_6I_6 = 0.1, \quad r_7I_7 = 6.6, \quad r_8I_8 = 0.7.$$

4. Determination of the potential of each junction point.

Pot. a = $230 - 7.0 = 223.0,$
Pot. b = $223 - 3.2 = 219.8,$
Pot. c = $219.8 - 0.6 = 219.2,$
Pot. a' = $115 + 2.8 = 117.8,$
Pot. b' = $117.8 + 0.8 = 118.6,$
Pot. c' = $118.6 - 0.1 = 118.5,$
Pot. d = $0 + 6.6 = 6.6,$
Pot. e = $6.6 + 0.7 = 7.3.$

5. Compute each load voltage by taking the difference between the potentials of its terminal points.

$$V_A = 223 - 117.8 = 105.2,$$
$$V_B = 219.8 - 118.6 = 101.2,$$
$$V_C = 219.2 - 118.5 = 100.7,$$
$$V_D = 118.6 - 6.6 = 112.0,$$
$$V_E = 118.5 - 7.3 = 111.2.$$

218. Railway Distribution Circuits. The long distances involved and the continual shift in the position and magnitude of the load make the problem of designing the distribution system for an electric railway a particularly difficult one. The trolley wire must be supplemented by heavy copper feeders connected in parallel with it, in order that the current requirements at any point on the system may be met without excessive voltage drop.

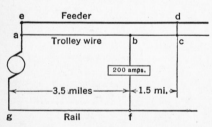

FIG. 169. Railway distribution circuit.

The circuit shown in Fig. 169, although impractical from both engineering and economical viewpoints, serves nicely as an introductory problem. A car drawing 200 amperes is located at bf, and a constant voltage of 600 is maintained at ag by the generator. The No. 0000 copper trolley wire is augmented by a 500,000-C.M. copper feeder, connected as shown. The resistance of the rail return path is 0.05 ohm per mile (both rails). Find the voltage at the car.

The trolley, ab, and the longer trolley-feeder path, $aedcb$, form two parallel paths. Since the drop in potential over each path must be the same, the following relationships are self-evident:

$$r_{ab}I_T = r_{aedcb}I_F,$$

and

$$I_T + I_F = 200 \text{ amperes,}$$

where I_T is the current taking the direct path over the trolley, and I_F follows the longer path, $aedcb$.

From Table III

$$r_{ab} = 0.05 \times 3.5 \times 5.28 = 0.924 \text{ ohm.}$$

From Table II

$$r_{aedcb} = (0.0216 \times 5.0 \times 5.28) + (0.05 \times 1.5 \times 5.28),$$
$$= 0.57 + 0.396,$$
$$= 0.966 \text{ ohm.}$$

Putting these resistance values in the previous equations and solving for I_T,

$$0.924 I_T = 0.966 \ (200 - I_T),$$
$$1.89 I_T = 193.2,$$
$$I_T = 102, \quad \text{and} \quad I_F = 98.$$

The value of the voltage drop from a to b becomes

$$0.924 \times 102 = 94.25 \text{ volts.}$$

The drop in the rail return path will be

$$0.05 \times 3.5 \times 200 = 35.0 \text{ volts,}$$

and the total drop between the generator and the car will be:

$$rI_{\text{tot.}} = 94.25 + 35.0,$$
$$= 129.25 \text{ volts.}$$

Therefore the car voltage $= 600 - 129.25,$
$$= 470.75.$$

Figure 170 shows a more practical form of railway distribution circuit. The feeder and trolley wire are connected at intervals of 200 to 300 ft., so that they may be treated in effect as a single large conductor. Suppose that it is required to estimate the sectional area of the feeder that will be needed to limit the voltage drop between the substation generator and the indicated loads to 200 volts, approximately. The substation voltage is 600.

Since a quick approximation is desired the so-called method of moments may be employed. This method requires the assumption that there is some point on the distribution system where the combined current demand of the individual loads may be concentrated with a resultant line drop equal to the average of the line drops produced by the individual loads. The location of this point may be found by a procedure similar to that employed in finding the lever arm of a resultant rotational force in mechanics. Let y = distance in miles from the substation to the point in question. Then in this example,

$$600y = 200 \times 1 + 400 \times 4,$$
$$= 1800,$$
$$y = 3.0 \text{ miles.}$$

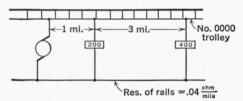

FIG. 170.   Practical railway distribution circuit.

The resistance of 3 miles of rail will be 0.12 ohm, and the rail rI drop will be:

$$600 \times 0.12 = 72.0 \text{ volts.}$$

The allowable drop in the trolley-feeder path will be $200 - 72$, or 128 volts, so that the resistance of the trolley-feeder path must be $128/600 = 0.213$ ohm, or 0.071 ohm per mile.

Using 10.58 C.M.-ohms per ft. as the resistivity of copper at 25°C., the total sectional area required will be:

$$A = \frac{10.58 \times 5280}{0.071} = 790,000 \text{ C.M.}$$

Subtracting the area of No. 0000 wire from this total area gives 578,000 C.M. as the area of feeder required. The nearest standard size of stranded copper is 600,000 C.M., which will give somewhat higher voltages at the loads.

Most railway distribution circuits are too complex to permit the use of the simple analytical methods so far described. Additional methods of solving circuit problems will be discussed in succeeding articles

219. Batteries. For complete information on the constructional features, chemical reactions and detailed operating characteristics of batteries the reader is referred to various textbooks specializing in this subject, one or two of which are listed in the bibliography at the end of this chapter. The present discussion is restricted to the general behavior of batteries as convenient sources of emf. in certain types of circuits.

A charged battery maintains a fairly constant difference of potential between its positive and negative plates so long as there is no current flow. This voltage is generally called the open-circuit voltage of the battery.

If a closed external circuit is connected to the battery terminals a current will be established, and a small part of the battery open-circuit voltage is neutralized by the internal rI drop associated with the passage of current through the battery plates and electrolyte. The battery is said to be discharging, and the voltage appearing at its terminals will be less than its open-circuit voltage and is called the terminal voltage of the battery.

If the battery terminals are connected to a power supply whose voltage is opposite to and greater than the open-circuit voltage of the battery a charging current will be delivered to the battery.

These voltage relationships may be summarized in the following equation:

$$E = V \pm rI, \tag{81}$$

where E = battery open-circuit voltage.
V = battery terminal voltage.
r = battery internal resistance.

The plus sign must be used when the battery is discharging, and the minus sign when the battery is being charged.

Batteries used as sources of emf. in circuit problems are assumed to have constant open-circuit voltages and constant internal resistances. The additional assumption is made that, when a battery is discharging, its current leaves from the positive terminal of the battery and flows from plus to minus in the external circuit. This is contrary to the actual direction of flow of the electrons constituting what we call current, but follows a long-established convention still prevalent in engineering practice.

220. Kirchhoff's Laws. Kirchhoff, a German physicist, formulated two simple rules which are of great assistance in the solution of circuit problems involving three or more unknowns.

1. The algebraic sum of all the currents approaching and leaving a junction point is zero. In other words, there can be neither accumulation nor loss of current at a junction point.

2. The algebraic sum of all the voltages in any closed path must equal the algebraic sum of all the RI drops in that same path.

In applying these laws to a complicated circuit, systematic procedure is essential. The following steps are suggested for the attack:

(a) Draw a schematic diagram of the circuit.

(b) Examine the circuit for possible simplification. It may be that there are several parallel paths containing no sources of voltage, which may be replaced by a single equivalent resistance.

(c) Letter or number all important junction points.

(d) Assume current directions in all the branches of the circuit, and indicate them on the diagram.

(e) Apply the first law, writing current equations for as many junction points as seem to be important to the problem. It is customary to call currents approaching a junction point positive, and currents leaving the point negative.

(f) Apply the second law, writing voltage equations for as many closed paths as appear necessary. It is customary to call voltages acting in a clockwise direction around the path positive, and opposing voltages negative. Hence all RI drops produced by a clockwise current will be negative and all others positive.

(g) Using these two groups of equations, proceed to evaluate the unknowns, either by simultaneous solution or by the use of determinants.

(h) Correct the original assumptions as to current directions if necessary. A negative sign attached to the computed current in any path means that the actual current in that path is opposite in direction to the assumed current.

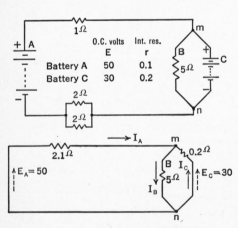

FIG. 171. Example of Kirchhoff's laws.

	O.C. volts E	Int. res. r
Battery A	50	0.1
Battery C	30	0.2

221. Networks. As an illustration of the method of applying Kirchhoff's laws to the solution of networks consider the following problem: Find the magnitude and direction of the current through battery C in the circuit shown in Fig. 171a.

Inspection of the figure shows several resistances in the path nAm which may be replaced by a single resistance of 2.1 ohms (including the internal resistance of battery A). To avoid confusion the circuit is redrawn in simplified form in Fig. 171b. Directions of the path currents I_A, I_B and I_C have been assumed and indicated. The dashed lines E_A and E_C indicate the battery open-circuit voltages.

By application of the first law at point m,

$$I_A + I_C - I_B = 0. \tag{I}$$

For the path $nAmB$ the second law gives

$$50 - 2.1I_A - 5I_B = 0. \tag{II}$$

In the path $nAmC$

$$50 - 2.1I_A - 30 + 0.2I_C = 0. \tag{III}$$

Rearranging the terms of equation I,

$$I_C = I_B - I_A. \tag{IV}$$

Substituting this value of I_C in equation III

$$50 - 2.1I_A - 30 + 0.2 (I_B - I_A) = 0,$$

or

$$20 - 2.3I_A + 0.2I_B = 0. \tag{V}$$

Multiplying equation V by 25, and combining with equation II to eliminate I_B,

$I_A = 9.23$ amperes.

$I_B = 6.12;\ \ I_C = -3.11.$

The negative sign attached to I_C indicates that the actual direction of I_C is opposite to the assumed direction. Battery C therefore is being charged.

In certain types of circuits the process of applying Kirchhoff's laws may be simplified considerably. Figure 172 illustrates such a case, in which three batteries

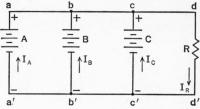

FIG. 172. Example of battery circuit.

	O.C. Volts	Int. res.
Battery A	100	0.08
Battery B	110	0.09
Battery C	120	0.10

Resistance $R = 1.5$ ohms.

are connected in parallel with a resistance load. It is required to find the magnitude and direction of the current in each battery. Current directions have been assumed and indicated in the diagram.

The connectors $abcd$ and $a'b'c'd'$ are assumed to be heavy copper straps of negligible resistance. Hence a voltmeter placed across the circuit at $a–a'$ will read exactly the same voltage as at $b–b'$, $c–c'$ or $d–d'$. Let V equal this voltage.

Since the three batteries are assumed to be discharging, the voltage relationships within each may be written in the following form:

$$E_A - V = r_A I_A, \quad \text{or} \quad I_A = \frac{E_A - V}{r_A}.$$

Since E and r are known for each battery we may write

$$I_A = \frac{100 - V}{0.08}. \tag{I}$$

$$I_B = \frac{110 - V}{0.09}. \tag{II}$$

$$I_C = \frac{120 - V}{0.10}. \tag{III}$$

$$I_R = \frac{V}{1.5}. \tag{IV}$$

Also

$$I_A + I_B + I_C = I_R. \tag{V}$$

Substituting the current equivalents in equation V,

$$\frac{100 - V}{0.08} + \frac{110 - V}{0.09} + \frac{120 - V}{0.10} = \frac{V}{1.5},$$

which is an equation with only one unknown, V.

Clearing fractions and solving,

$$V = 107.13 \text{ volts}.$$

$$I_A = -89, \quad I_B = 32, \quad I_C = 129, \quad I_R = 72.$$

222. "Short-circuit Current" Method. This ingenious method of solving networks, devised by Kouwenhoven and Pullen,[*] is particularly valuable for combinations of generators (or batteries) and resistances in parallel.

Consider the circuit shown in Fig. 172 again, with its current and voltage relationships restated in general terms.

$$I_A + I_B + I_C = I_R, \tag{1}$$

and

$$E_A - r_A I_A = E_B - r_B I_B = E_C - r_C I_C = R I_R = V. \tag{2}$$

---

[*] "A New Method of Calculating Circuits," W. B. Kouwenhoven and M. W. Pullen, *Electrical Engineering*, November, 1933, pp. 776–779.

Rearrange equation 1,

$$I_A = I_R - I_B - I_C. \tag{3}$$

Select from equation 2 the particular terms applying to battery A,

$$E_A - r_A I_A = V. \tag{4}$$

Replace the I_A of equation 4 with its value obtained from equation 3,

$$E_A - r_A (I_R - I_B - I_C) = V. \tag{5}$$

Rearrange the order of the terms and divide both sides of equation 5 by r_A.

$$\frac{E_A}{r_A} + I_B + I_C - I_R = \frac{V}{r_A}. \tag{6}$$

Select from equation 2 the particular terms applying to battery B, and divide by r_B.

$$\frac{E_B}{r_B} - I_B = \frac{V}{r_B}. \tag{7}$$

Repeat for battery C.

$$\frac{E_C}{r_C} - I_C = \frac{V}{r_C}. \tag{8}$$

For the load we may write

$$I_R = \frac{V}{R}. \tag{9}$$

Add equations (6), (7), (8) and (9) algebraically.

$$\frac{E_A}{r_A} + \frac{E_B}{r_B} + \frac{E_C}{r_C} = V\left(\frac{1}{r_A} + \frac{1}{r_B} + \frac{1}{r_C} + \frac{1}{R}\right). \tag{10}$$

The ratio E_A/r_A is called the fictitious short-circuit current (I_{As}) of battery A, so that the left-hand side of equation 10 may be written

$$I_{As} + I_{Bs} + I_{Cs}.$$

The terms within the parenthesis may be replaced by $1/R_{eq}$, where R_{eq} is the resistance equivalent to r_A, r_B, r_C and R in parallel. Therefore equation 10 becomes

$$(I_{As} + I_{Bs} + I_{Cs}) R_{eq} = V.$$

Hence to solve a circuit problem by this method, proceed as follows:

1. Calculate the " short-circuit current " of each battery by dividing the battery emf. by the resistance of its branch.

2. Add these short-circuit currents algebraically.

3. Compute the equivalent resistance of the various parallel branches.

4. Multiply the sum of the short-circuit currents by the equivalent resistance, obtaining the voltage V.

5. Return to each branch, and calculate the branch current.

Applying this method to the problem illustrated in Fig. 172

$$I_{As} = \frac{100}{0.08} = \frac{10,000}{8} = 1250.$$

$$I_{Bs} = \frac{110}{0.09} = \frac{11,000}{9} = 1222.$$

$$I_{Cs} = \frac{120}{0.1} = \frac{1200}{1} = 1200.$$

$$\text{Sum} = \overline{3672}.$$

$$R_{eq} = \frac{1}{\dfrac{1}{0.08} + \dfrac{1}{0.09} + \dfrac{1}{0.1} + \dfrac{1}{1.5}} = \frac{1}{\dfrac{100}{8} + \dfrac{100}{9} + \dfrac{10}{1} + \dfrac{2}{3}},$$

$$= \frac{72}{2468},$$

and

$$V = 3672 \left(\frac{72}{2468}\right) = 107.13 \text{ volts,}$$

from which,

$$I_A = -89, \quad I_B = 32, \quad I_C = 129, \quad I_R = 72.$$

223. Schutt Method. C. E. Schutt,[*] in 1923, demonstrated a method of attacking circuit problems that proves particularly valuable for the types of circuits encountered in the trolley networks of city railway systems.

The loop or mesh shown in Fig. 173 will be used as an example. Current is entering the loop at junction points a, c, d, f and h, and leaving at points b, e and g. It is desired to find the magnitude and direction of the current in each of the eight sections of the loop. The procedure may be outlined as follows:

1. Let the current entering at any junction point, as a, be assumed to start around the loop in a clockwise direction. Compute the ficti-

* " A New Method of Determining Correct Values of Current Flow for Electric Railway Systems," C. E. Schutt, *Electric Traction*, Vol. 19, 1923, pp. 422–425; 568–570; 607–611.

tious current in each section by applying Kirchhoff's first law to each junction point in turn. Thus $i_2 = 100$, $i_3 = -200$, $i_4 = -140$, $i_5 = 60$, $i_6 = -90$, $i_7 = 180$, $i_8 = -150$, $i_1 = 0$.

2. Calculate the fictitious voltage drop in each section, and add algebraically. Thus

$$r_2i_2 = 1.0 \qquad r_3i_3 = -4.0$$
$$r_5i_5 = 0.6 \qquad r_4i_4 = -2.8$$
$$r_7i_7 = 4.5 \qquad r_6i_6 = -2.7$$
$$\underline{r_1i_1 = 0.0} \qquad \underline{r_8i_8 = -3.75}$$
$$6.1 \qquad\qquad -13.25$$

$$\Sigma ri = -7.15 \text{ volts}$$

3. Divide the net fictitious ri drop by the sum of the section resistances to obtain a corrective current. Thus

$-7.15 \div 0.15 =$
   -47.7 amperes.

4. Introduce this corrective current in each section, and combine it algebraically with the fictitious current already present. If a positive corrective current results from step 3, introduce it in the loop as a counter-clockwise component. If the corrective current is negative, as in this example, consider it as flowing clockwise around the loop.

Thus

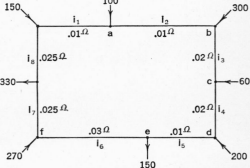

FIG. 173.   Circuit suitable for Schutt method.

$$i_2 = 100 + 47.7 = 147.7.$$
$$i_3 = -200 + 47.7 = -152.3.$$
$$i_4 = -140 + 47.7 = -92.3.$$
$$i_5 = 60 + 47.7 = 107.7.$$
$$i_6 = -90 + 47.7 = -42.3.$$
$$i_7 = 180 + 47.7 = 227.7.$$
$$i_8 = -150 + 47.7 = -102.3.$$
$$i_1 = 0 + 47.7 = 47.7.$$

These are the true currents in the loop, with positive values interpreted as clockwise currents.

Notice that this method is in perfect accord with Kirchhoff's laws. The second step produces an apparent violation of Kirchhoff's second law, in that Σri around the loop does not equal zero. This discrepancy is removed by the third and fourth steps in which an additional ri drop is introduced with the proper magnitude and algebraic sign to bring $\Sigma ri = 0$, as required.

The reader is referred to the original articles for additional details on the method, particularly its application to two or more interconnected loops.

BIBLIOGRAPHY

1. Storage Batteries, VINAL, 2nd edition, John Wiley & Sons.
2. Elements of Storage Batteries, JANSKY and WOOD, McGraw-Hill Book Co.
3. Wiring for Light and Power, CROFT, 4th edition, McGraw-Hill Book Co.
4. Standard Handbook for Electrical Engineers, 6th edition, McGraw-Hill Book Co.

PROBLEMS

1. It became necessary to wind new field coils to replace burned-out coils on a shunt motor, but owing to an error the new coils were only 80% as long (measured along the polar axis) as the original ones. The internal and external diameters of the coils and the wire size were all the same as in the original coils. Compare the currents of the two sets of coils. Compare their RI^2 losses.

2. A given spool wound full of No. 18 copper wire has a resistance of 12 ohms. If the same spool should be wound full of No. 12 wire what would be its approximate resistance?

3. A coil of No. 14 wire has a resistance of 3.87 ohms at 25°C. What will be the resistance at this temperature of a coil of No. 8 wire having the same total weight?

4. A steady source of 120 volts supplies current to three loads in parallel. The first load takes 5 amperes and is 140 ft. away from the source. The second takes 10 amperes and is 50 ft. beyond the first load. The third takes 8 amperes and is 150 ft. beyond the second. The line wires are No. 12. What are the voltages at the loads?

5. A load 500 ft. away from the generator is drawing 40 amperes. The voltage at the load is 100.

(a) If a two-wire transmission line is to be used, determine the proper wire size that will limit the voltage drop in the line to 4 volts.

(b) Determine the proper wire size if the load voltage becomes 200, the power transmitted, the power loss due to heating and the distance remaining the same as in (a).

6. How much saving in copper could be secured by using a three-wire system of transmission, for the same power, power loss and distance as in the previous problem? Voltage between neutral and each outside wire to be 100. Neutral to have half the sectional area of each outside wire.

7. A two-wire transmission line 40 miles long has 45 poles per mile. The average insulation resistance of one insulator is 50 megohms. The line voltage is 22,000 volts. Find the total insulation resistance in ohms between line wires, the total leakage current and the total power lost by leakage.

8. A concentrated load of 20 amperes is located 500 ft. from a 115-volt source. What size of copper wire is required to maintain a voltage of 105 volts across the load?

9. What size of aluminum wire could be substituted for the copper wire in the previous problem if the rI drop is to be kept the same? Compare the relative weight of wire required in the two cases.

10. The accompanying figure shows an anti-parallel distribution circuit. The supply voltage is held constant at 115 volts. What size of wire should be used in order that a voltage of 100 shall be maintained across the 20-ampere load?

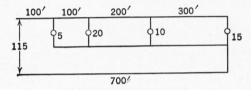

Prob. 10. Ch. 16.

11. If No. 1 wire were used in the circuit of the preceding problem, what would be the voltage across each load?

12. Three different wire sizes are to be used in the circuit shown, in order to equalize more nearly the rI drop. Determine the proper wire size to maintain 110 volts across the first load, 105 across the second and 102 across the third.

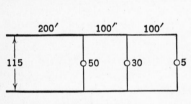

Prob. 12, Ch. 16.

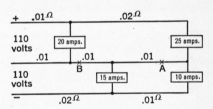

Prob. 13, Ch. 16.

13. The plan of a three-wire system is shown in the figure, the loads being of constant resistance. Calculate the voltage at each load. What will be the effect of breaking the neutral conductor at B? What will be the voltage at each load if the neutral is broken at A?

14. A car drawing 200 amperes is 3 miles away from the power house. The car is supplied by direct trolley connection from the power house, and also by a feeder which connects with the trolley 5 miles from the power house. The resistances per mile are: trolley, 0.25; feeder, 0.12; rail return, 0.05. The voltage at the power house is 600. Find the feeder current and the voltage at the car.

15. A generator whose terminal voltage is maintained at a constant value of 600 feeds power to a trolley system. Resistances are as follows: trolley, 0.3 ohm per mile; track, 0.05 ohm per mile. Five miles from the generator a battery of 550-volt open-circuit voltage and an internal resistance of 0.25 ohm is connected from trolley to rail.

(a) A car drawing 100 amperes is just opposite the battery; what current is supplied by the generator?

(b) A car drawing 100 amperes travels from the battery location towards the generator. For what position of the car will the battery be just " floating " on the line?

16. At the end of a transmission line having a resistance of 0.3 ohm there is floated a battery of 250 cells, each of which has an open-circuit voltage of 2.1 volts and an internal resistance of 0.001 ohm. If the station voltage is maintained at 560 volts, what current will the battery supply when there is a load of 400 amperes at the end of the line close to the battery terminals? What current will the load take if the battery supplies 100 amperes; if the battery carries zero amperes?

17. An interurban line is to be supplied with current from a No. 0000 trolley, assisted by a feeder tied in parallel with it at close intervals. Substations maintaining voltages of 600 volts will be connected to each end of a 6-mile section. If a car drawing 500 amperes is located 2 miles from one end of this section, what size of feeder will be necessary in order that the voltage at the car will be 500 volts? Track resistance is 0.04 ohm per mile.

18. A 600-volt generator supplies a streetcar line as follows: length of track is 5 miles, with a resistance of 0.04 ohm per mile; trolley wire resistance is 0.3 ohm per mile; feeder resistance is 0.01 ohm per mile. The feeder parallels the trolley and is connected to it at each end of the 5-mile length. A car on the system takes 100 amperes. Find the car's distance from the generator to the point where the trolley-to-track voltage is lowest; also find that voltage.

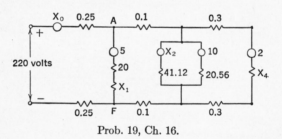

Prob. 19, Ch. 16.

19. Find the unknown currents X_0, X_2. Find the unknown resistances X_1, X_4. Find the voltage A–F.

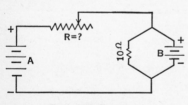

Prob. 20, Ch. 16.

20. Find the value of R so that batter B will neither charge nor discharge.

	A	B
Open-circuit volts	75.	20.
Internal resistance	2.	1.

21. Determine the magnitude and direction of the battery currents in the circuit shown.

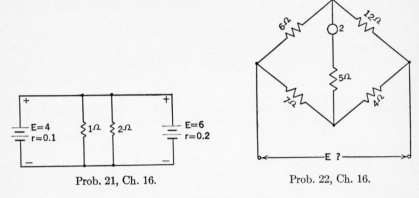

Prob. 21, Ch. 16.   Prob. 22, Ch. 16.

22. Find what voltage must be applied to the given network in order to produce a current of 2 amperes in the middle path. Find the total current in the supply line.

23. A variable-load resistance is connected to the terminals of a battery whose open-circuit voltage is 50 and whose internal resistance is 1 ohm. For what value of load resistance will the power delivered to the load be a maximum if the battery resistance and open-circuit voltage remain constant?

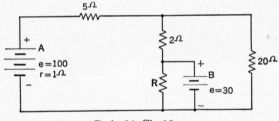

Prob. 24, Ch. 16.

24. Find the internal resistance of battery B in the circuit shown below. Resistance R is 1.2 ohms and is drawing 480 watts from the system.

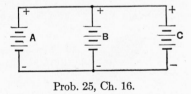

Prob. 25, Ch. 16.

25. Find the magnitude and direction of the current in each branch.

	A	B	C
Open-circuit volts	49	48	44
Internal resistance	0.1	0.12	0.15

26. Find the magnitude and direction of the current in each part of the circuit.

	A	B	C
Open-circuit volts	60	58	54
Internal resistance	0.13	0.15	0.17

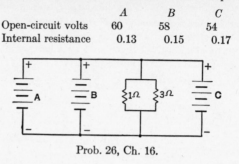

Prob. 26, Ch. 16.

27. Two separately excited shunt generators are connected as shown below, and are driven at constant speeds and supplied with constant field excitation. Find the value of R required to make generator B motorize and draw a 20-ampere armature current.

	A	B
Generated volts	600	550
Armature resistance	0.1	0.15

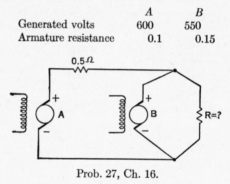

Prob. 27, Ch. 16.

28. In the accompanying circuit, generator A is separately excited and generates a constant voltage of 100 volts. Its armature resistance is 0.2 ohm. Battery B has

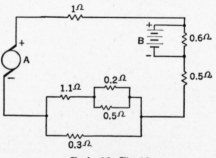

Prob. 28, Ch. 16.

an open-circuit voltage of 10, and an internal resistance of 0.3. Compute the value of the current through the battery and determine its direction.

29. A battery consisting of 60 cells has a resistance of 10 ohms connected across its terminals.   Each cell has an emf. of 2 volts and a resistance of 0.01 ohm.

(a) A 1-ohm resistance is connected from the midpoint of the 10-ohm resistance to the midpoint of the battery.   Find what current flows in the 1-ohm resistance.

(b) The 1-ohm resistance of (a) is replaced by a battery of 10 volts emf. and 1-ohm resistance.   Find the current in this battery.

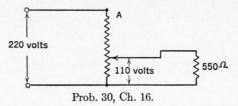

Prob. 30, Ch. 16.

30. A 220-ohm slide-wire rheostat is connected across a 220-volt line, as shown. A 550-ohm resistance is connected between the slider and one end of the rheostat, and the slider is then moved until the voltage across the 550-ohm resistance is 110. Find the resistance of the rheostat section between the slider and terminal A.

31. Find the value of the current in resistance R.

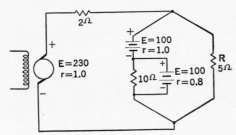

Prob. 31, Ch. 16.

32. A railway distribution circuit is shown, with the total resistances of each part of the circuit given.   The resistance of the series generator used as a negative booster

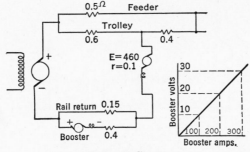

Prob. 32, Ch. 16.

is negligible and its characteristic curve is shown.   The load consists of a series motor whose counter-emf. is 460 volts and whose resistance is 0.1 ohm.   The feeder current is 60% of the current in the rail return path. Determine the current drawn by the series motor, and its terminal voltage.

33. Find the magnitude and direction of the current in each section of this loop.

Prob. 33, Ch. 16.

APPENDIX

224. Prediction of External Characteristics.

A. Separately excited generator with demagnetizing ampere-turns created by brush shift.

EXAMPLE. Given the following data: poles = 6; constant shunt ampere-turns per pole = 3500; armature, 78 slots; 1404 conductors; simple lap winding; armature circuit resistance, 0.11; speed, 1000 rpm.; brushes placed one slot ahead of neutral position.

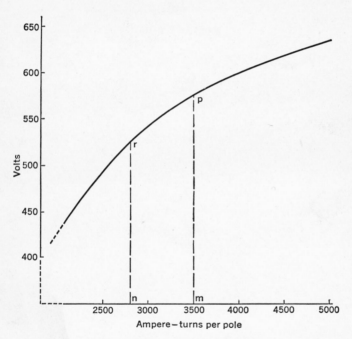

FIG. 174.   Saturation curve at 1000 rpm.

Figure 174 shows a portion of the saturation curve of this machine for a speed of 1000 rpm. At no load the voltage drops due to armature resistance and armature demagnetizing action are negligible, and the terminal voltage will be determined entirely by the amount of shunt field excitation. Accordingly $V_{\text{no-load}}$ = ordinate mp = 575 volts. To determine another point on

295

the external characteristic curve an armature current will be assumed and its demagnetizing action will be computed first.

Let $I_a = 120$ amperes.

The path current $= 120/6 = 20$ amperes.

The demagnetizing band width is 2 slots, or 36 conductors.

The demagnetizing NI per pole $= 36 \times 20 = 720$.

The net NI per pole $= 3500 - 720 = 2780$.

The $K\Phi N$ = ordinate nr of the saturation curve $= 525$. Now the RI drop can be determined.

$$R_a I_a = 0.11 \times 120 = 13.2 \text{ volts,}$$

and V, the terminal voltage $= 525 - 13.2 = 511.8$.

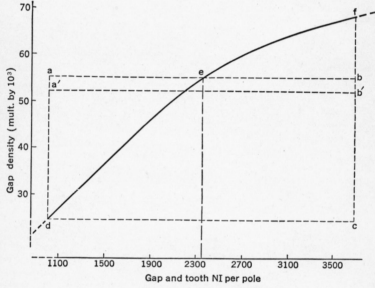

Fig. 175. Gap density vs. gap and tooth NI.

By repeating this process for other values of I_a, a sufficiently accurate determination of the curve can be obtained.

B. Separately excited generator with the flux distorted by armature reaction.

The data of Example A will be used, except that the brushes are fixed at the geometric neutral.

The no-load voltage = ordinate $mp = 575$ volts.

Let $I_a = 100$ amperes, and assume that the pole arc is 70% of the pole pitch, or 9 slots.

The path current $= 16.7$ amperes.

The reaction band under one pole = 9 × 18 = 162 conductors. The reaction ampere-turns at each pole tip = 1/2 × 162 × 16.7 = 1350. From the B-H curves and design data of this machine the gap density resulting from a shunt field excitation of 3500 is about 55,000 lines per sq. in. and the corresponding gap-and-tooth mmf. is about 2345.

The curve shown in Fig. 175 gives the relation between gap density and gap-and-tooth mmf. for the magnetic circuit.

The mmf. at the low-density pole tip will be

$$2345 - 1350 = 995,$$

with a corresponding density of 25,000.

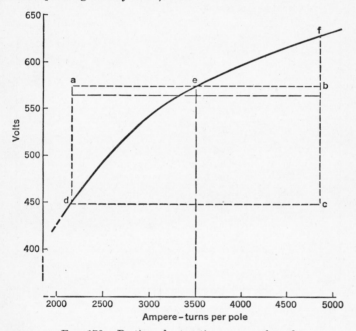

Fig. 176. Portion of saturation curve, enlarged.

The mmf. at the high-density tip will be

$$2345 + 1350 = 3695,$$

with a density of 68,000.

The area of the rectangle $abcd$, Fig. 175, is increased by the area efb, but is decreased by the larger area aed. Measurements of these areas with a planimeter indicate a net reduction of about 10% in area, which brings the average density line ab to a new position $a'b'$, and the average gap density becomes 52,000.

The gap flux therefore will be 52/55, or 94.5% of the amount produced at no load, and $K\Phi N$ becomes 544 volts.

The RI drop in the armature circuit = 11 volts.

The terminal voltage becomes 544 − 11 = 533 volts, for a load current of 100 amperes.

Repeating this process for other assumed values of I_a will give sufficient points to determine the trend of the curve.

Since the design data required to determine the curve of gap density vs. gap-and-tooth mmf. will not always be available, a more approximate result can be secured by a similar process utilizing the complete saturation curve.

That portion of the saturation curve covering the vicinity of the no-load

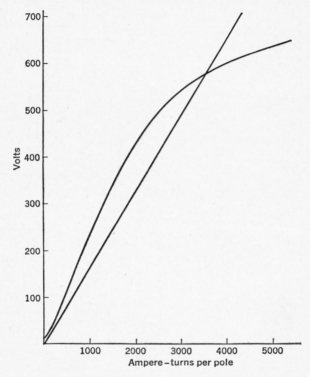

Fig. 177.   Saturation curve and resistance line.

voltage is replotted to a larger scale as in Fig. 176.   The points corresponding to 3500 − 1350 and 3500 + 1350 ampere-turns per pole are marked at d and f respectively, and the areas aed and efb are measured with a planimeter.   In this manner the net area is found to be 92.3% of the original rectangle $abcd$, which places the new voltage ine at 565 volts.   With this value of $K\Phi N$ the terminal voltage becomes 554, which is about 4% greater than the value determined by the previous method.

C. Self-excited generator with demagnetizing ampere-turns created by brush shift.

The data of Example A will be used. Let the initial shunt field excitation be set at 3500 ampere-turns per pole, giving a no-load terminal voltage of 575 as indicated by the intersection of the saturation curve and the shunt field resistance line (Fig. 177).

Let $I_a = 60$ amperes.

The armature $RI = 6.6$ volts.

The demagnetizing NI per pole $= 360$.

A reduction in flux will occur, owing to the demagnetizing NI and to the reduction in shunt field current. A further reduction in terminal voltage will

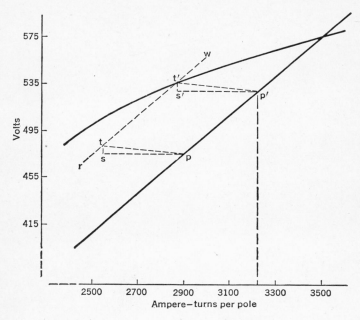

FIG. 178. Part of Fig. 177, enlarged.

be caused by armature RI drop, and the conditions governing the new values of generated voltage and terminal voltage may be stated as follows:

1. The generated voltage will slide down the saturation curve to a point whose abscissa is the excitation produced by the new shunt field ampere-turns less the demagnetizing ampere-turns.

2. The terminal voltage will slide down the shunt field resistance line to a point whose abscissa is the new shunt field ampere-turns.

3. The vertical distance separating the generated and terminal voltages is equal to the armature RI drop.

4. The horizontal distance separating these voltages is equal to the demagnetizing NI.

The voltages required to satisfy these conditions may be determined graphically. The upper portion of Fig. 177 has been enlarged as shown in Fig. 178. From a convenient point p on the shunt field resistance line the demagnetizing NI have been laid off to scale as the line ps. From the point s the armature RI drop is erected to t. The straight line rtw is drawn through t parallel to the shunt field resistance line. Its intersection with the saturation curve occurs at about 535.6 volts, which is E, the new value of the generated voltage. The new terminal voltage $= E - R_aI_a$, or $535.6 - 6.6 = 529$ volts. The new shunt field excitation, indicated by the abscissa of the point p', is 3215 ampereturns.

To determine the terminal voltage corresponding to another current, say 40 amperes, a triangle exactly similar to tsp is required, with each dimension

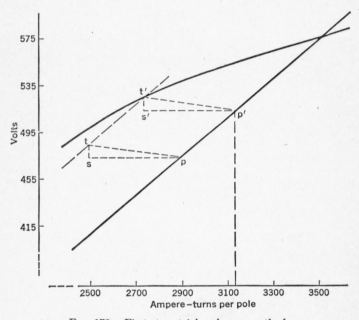

FIG. 179.   First step, trial-and-error method.

reduced to 40/60 of its present value, but with its apex still lying on the shunt field resistance line. Drawing a line through the new location of t parallel to the shunt field resistance line, and extending it until it cuts the saturation curve, will determine the new generated voltage, and V can be found as before.

D. Self-excited generator with the flux distorted by armature reaction.

A laborious trial-and-error process is necessary in this case. The data of Examples A and B will be used. Let $I_a = 100$ amperes, for which $R_aI_a = 11$ volts and the reaction ampere-turns at each pole tip $= 1350$.

Assume that these reaction ampere-turns have a demagnetizing effect equivalent to $400NI$. Construct a triangle *tsp* (Fig. 179), with the altitude equal to 11 volts and the base equal to $400NI$. Fit this triangle between the saturation curve and the shunt field resistance line as in Example C, by drawing a line through t parallel to the shunt field resistance line. By this process the following tentative values of E, V and shunt NI are obtained:

$$E = 524; \quad \text{shunt } NI = 3130; \quad V = 513.$$

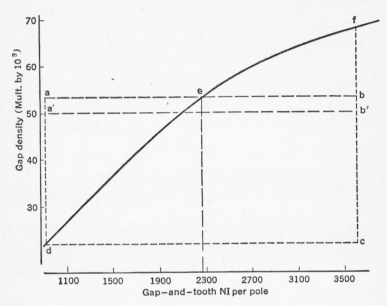

Fig. 180. Second step, trial-and-error method.

It is now necessary to refer to the curve of gap density vs. gap-and-tooth NI (Fig. 180) and to proceed as in Example B. The values of flux and flux density corresponding to $3130NI$ are 2.35×10^6 and 53,400 respectively, and the gap-and-tooth NI at the center of the pole face is 2250. The gap-and-tooth NI at one pole tip will therefore be $2250 + 1350 = 3600$, and at the other pole tip it will be $2250 - 1350 = 900$. By measuring the areas *aed* and *bef* with a planimeter a net reduction in area of 10.8% is noted. This reduces the average gap density to 50,000, as compared with 51,000 obtained by dividing the generated voltage (524) by KN (0.234×10^{-3}) and then by the gap area (44 sq. in.).

If the discrepancy between the gap-density values obtained in this trial is too great, it is necessary to assume a different value for the demagnetizing effect of the reaction NI. The proportions of the triangle *tsp* will have to be altered accordingly, new values of voltage and shunt ampere-turns obtained, new boundaries established on the curve of Fig. 180 and the net reduction in

area determined as before. Additional points on the characteristic curve
must be determined in the same manner.

In the absence of sufficient design data, an estimate of the influence of armature reaction on the external characteristic curve can be obtained with the help
of the saturation curve.   In Fig. 181, portions of the saturation curve and the
shunt field resistance line of the machine used in the previous examples are
drawn to an enlarged scale.   Let $I_a = 100$ and the demagnetizing effect of
the reaction NI be estimated at $200NI$.   The triangle tsp with an altitude of

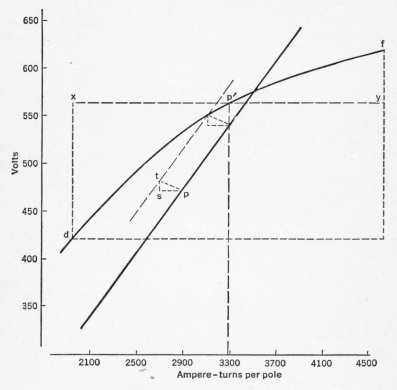

Fig. 181.   Trial-and-error method utilizing saturation curve.

11 volts and a base of $200NI$ is fitted between the saturation curve and the
shunt field resistance line as shown, giving the following values:

$$E = 551; \quad V = 540; \quad \text{shunt } NI = 3290.$$

The abscissa of the point x is $3290 - 1350$, and of point y it is $3290 + 1350$.
By means of a planimeter the new position of the line $xp'y$, such as will bring
the areas $xp'd$ and $yp'f$ into balance, occurs at 550 volts, which checks closely
the value of E determined by the assumed proportions of the triangle tsp.

This trial-and-error process must be repeated for a sufficient number of values of I_a to determine the trend of the desired characteristic.

E. Cumulative compound generator with demagnetizing ampere-turns created by brush shift.

For convenience let series coils of 16 turns be added to the machine of the previous examples. The shunt field is self-excited with the long shunt connection. The new armature circuit resistance is 0.14 ohm. The no-load voltage is 575, as before.

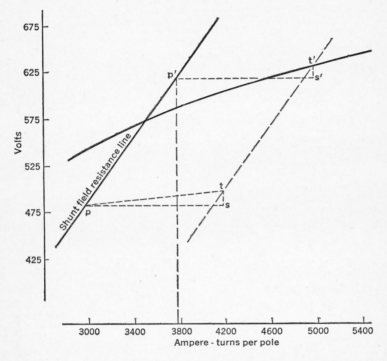

Fig. 182. Determination of terminal voltage, compound generator.

To illustrate the procedure, assume $I_a = 120$, for which $R_a I_a = 16.8$, and the demagnetizing $NI = 720$ as in Example A. The series $NI = 1920$, giving a net increase of $1200NI$. Construct the right triangle tsp (Fig. 182) with the base $= 1200NI$, laid off to the right of point p on the shunt field resistance line, and the altitude $= 16.8$ volts. Draw a line through t parallel to the shunt field resistance line, and extend it to the saturation curve at t'. The values of E, V and shunt NI as determined by the new location of the triangle at $t's'p'$ are as follows: $E = 632.8$; $V = 616$; shunt $NI = 3750$. By choosing other values of I_a and changing the dimensions of the triangle *tsp* to correspond, a sufficient number of points on the characteristic curve may be determined.

F. Cumulative compound generator with the flux distorted by armature reaction. Consider the machine of the preceding example to be operating with its brushes at the geometric neutral. To find the terminal voltage corresponding to a selected armature current a laborious trial-and-error method is required.

Let $I_a = 100$, for which $R_a I_a = 14$. As a trial value let $400NI$ be the demagnetizing effect of the reaction NI. Since the series field is producing a

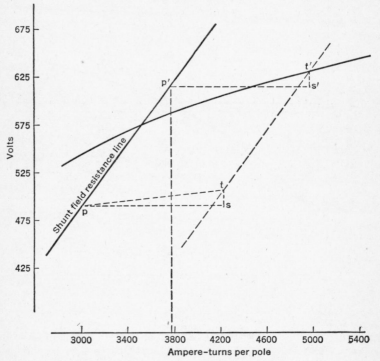

Fig. 183. Trial-and-error process, compound generator.

magnetizing effect of $1600NI$ the net magnetizing effect will be $1600 - 400 = 1200$. Construct the right triangle *tsp* (Fig. 183) with a base of $1200NI$, laid off to the right of the shunt field resistance line, and an altitude of 14 volts. By fitting this to the curves the following tentative values are obtained:

$$E = 634; \quad V = 620; \quad \text{shunt } NI = 3780.$$

By referring to the saturation curve, Fig. 183, the value of E corresponding to the sum of the shunt and series NI (5380) is 646 volts. By dividing by $KN = 0.234 \times 10^{-3}$ the value of Φ is found to be 2.755×10^6, and the flux density at the center of the pole face $= 2.755 \times 10^6/44 = 62,700$. The gap-

and-tooth NI for this density is 2940, from Fig. 184. Since the reaction NI at each pole tip is 1350 for $I_a = 100$, the gap-and-tooth NI at one tip will be $2940 + 1350 = 4290$, and at the other tip it is $2940 - 1350 = 1590$. Measuring the areas *aed* and *bef*, the position of the line indicating the average gap density under the pole face is located at 60,700, for which $\Phi = 2.67 \times 10^6$ and $E = 626$, as compared with the value of 634 obtained from the position of the triangle $t's'p'$, Fig. 183.

If the difference between the two values of E obtained on the first trial is too great the proportions of the triangle *tsp* must be altered by assuming a differ-

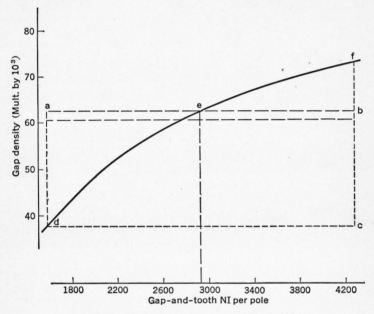

FIG. 184. Gap density vs. gap-and-tooth NI.

ent value for the demagnetizing effect of the reaction NI and proceeding as before. Additional points on the characteristic curve may be obtained by assigning other values to I_a and following the outlined procedure to determine satisfactory values of E and V.

If insufficient design data are available the saturation curve may be used to determine the approximate demagnetizing effect of armature reaction, as suggested in the preceding examples.

To illustrate, let $I_a = 100$, and assume that the demagnetizing effect of armature reaction is $200NI$. Construct the triangle *tsp* with a base $= 1600 - 200 = 1400NI$, and an altitude of 14 volts. By fitting this triangle to the saturation curve and the shunt field resistance line as shown in Fig. 185 the associated values of E, V and shunt NI are as listed below:

$$E = 639; \quad V = 625; \quad \text{shunt } NI = 3800.$$

Locate the point x on the saturation curve with an abscissa equal to the sum of the shunt and series NI, or 5400. Add and subtract the reaction NI of 1350, obtaining $6750NI$ and $4050NI$ for the pole tip conditions. Measure the areas axd and bxf, and locate the line indicating the resultant voltage, which in this trial is 633 volts. By comparing this with the 639 volts determined by the tentative selection of the proportions of the triangle tsp, a decision can be made as to the need for an additional trial.

By repeating this process with other selected values of I_a the trend of the characteristic curve can be determined.

G. Series generator with demagnetizing ampere-turns created by brush shift.

The machine used in the preceding examples is converted to a series generator by removing its shunt and series field coils and placing a series coil of 45

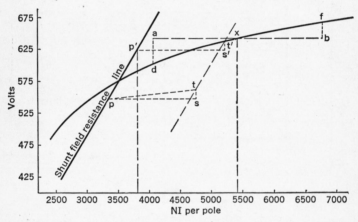

Fig. 185. Trial-and-error process based on saturation curve.

turns on each pole. The armature, frame and operating speed are unaltered; the new armature circuit resistance is 0.19 ohm.

Let $I_a = 100$ amperes and a brush shift of one slot be assumed as in Examples A, C and E. Then $R_a I_a = 19$ volts, and the demagnetizing $NI = 600$. The series $NI = 45 \times 100 = 4500$, and the net $NI = 4500 - 600 = 3900$. From the saturation curve, Fig. 174, the value of E corresponding to this excitation is 594. Therefore, the terminal voltage $V = 594 - 19 = 575$.

Additional points on the characteristic curve can be determined by assuming other values of I_a and proceeding as outlined above.

H. Series generator with the flux distorted by armature reaction.

As an illustration the machine of Example G will be used. The brushes are placed at the geometric neutral; the speed and the armature circuit resistance are unaltered.

Let $I_a = 100$, for which $R_a I_a = 19$, and the series $NI = 4500$. From the saturation curve, Fig. 174, the generated voltage produced with this excitation is 617.   The flux per pole $= E/KN = 2.64 \times 10^6$, and the density at the center of the pole face $= \Phi/A = 60,000$.   The gap-and-tooth NI for this density is 2685, from Fig. 186.   Adding and subtracting 1350 to obtain the density values at the pole tips and measuring the areas adx and bxf, the value of the average gap density is found to be 57,300, for which $\Phi = 2.52 \times 10^6$; $E = 590$; $V = 571$.

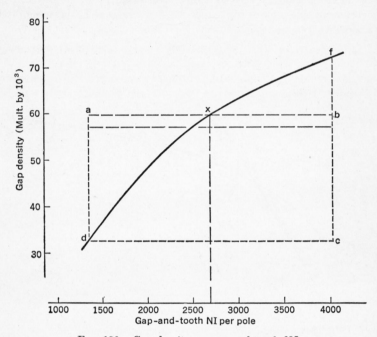

FIG. 186.   Gap density vs. gap-and-tooth NI.

Additional points on the characteristic curve may be obtained by assuming other values of I_a and repeating the process just described.

If insufficient design data are available, an estimate of the demagnetizing effect of the reaction NI may be obtained with the help of the saturation curve.

Let $I_a = 100$.   Then $R_a I_a = 19$;   series $NI = 4500$;   and $E = 617$. Assuming the $4500NI$ to be effective at the center of the pole face, the NI at one pole tip is $4500 - 1350 = 3150$, and at the other it is $4500 + 1350 = 5850$.   By measuring the areas axd and bfx, Fig. 187, the new value of E is found to be 612.   The terminal voltage is $612 - 19 = 593$.

225. Tirrill Regulator.   Sudden changes in the load supplied by a generator tend to produce fluctuations in its terminal voltage.   Some automatic means of producing equally rapid corrective changes in generated voltage is necessary if such fluctuations are to be closely restricted.   One device, commonly called the Tirrill regulator, produces rapid periodic changes in field current by

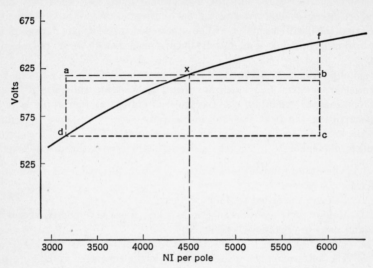

FIG. 187.   Use of saturation curve for voltage prediction.

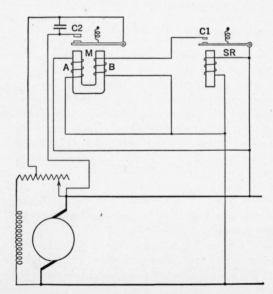

FIG. 188.   Schematic diagram of Tirrill regulator.

means of vibrating contacts. When the contacts close, a portion of the field rheostat is short-circuited and the field current increases; when they open, the short circuit is removed and the field current decreases. Although it is likely that the Tirrill regulator will be superseded by electronic devices in the near future the principle of operation is so ingenious as to deserve brief mention here.

A simplified diagram of a modern regulator of this type is shown in Fig. 188. The rugged contacts, $C2$, which are closed by a spring and opened by the electromagnet, M, maintain the average field current at the proper level by short-circuiting the field rheostat periodically. Quick response is secured with the help of a sensitive relay, SR, whose contacts, $C1$, control the current of coil B on magnet M. The regulating action may be outlined as follows:

1. When the terminal voltage drops below the desired level, the magnet of relay SR releases and $C1$ is closed by the spring.

2. Coil B is energized through contact $C1$.

3. Magnet M releases because coils B and A are both energized and are wound so as to oppose each other.

4. The spring closes $C2$ and short-circuits a section of the field rheostat.

5. The field current increases and builds the generated voltage up to a higher level.

6. As the terminal voltage climbs above the desired value, SR overpowers the spring and opens $C1$.

7. Coil B is deenergized, and coil A acts to open $C2$.

8. The added resistance in the field circuit reduces the generated voltage, thus completing the cycle.

226. Armature Winding Faults. Motors or generators that have been in service for some time may begin to spark seriously at the commutator, the sparking being accompanied by excessive temperature rise in the winding and often by localized blackening and pitting of the commutator surface. If careful inspection of the commutator reveals no superficial cause, such as particles of carbon or copper wedged between the bars, it is likely that a fault has developed in one or more of the winding elements. The armature should then be removed in order to facilitate the determination of the kind of fault and its location.

(a) Short-circuited element. A winding element may become short-circuited in various ways. There may be a partial breakdown of the insulation between turns, or a drop of solder may become lodged between adjacent commutator bar risers.

The location of a short-circuited coil may be determined by means of the test circuit shown in Fig. 189. Two probes (A, B), connected to a low-voltage source, are placed in contact with adjacent commutator bars, the milli-voltmeter circuit is then closed at C and its reading noted. Voltage readings are taken in this manner with the probes advanced one bar at a time until the entire commutator has been explored. If on arriving at the bars connected to element D no appreciable deflection can be observed this element must be short-circuited.

(b) Open-circuited element. If a winding element becomes open-circuited owing to a break in the wire or a poorly soldered connection at a commutator bar its location may be discovered by the same test recommended for short-circuited elements. The procedure to be followed is exactly the same; in fact, the two tests may be conducted simultaneously. If the probes arrive at the terminal bars belonging to an open-circuited element the millivolt-meter deflection will become much greater than normal. The normal arma-

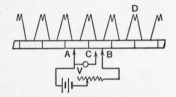

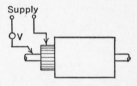

Fig. 189. Location of shorted coil.   Fig. 190. Detecting a ground.

ture winding may be considered a closed loop with numerous taps brought out to convenient terminals called commutator bars. Between any two adjacent bars there is a short path containing one element ($1/2\ p$ elements in a wave winding with p poles) and a long path containing all the remaining elements. If an element is open-circuited the short path between its terminals is out of

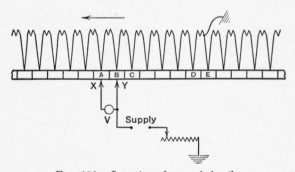

Fig. 191. Location of grounded coil.

service and the test current entering the winding at these terminals must take the long and relatively high-resistance path, thus accounting for the larger millivoltmeter reading obtained under such conditions.

(c) Grounded element. If metallic contact is established between a wind-ing element and the armature iron, as might be produced by a localized break-down of the slot insulation, the element is said to be grounded.

One method of detecting the presence of a ground in an armature is illus-trated in Fig. 190. One side of the power supply is connected through a volt-meter to the shaft, and the other side is placed in contact with any commuta-

tor bar.   If the voltmeter deflection is not more than about 0.5% of the supply
voltage the armature may be considered to be free from grounds.   If the voltmeter shows an appreciable deflection, thus indicating the presence of a
ground, it is advisable to apply an additional test to discover the location of
the defective element.

A convenient method of locating a grounded element utilizes the circuit
shown in Fig. 191.   A convenient supply voltage, say 115 volts, is connected

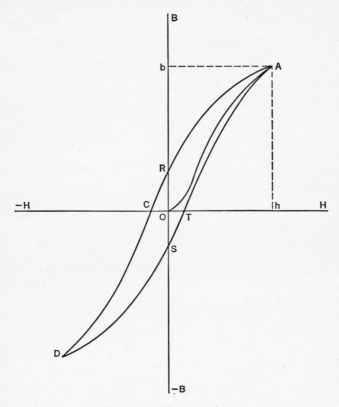

FIG. 192.   Hysteresis loop.

through a rheostat to the armature shaft, and the reading of the millivoltmeter,
V, is noted when the probes X, Y are placed in contact with adjacent bars
A, B, selected at random.   Call this reading V_1.   Swing probe X to bar C, Y
remaining at B, and call the new reading V_2.   If $V_2 > V_1$, bar C is nearer the
grounded element than bar A.   The greater this voltage inequality, the
shorter is the path from the grounded element to bar C, as compared with the
path in the other direction to bar A.

With the ground as shown in Fig. 191, $V_2 > V_1$.   If probe X is kept to the
right of Y and the armature rotated in the direction of the arrow the millivolt-

meter readings will increase steadily until Y and X come in contact with D and E respectively, when the reading becomes zero, thus marking the location of the ground.

The theory of this method is based on the obvious fact that two parallel paths exist in the winding between the point of contact of probe Y and the grounded element. Since the RI drop over each of these paths must be the same, the path with the smaller number of elements will show the larger bar-to-bar drop.

227. The Hysteresis Loop. In Art. 84, Chapter 7, the relationship between magnetic flux density and exciting ampere-turns was discussed. The B–H curves of the various magnetic materials shown therein are average values; cast iron, for example, has a single B value of 80,000 lines per square inch corresponding to an H value of 900 ampere-turns per inch. A more detailed investigation of the B–H relationship will reveal, however, that the exact value of B which can be produced by a given value of H depends very noticeably upon the recent magnetic history of the sample under test.

Let a demagnetized sample be selected and be subjected to steadily increasing values of H, until a maximum of Oh (Fig. 192) is reached. The curve OA represents the corresponding values of B. If H is decreased to zero, B drops to a residual value OR, and a certain amount (OC) of negative H is required to bring B down to zero. The value of H indicated by OC is sometimes called the coercive force. Further increases of H in the negative direction will carry B down to a negative value D. If H is now decreased to zero and increased in the positive direction to h again the values of B follow the curve DST to a point that practically coincides with A, completing what is known as the hysteresis loop.

228. Hysteresis Loss. An enlarged portion of Fig. 192 is shown in Fig. 193. It will be shown that the shaded area $ORbATO$ produced by the integration of $H\,\Delta B$ between the limits $\Delta B = 0$ and $\Delta B = b$ is proportional to the magnetic energy storage occurring while H is being increased.

Let a closed magnetic circuit of length l inches be formed of the iron sample under test, and let it be closely wrapped with a coil of N turns carrying i amperes. Then $H = Ni/l$ ampere-turns per inch $= k_1 i$.

Any small increment in flux density such as ΔB can be replaced by a proportional increment of flux $\Delta\phi$, since $\phi = BA$. If this increment of flux occurs during a time interval Δt the average rate of change of flux is $\Delta\phi/\Delta t$. Since the flux is linked with N turns a back voltage of $N(\Delta\phi/\Delta t) = e$ will be generated while the flux is changing. Then $\Delta B/\Delta t = k_2 e$, and the incremental area $H\,\Delta B = k_1 i \times k_2 e \times \Delta t =$ energy, since the product of current, voltage and time is energy.

By a process of elimination it is evident that the energy represented by the above expression is stored in the magnetic circuit since it is neither the energy input to the coil $(Vi\,\Delta t)$ nor the energy converted into heat $(Ri^2\,\Delta t)$. The shaded area therefore is proportional to the magnetic energy storage while H is increased from OT to Oh.

By similar reasoning it may be shown that the cross-hatched area RbA represents a return of some of this stored energy to the electric circuit; and that energy storage again occurs when the shaded area RCO is traversed.

The upper half of the hysteresis loop has now been covered, with the result that the area representing energy returned to the electric circuit is less than the area representing energy drawn by the amount included within the boundaries of the hysteresis loop. A similar loss of energy occurs when the lower half of the loop is traversed. Experimental evidence indicates that the energy represented by the area within the complete hysteresis loop is converted into heat within the magnetic material, presumably as a result of some form of molecular friction accompanying the change in magnetic flux density. The hysteresis energy loss per unit volume of a given material is thus directly proportional to the area of the hysteresis loop obtained by testing a sample of the material.

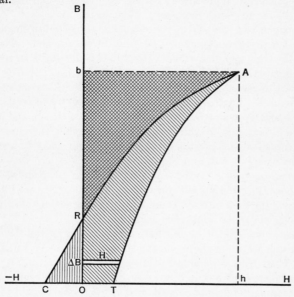

Fig. 193. Enlarged portion of hysteresis loop.

The hysteresis power loss per unit volume naturally involves the time element. That is, a sample showing a hysteresis energy loss of W watt-seconds per cubic centimeter will have a hysteresis power loss of W/t watts per cubic centimeter, if t = number of seconds required to complete one hysteresis loop.

Steinmetz discovered, by making numerous hysteresis loop determinations on the same sample carried up to many different values of maximum flux density, that the loop area is quite closely proportional to $B_{max.}^{x}$, and that x

may be taken as 1.6 for most magnetic materials and operating densities. Hence the hysteresis power loss may be expressed in the following terms:

Hysteresis loss, watts per cubic centimeter $= c(k/t)B_{max}^{1.6}$, where c is a conversion factor for the units involved, and k is the so-called hysteresis coefficient, varying from 0.012 for cast iron down to 0.0001 for Permalloy.

If the magnetic material is carried through the hysteresis loop repeatedly, perhaps by connecting the exciting coil to an alternating-current source, the hysteresis loss may be expressed in terms of the number of cycles or complete loops traversed per second.

$$\text{Hysteresis loss, watts per cubic centimeter} = ckfB_{max}^{1.6},$$

where f is the number of cycles per second or the frequency.

INDEX

Numbers refer to pages